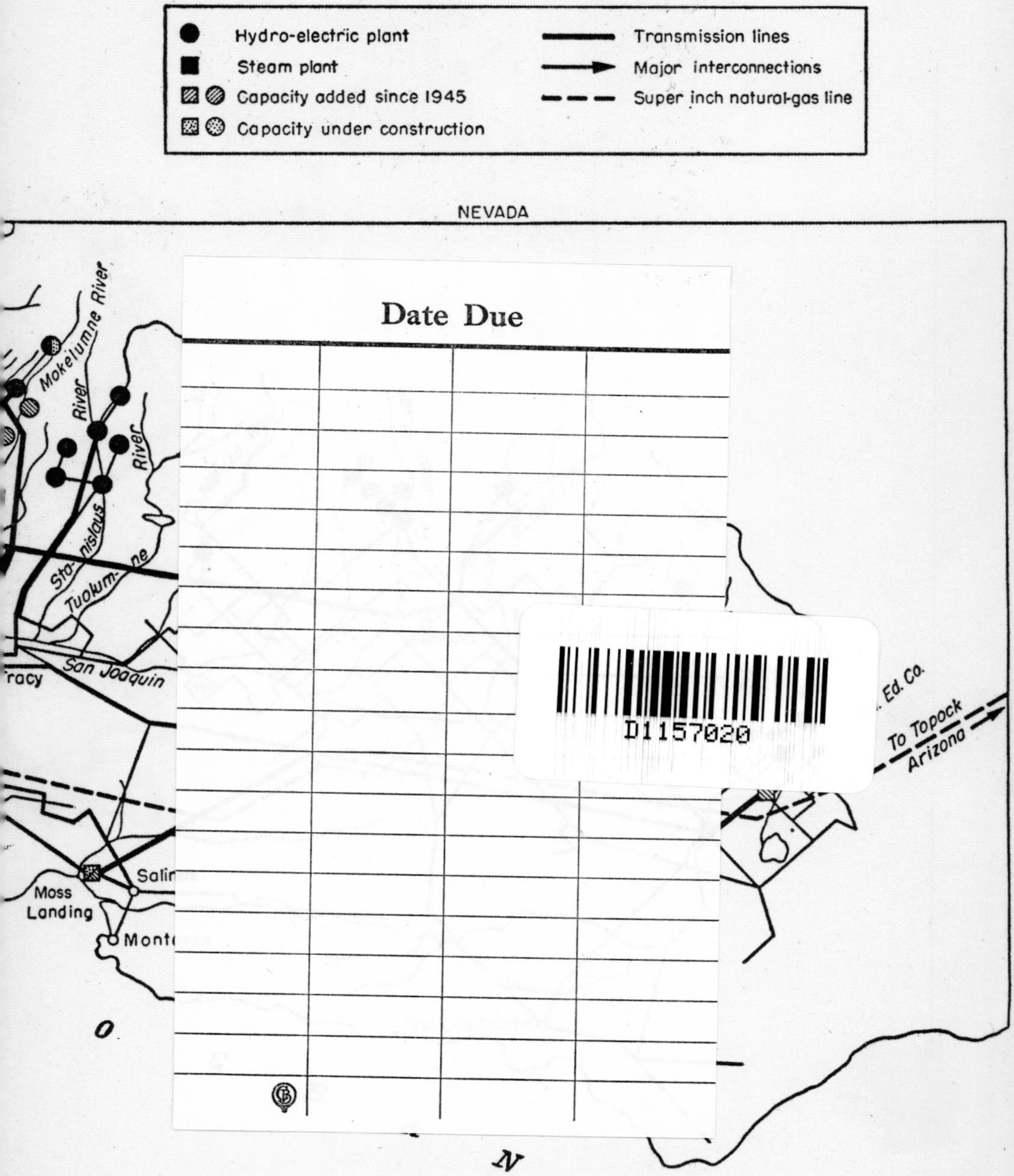

Hydro-electric plant
Steam plant
Capacity added since 1945
Capacity under construction
Transmission lines
Major interconnections
Super inch natural-gas line
NEVADA
Mokelumne River
River
Sta-
nislaus
Tuolum-
ne
River
San Joaquin
Moss
Landing
Ed. Co.
To Topock
Arizona
O
N

P·G·and E·
OF CALIFORNIA

Tower at Carquinez Strait crossing, symbol of electric power that leaps across mountains, canyons, valleys to serve the vast P. G. and E. system.

P·G·and E·
OF CALIFORNIA

THE CENTENNIAL STORY OF
PACIFIC GAS AND ELECTRIC COMPANY
1852–1952

by CHARLES M. COLEMAN

FIRST EDITION

McGRAW-HILL BOOK COMPANY, INC.

NEW YORK TORONTO LONDON

P. G. AND E. OF CALIFORNIA: *The Centennial Story of Pacific Gas and Electric Company,* 1852-1952

Library of Congress Catalog Card Number: 52-10331

Preface

INTO THESE pages is compressed the many-sided centennial story of a widespread public utility. Compression was necessary, for the story was to deal with more than 520 utility companies which over one hundred years have been welded into the present single organization. Obviously, each could not be treated in detail.

There was, also, the necessity of choosing between various approaches—whether this should be a history of technological, financial, or economic accomplishment. To cover all these phases the work would have been of encyclopedic proportions. Consequently the reader will find here a less exhaustive account but one designed to give emphasis to the daring enterprise, the courage, and the vision of the men who laid the foundations and built upon them the structure that is now Pacific Gas and Electric Company.

It is essentially a tale of men and leaders of men; one of risk and toil, and not a little privation, trouble, and heartbreak, counterbalanced in the end by magnificent achievement. It is a recital of engineering feats accomplished despite great obstacles, of pioneering in the little-known field of electricity, of bold venturing of capital to perform a public service.

Significance of the events recorded here lies in the immeasurable benefits conferred upon all Northern California by the utility pioneers and their successors. Provision of light, heat, and power in many instances has made possible the establishment and extraordinary development of the region's industry, commerce, and agriculture. Gas and electric services, spreading far from small beginnings, have brought to the whole people of

Northern California, rich and poor alike, comforts and conveniences of living that no monarch of olden times enjoyed.

The life story of Pacific Gas and Electric Company parallels in point of time the life story of the Golden State. Starting within two years of each other—1852 and 1850—each has attained similar high rank in a century of growth: California, the second largest state of the Union in population; P. G. and E., the first or second largest gas and electric utility in the United States, according to the medium of measurement employed. The Company's size is important only because, by being large, the system is able more efficiently and more economically to perform the public services to which it is dedicated.

In this chronicle of Pacific Gas and Electric Company's origin and development is to be found evidence of the part played by the gas and electric utilities in advancement of the economic welfare of the state and the nation.

Charles M. Coleman

Acknowledgment

PREPARATION of the manuscript for this history of P. G. and E. could not have been completed without the generous aid of a veritable legion of helpful persons both within and outside the Company. To all of them, too numerous to list individually, I offer my grateful acknowledgment.

Bancroft Library of the University of California, the State Library at Sacramento, the Mechanics Institute Library and the Public Library in San Francisco have provided a great wealth of data; the Company's own James H. Wise Library, under direction of Mrs. Agnes Reinero, has been of incalculable assistance. Librarians of the Historical Society of California and Wells-Fargo Bank History Room have responded promptly and effectively to our requests.

Interviews and correspondence with surviving members of the distinguished company of pioneers yielded a store of information for the book. For their assistance I am obligated to Messrs. Eugene J. de Sabla, Jr., John S. Drum, Prince André Poniatowski, and William B. Bosley.

While facts have been gleaned largely from Company archives, the search for them has entailed much extra labor in unearthing sources. For this I am indebted especially to Mr. W. A. Worthington, assistant engineer in charge of the Statistical Department, to Mr. Raymond Kindig, secretary of the Company, and to Mr. E. E. Manhard, assistant secretary.

Mention must also be made of the work of the late Charles L. Barrett, who succeeded his father as secretary of the San Francisco Gas Light Company and its successor, San Francisco Gas and Electric Company. Mr. Barrett's historical writings proved rich sources of information as were the files of Pacific Service Magazine, edited by the late Frederick S. Myrtle. Mr. R. W. Van Norden contributed much information regarding the South Yuba Water Company.

To Mrs. Violet G. Homem, who prepared the index and accomplished much of the initial research, and to Miss Ruth Hoehn, my secretary, who has patiently and competently typed and retyped hundreds of pages of copy, I must also acknowledge my debt.

Finally to Mr. John P. Coghlan, vice-president and assistant to the president, who has supervised the history project, do I tender my thanks for his ever helpful and wise counsel.

Charles M. Coleman

Contents

PART THREE

APPENDIX

In the Beginning

CHANGE was on the march in the slumbering Spanish-Mexican colony of California as the first half of the nineteenth century drew to a close.

Under the rule of Mexican governors, Alta California had made little or no progress. The once-prospering missions had fallen into decay after their enforced secularization. The few widely separated pueblos, sparsely populated, were at a standstill. The presidios were manned by scant squads of ragged and indolent soldiers. The only foreign trade was that brought by the hide and tallow ships of New England and occasional fur buyers who, like the hide dealers, came with cargoes of barter goods.

Life revolved in leisurely tempo around the feudal ranchos of the land-grant barons who measured their wealth in square leagues of range land and in thousands of cattle, sheep, mules, and horses. In the words of one historian, "By 1840, the old California, with its Spanish institutions and background, stood close to the end of its tranquil, romantic day."

In 1840 there were only 380 foreign residents in all California. They were a cosmopolitan, mixed lot—sailors who had left their ships for the easier life ashore, fur trappers and "mountain men" who had deserted the nomad's trail, adventurers of all kinds and occasional Americans who had been drawn West by tales of the new Promised Land. The first real American settlers began dribbling in by wagon train in 1841. By 1845 there were not more than 680 foreign residents as distinguished from native Californians.

As early as 1826 a British Navy officer, Capt. Frederick W. Beechey in command of H.M.S. *Blossom,* had written after a visit to San Francisco Bay, "California must awaken from its lethargy or fall into other hands." The awakening and the fall came with a resounding bang just 20 years later when Commodore Sloat raised the American flag at Monterey July 7, 1846, and proclaimed, "Henceforward, California will be a portion of the United States."

Yet even as a territorial possession of the United States, the province might have held longer to its slow pace had it not been for Marshall's discovery of gold at Coloma only 18 months later. The explosive impact of the gold rush transformed with unprecedented speed the backward Mexican outpost into a full-fledged state of the Union, equipped with laws and all the machinery of stable government. The hordes of forty-niners, with characteristic Yankee initiative, planted a new government and a new economy of commerce and industry in the virgin soil that had known only the pastoral regime of the ranchos and missions.

The U.S. Census of 1850, the year California was admitted to the Union, fixed the state's population at 92,597, but the figure did not include residents of San Francisco. The census was taken there, but the records were lost in one of the many fires that leveled the shacks of the mushroom town. The nearest official count of the city is a state census made in 1852 which credited San Francisco with 36,751 inhabitants.

Included in the surging influx of newcomers were men of all professions and trades, many with college education and training. Almost without exception they hurried into the foothills of the Sierra in search of gold. Some quickly found wealth and returned to the coastal settlements; some failed to "strike it rich"; some were physically unfit for the rigors of labor in the placers. Many a man quickly discovered that his fortune was to be gained not in digging for gold but in following more familiar pursuits. It was these men who became the first citizens of San Francisco, Sacramento, San Jose, and the booming mining towns. From their ranks came the earliest leaders in business and the professions. They were also largely responsible for the quick transplanting of the arts and sciences, the cultures as well as the economy, of the Atlantic states to this pioneer land on the remote western fringe of the continent.

Many a present-day mercantile firm in San Francisco had its origin in 1849 and the turbulent decade that followed. The early merchants included not only purveyors of the necessities but dealers in wares of another sort, such as a music store founded in 1850 and a bookstore that has been operating ever since that year.

The gold miners and their brother pioneers in the towns were quick to satisfy their hunger for the luxuries and refinements of life. The newly rich brought treasures of art from Europe. They ransacked the markets of the world for materials and furnishings for their mansions. This writer recalls seeing in the ghost town of Yankee Jim in Placer County a spinet which had traveled by ship around Cape Horn in 1849 and then by freight wagon to the mountain mining town. It was one of many such importations.

No reader of California history can fail to note the speedy transition from the lethargy of the Mexican outpost to the drive and push of the new American state. These were the conditions and circumstances which in 1852 brought about establishment of the first gas service in California, the seed from which grew the present Pacific Gas and Electric Company system.

But before that story can be told, the background upon which, nearly half a century later, the present great P. G. and E. hydroelectric generating system was started must be sketched into the picture.

Long before the physicists and engineers had found a way to produce electricity for light and power purposes, the gold miners of the Sierra unwittingly were laying the foundation for the building of the water-powered electric plants that now dot the foothills from the Kern River in the south to the Pit in the north. The explanation is obvious—*water,* the prime necessity of placer mining as it is of hydroelectric operation.

The gold miners knew a good deal about water power. Many of them came from New England where the colonists had followed ancient custom by installing water wheels to operate their flour and textile mills. James Marshall was building a water-powered lumber mill at Coloma for John A. Sutter when he found those flakes of gold in the tailrace.

In the first frenzied scratching of sand bars and gravel banks the miners used only shovel and pan or rocker to recover the precious metal. Before long, however, the easy fortunes the early comers had picked up were no longer to be had. Then the Long Tom, an elevated flume into which the gravel was thrown, and the sluice box were introduced to save labor and time. For these devices a constant flow of water was needed, especially when the claims were distant from the living stream. Inventive workers soon discovered that with a greater volume of water, whole banks of gold-rich gravel could be washed into the sluice boxes. Thus hydraulic mining was born.

So while the Argonauts delved for gold, others saw fortunes to be made in digging ditches and building flumes to deliver streams of water under gravity pressure for the miners' use. Starting with one short ditch in Nevada County in 1850, mining men built a vast network of waterways that reached into every canyon where placers were being worked. In his classic report of 1868 on "Mineral Resources of the West," J. Ross Browne declared that by 1863 the conduit system of Northern California included 5,328 miles of "artificial water courses." These and others built later were the heritage left by the gold miners to the hydroelectric men who followed.

Thus it happened that, although P. G. and E. traces its lineage as a gas and electric utility back to the San Francisco Gas Company which was incorporated in 1852, the earliest company on its corporate "family tree" is the little Rock Creek Ditch Company organized in 1850 in Nevada County and later consolidated into the South Yuba Water Company's far-flung canal network which eventually became a part of the electric system.

The gold-rush men made other contributions to hydroelectric development in Northern California. One came from Lester A. Pelton, the millwright whose inventive genius produced the water wheel that bears his name. Pelton saw the need for more efficient power to operate the hoists and other machinery of the deep mines of the Sierra. Knowing nothing of electricity, he could not guess that the Pelton wheel would become a vital part of modern hydroelectric equipment. Pelton wheels today drive the generators in many a hydro powerhouse in the West and elsewhere in the world.

But more important perhaps than Pelton's contribution to hydroelectric development was that which arose from the water know-how of the gold miners. They left a vast water system and legal rights to water sources; and they left, too, a generation of men who knew how to build tunnels, canals, and flumes, how to lay pipe in rugged terrain, how to handle water and where to find it. That was a mighty aid to the electrical engineers when they began to build water-powered plants.

A forty-niner, Peter Donahue, founded the San Francisco Gas Company in 1852, brought the first gas light to California.

Associated with his brother Peter in the San Francisco Gas Company, James Donahue was president from 1856 to 1862.

At the Oriental Hotel, "brilliantly lighted with gas," the introduction of gas street lights in San Francisco was celebrated with a banquet in 1854.

PART ONE

[1852-1905]

Years of gas and electric pioneering—Evolution to higher levels of service—Years of sharp competition—Gradual system consolidation—Years of steady expansion in step with the forward march of Northern California. The men who led the way—the Donahues—George H. Roe—Martin and de Sabla—W. H. Crocker and Prince Poniatowski.

CHAPTER I

Fiat Lux

SAN FRANCISCO walked in darkness until some time after the American invasion descended upon it in 1848 and 1849. Its streets, or the muddy trails that passed for streets, were unlighted; its business places, pleasure resorts, and dwellings were lighted only by oil lamps and candles.

The settlement on the cove of the Bay south of Telegraph Hill boasted considerably less than a thousand residents in 1848 when news of Marshall's discovery of gold leaked out. The town was almost depopulated by the first stampede of fortune seekers to the mountains, but within months it became a maelstrom of newcomers outfitting for the placers, and miners returning heavy with gold "dust" or with empty pockets.

In the first nine months of 1849 some 550 ships dropped anchor in San Francisco Bay, each jammed with gold-hungry passengers. Most of the ships' crews joined the flight to the "diggings." Among them was Peter Donahue, who was to become one of San Francisco's foremost citizens.

Peter Donahue, a machinist and foundry worker, came to California on the steamship *Oregon* by way of Peru and Panama. He had worked his way from Panama as engineer of the ship. With the canny foresight that marked his career he had fattened his purse with the proceeds of a large shipment of scarce onions he had put aboard his ship en route from Panama. The onions were sold in San Francisco to a dealer who promptly disposed of them at one dollar apiece, chiefly to sufferers from scurvy.

Donahue tried his hand at gold mining, but after a few months in the placers he had only ill health and diminished capital to show for his labor. One day he overheard a conversation of two strangers which convinced him his brother James must be in San Francisco. Acting on the tip, he returned to the Bay city and found his brother after a long search.

The brothers turned their backs on the gold fields and opened a blacksmith shop in an old adobe building on Montgomery Street near the foot of Telegraph Hill. The shop prospered, and in 1851 they established a foundry to meet a pressing demand for castings. They moved to new and larger quarters close to the water's edge at Mission and First Streets. The plant was called Union Iron and Brass Foundry. At about this time a third brother, Michael, joined Peter and James. They made a strong team in the foundry—James was a boilermaker, Peter a machinist, and Michael a molder—but after a few years Michael moved to Davenport, Iowa, settled down, and eventually became mayor of the city.

Peter Donahue was still in his twenties at that time but already he showed signs of initiative and business capacity. He had no thought of going on as the village blacksmith. One Sunday in 1850 he sought relief from the forge and anvil by going for a walk with a friend, Martin Bulger. The westerly breeze carried a bit of a nip and the Bay waters danced in the clear sunlight. The men climbed the sand hills that rose west of Kearny Street to gain a view of the straggling town. Donahue was impressed by what he saw and, turning to his companion, said:

"Bulger, this is going to be a great city at no distant day; there will have to be gasworks and water works here, and whoever has faith enough to embark in either of these enterprises will make money."

The idea stuck in the young man's mind. He discussed it with his brothers, but they were not enthusiastic. He persisted, saying at one time, "Give me the privilege of supplying this city with gas and I care not for any other fortune." His faith and vision saw far beyond the realities of the San Francisco of that day.

The tides of the Bay then lapped close to Battery Street and to Sansome in some spots. The town centered on Portsmouth Square. South of California Street and west of Stockton there were only hills and sand dunes. A cluster of shacks marked Happy Valley around Third and Howard Streets. The area in the vicinity of Turk and Taylor Streets, which was called St. Ann's Valley, had attracted a few dwellers because of its small stream of clear water. A winding road led to distant Mission Dolores. There was a limited water supply, and firewood was brought in from the peninsula or from across the Bay.

The only street lighting San Franciscans enjoyed in 1850 was provided by oil lamps installed along Merchant Street by James B. M. Crooks in October of that year. Their cost was paid by the property owners. Crooks extended his private system until in February, 1852, about 90 lamps were in operation on Montgomery, Clay, Washington, and Commercial Streets. The fire of May 4, 1852, destroyed all but four of these beacons, and the common council then gave Crooks a contract to erect new standards to light the area bounded by Battery, Kearny, Jackson, and California. His flickering oil lamps served partly to relieve the blackness of night until the brighter gas lamps supplanted them.

Peter Donahue at last convinced his brothers they should join him in the gas project, and they went to work on plans, undeterred by the fact that none of them knew anything of gas manufacture. The industry then was unknown in the West. The first gas company in the United States had been organized in Baltimore in 1816. Boston and New York did not have gas light until 1822 and 1823; Chicago not until 1850; and Los Angeles not until 1867. The gas, extracted from coal in retorts subjected to high heat, gave a poor soot-laden flame compared to today's natural product.

The Donahues began to study all the information on gas making they could find. They were helped by a bright young clerk in the foundry—Joseph G. Eastland—who became deeply interested in the project. Confident of their ability to find a way, James Donahue applied for and received from the common council in July, 1852, a franchise to erect a gasworks, lay pipes in the streets, and install street lamps to light the city with "brilliant gas" at a cost of 32½ cents per lamp per night. Gas was to be supplied to householders "at such rates as will make it to their interest to use it in preference to any other material."

The brothers had a franchise but they lacked a gas plant and pipe, the money for construction, and, most important, a man able to build and operate the plant. Undaunted, they proceeded to organize the San Francisco Gas Company, first gas utility in all the West. The company was incorporated August 31, 1852, with $150,000 authorized capital stock. The official seal bore the inscription "Fiat Lux," the same slogan as that adopted years later by the University of California.

There were 11 original stockholders. The three Donahues subscribed for 610 of the 1,500 shares authorized at $100 par value. The first officers were: Beverley C. Sanders, president; J. Mora Moss, vice-president; John Crane, secretary. These, with James Donahue, John H. Saunders, and Giles H. DeVoe, constituted the board of trustees. While all authorities give Peter Donahue the major role of originator and organizer of the gas project, he did not appear as an officer of the company until long afterward. Occupied with other business, he left to brother James the guidance of the gas enterprise.

For the gas plant, a tract 275 feet by 137½ feet, bounded by First and Fremont, Howard and Natoma Streets, was purchased for $22,000. The Fremont Street side was at tidewater where lighters could be landed with coal from Australia and building materials and equipment from the East. The Donahues' foundry was equipped with only one cupola for casting the 21 iron retorts needed for the manufacture of gas, but slowly the work was done.

Other obstacles stood in the way. There was no pipe on the Pacific Coast, not enough money yet available for its purchase, and still no engineer to design and operate the plant. So Peter Donahue went to New York. He had only $5,000 in cash, but Peter Taggart, an old friend in Paterson, New Jersey, loaned him $2,000 more and gave him credentials to R. D. Wood & Company, pipe manufacturers of Philadelphia. Thus armed, he bought the pipe on terms of $5,000 cash and the balance in due time. Other equipment was bought for immediate shipment.

The problem of finding a capable engineer was solved by a happy chain of circumstances. While still serving his apprenticeship as a youth in New Jersey, Peter had known young W. W. Beggs, a son of Hugh Beggs, his employer. On his return he found the younger Beggs in Paterson and learned that his old friend had become an expert gas engineer. He had the man he needed. Beggs came to San Francisco, completed the Howard Street works, and remained as operating engineer for 17 years. When he died he was succeeded after a brief interval by his brother James.

Work on the gas plant was started in November, 1852. On February 11, 1854, the plant was ready for operation and gas was turned into the pipes on that day. In celebration of the event, the company entertained public officials and leading citizens at a gala banquet at the Oriental Hotel, at Battery and Bush Streets. The engraved invitation read:

Office of the San Francisco Gas Company

February 8, 1854

Sir:

The Trustees of the San Francisco Gas Company request the honor of your company at the Oriental Hotel from 7½ to 9 o'clock on Saturday Evening, the 11th inst., on the occasion of their introducing Gas Light into the Streets of San Francisco.

Respectfully,

John Crane, *Secretary*

San Francisco's welcome to the new illuminant was outspoken. The *Daily Alta California* described its benefits as "incalculable." Let the *Alta's* reporter tell the story of the banquet in the quaint journalese of the period:

"SAN FRANCISCO BY GAS-LIGHT—Last evening, between six and seven o'clock, the streets of San Francisco were lighted with gas for the first time. Some of the lamps have been lighted within two or three nights past, but last night was the first general illumination. It was not a very favorable evening for the exhibition of the gas-light, as its brilliancy paled somewhat beneath the rays of Luna, who exhibited a full face last evening, and seemed to be enjoying a sort of a quiet laugh at the gas-light. Nevertheless, a cheerfulness seemed to pervade the streets that has never been among us before. In travelling over the muddy side-walks and in wading through the street crossings, there was a light ahead which showed the pedestrian how to pick his way, and seemed as a sort of a guiding star through the mud. The lights burned very brilliantly, and it required only a larger number of them to render our streets as light as day. The good results from the introduction into the city are almost incalculable. Beside the greater accommodation, the safety of life and property will be very much increased, and when the streets are more generally lighted, the frequent midnight robberies and burglaries will materially decrease in number. Eighty-four gas-lamps were lighted last evening.

"The gas works are at the corner of First and Howard streets, and the pipes, thus far, are laid in the following districts:—In Montgomery Street, from Bush to Jackson; in Kearny Street, from Sacramento to Jackson; in Dupont Street, from Clay to Jackson. They are also laid between Montgomery and Dupont streets on Clay, Commercial, and Washington streets.

"In accordance with an invitation from the trustees, between two and three hundred gentlemen assembled at the Oriental Hotel, which was brilliantly lighted with gas, to partake of a collation provided for the occasion. About 9 o'clock the party went into the dining room of the hotel, where an elegant spread was laid out, of which the guests partook, occasionally, as is usual on such occasions, washing down the edibles with some drinkables. When the inner man was sufficiently satisfied with the solids, the guests were requested to come to order by W. R. Gorham, Esq., Sheriff, and J. M. Moss, Esq., President of the Gas Company [Moss actually was vice-president at that time], took his stand at the head of the table. Mr. Moss stated that there had been over three miles of gas pipe laid, and as a specimen of the workmanlike manner in which it had been done by the mechanics of this city, no leakage had been discovered. Mr. Moss, in speaking of the price charged for gas, ($15 per thousand cubic feet) made the following comparison between the price here and in New Orleans, by which it appears taking everything into consideration, that on the score of cheapness we are fifty per cent in advance of New Orleans. In New Orleans, he said, the price of gas was $8 per thousand cubic feet, coal was five to six dollars per ton, money was worth ten per cent and labor about two dollars per day. Here gas was $15 per thousand, coal from thirty-six to forty dollars per ton, money thirty-six per cent, and labor from six to seven dollars per day. Mr. Moss in concluding gave a toast, 'The Mayor, Recorder and Council of San Francisco,' to which Judge Baker responded in a few happy remarks. . . .

"Mayor Garrison arose to speak, and before he had uttered three words, some wag below had got at the meter in the house, and turned off the gas, leaving the room and guests in total darkness for a few minutes, which were principally occupied in laughing at the unexpected interlude. . . .

"The utmost good feeling and harmony prevailed, and all seemed highly gratified at the success of the gas company in introducing into our city their brilliant lights. All present seemed to enjoy themselves; and from appearances when we left, there were a few in the large party who partook of the collation who seemed to be getting into a condition in which they would find the gas light 'mighty convenient' in illuminating their paths to their respective lodgings."

Gas light gained immediate public favor. In 1854, the first year of operation, there were 237 customers; 563 the next year. By the end of 1855 more than 6½ miles of pipe had been laid and 154 street lamps were in operation. The original rate of $15 per thousand cubic feet of gas soon was reduced to $12.50 and then to $10, with a downward sliding scale to a minimum charge of $7.50 for maximum consumption.

The first contract for lighting the city's streets called for lamps at intervals within the area bounded by California Street on the south, Dupont Street (later renamed Grant Avenue) on the west, Jackson on the north, and the Bay shore on the east. As the city grew year after year, the mains were extended until at last they formed a giant network from the water front to the ocean beach.

A picturesque figure of the gas era of street lighting, which survived in San Francisco probably longer than in most of the big cities, was the lamplighter. As the shadows of dusk fell over the pavements, the lamplighters began their rounds, trotting from post to post with torch in hand. They became the symbol of the end of the day's activities and the coming of night, promising protection against its terrors and mysteries by their gift of light at every street corner. At first the lamplighters carried ladders and climbed to every lamp, but this method was changed in the early sixties. Jacob Radstone, in charge of the meter repair shop, invented a torch, a shielded flame on the end of a long staff equipped with a device to turn the gascock on and off without aid of a ladder.

The last of San Francisco's gas street lights were not abandoned until December 27, 1930, long after electricity had been proved more efficient for the task. The peak of gas lighting in the city was reached in 1915, the Panama Pacific International Exposition year, when on February 10 a total of 8,483 street lamps was in use and each one had to be turned on and off by hand at dusk and dawn. Many a P. G. and E. man started his career as a lamplighter.

Peter Donahue's dream of a great city by the Golden Gate proved more true with every passing decade and his little gas company expanded at similar pace, building additional plant facilities and laying more and more miles of main. Even before the first gas lights were turned on, the company found need for more capital and greater plant capacity. Capital stock authorized was raised from $150,000 to $450,000 in January, 1854; to $1,000,000 in 1855; to $2,000,000 in 1862; to $6,000,000 in 1866; and to $10,000,000 in 1873.

Between 1852 and 1905, when the successor of the pioneer company, San Francisco Gas and Electric Company, was merged into P. G. and E., only nine presidents held office:

Beverley C. Sanders	1852–1855
James Donahue	1856–1862
J. Mora Moss	1862–1865
Peter Donahue	1866–1867
Joseph A. Donohoe	1868–1869
Peter Donahue	1870–1883
Eugene P. Murphy	1884

Joseph B. Crockett	1885–1901
W. B. Bourn	1902–1905

In the same period of 53 years, only four men held the position of secretary. John Crane, the first of the four, was succeeded in 1856 by Joseph G. Eastland, who served through 1878. He was followed by William G. Barrett, who since 1860 had been with the company as assistant bookkeeper, then cashier, and as secretary from 1879 to 1901. His son, Charles L. Barrett, who had been with the company since 1879, succeeded his father as secretary in 1902. When P. G. and E. was formed he became assistant secretary of the new corporation, and later a director, remaining on active duty until his death, June 2, 1934. His was an unusual record—55 years of unbroken service with one organization and its successors.

CHAPTER 2

Bring Me Men

GRAVEN over the stone entrance of the California State Office Building in Sacramento is a ringing line from the "Coming American," written many years ago by poet Sam Walter Foss:

"Bring me men to match my mountains"

The call was answered in the fifties and succeeding years by a long line of "men with empires in their purpose, and new eras in their brains."

Peter Donahue was the first of the gas and electric utility builders. Born of Irish parents in Glasgow, Scotland, January 11, 1822, he had few advantages during his boyhood and little schooling. When he was eleven, his mother emigrated to America, settling in Matteawan, New York, with her family of sons, Peter, James, and Michael.

Peter spent his youth mostly learning a trade, first in a cotton mill, then as an apprentice in a locomotive works, and later in the shop of Hugh Beggs at Paterson, New Jersey, where his pay was $1.50 a day. As a journeyman machinist, young Peter held jobs in several foundries until 1847 when he was appointed assistant engineer of a new steamship built in New York for the Peruvian government and about to sail for its home port. The craft was said to be the first American-built steamship ever to pass through the Strait of Magellan.

Soon after he arrived at Callao, Peru, news of discovery of gold in California was received, and Peter booked passage to San Francisco on the S.S. *Oregon,* which also had been built at the plant where he had worked in New York. An attack of malaria forced him to interrupt his voyage at Panama where he remained until the *Oregon* returned. After superintending repairs to the ship's boilers, for which he was paid $1,000, he again went aboard the *Oregon,* this time as engineer, and sailed for the Golden Gate. He was twenty-seven years old when he reached San Francisco in June, 1849, armed with his youth, his trade, and some $6,000 he had saved.

(Some accounts of his life declare that Peter and James Donahue started their first blacksmith shop with capital of only $500. If this be true, Peter must have lost heavily in his mining or other ventures, or the estimate of his wealth when he reached San Francisco has been considerably exaggerated.)

Then followed the fruitless experience in the placer diggings at Auburn and Kelly's Bar on the north fork of the American River. When the brothers established the Union Iron and Brass Foundry at First and Mission Streets, they entered a virgin field in the city and one that paid. Fires were frequent, and they were able to buy scrapped stoves, ruined machines, and other iron at salvage rates for melting in their single cupola. There was a shortage of cooking ranges in the city so the Donahues designed a simple model made from surplus boiler plates. The foundry is credited with making the first casting, a shaft bearing for the S.S. *McKim,* and with building the first quartz mill, the first locomotive, and the first printing press manufactured in California. Much of its work was for ship repairs. In 1859 the Donahues built machinery for the *Saginaw,* first warship built on the Pacific Coast.

With the gas company well started, Peter Donahue, always alert for new business, established a line of river steamers to compete with those operated by the California Steam Navigation Co. A bitter fight followed but he managed to reduce fares to 20 per cent of their former high level. He placed two small steamers, the *Goliath* and the *Herman,* in coastal trade. Obtaining a franchise for the Omnibus Street Railroad in 1861, he became president of the first streetcar line built in San Francisco.

In the same year he obtained a contract to build the monitor *Camanche* for the United States government. The frames of the ship and its equipment were fabricated in New Jersey and shipped around the Horn in the S.S. *Aquila.* The ship arrived safely in port late in 1863, then sank at dockside during a storm. To complete his contract, Donahue imported divers from New York to retrieve the cargo from the Bay bottom. The *Camanche,* which was similar in design to the turreted *Monitor* of Civil War fame, was assembled and launched in 1864 under Donahue's direction, but it never fired a shot in defense of the Pacific Coast, the task to which it was assigned. In 1899 it was sold for junk and its hull converted to use as a coal barge.

James Donahue found his time so taken with affairs of the gas company that in 1853 he and brother Michael sold to Peter their interest in the foundry. The firm name was changed to Union Iron Works, Peter Donahue, Proprietor. In the next 10 years Peter's enterprises multiplied so rapidly that he was unable longer to carry the responsibilities of the ironworks. In 1863 he sold two-thirds of his foundry interest and in 1865 disposed of the remaining third.

At this point Irving M. Scott, who had joined the firm in 1860 as a draftsman, acquired a share in the new partnership and started the career that was to place him at the head of the great Union Iron Works. When, in 1883, under Scott's leadership, shipbuilding was made the major activity, a tract of 32 acres in the Potrero was purchased, the business was incorporated, and the plant moved to the new site. From Peter Donahue's blacksmith shop had sprung a vast shipyard, destined to build the battleship *Oregon* of Spanish-American War fame and fleets of other ships of war and commerce. Since 1905 the yard has been owned by Bethlehem Pacific Coast Steel Corporation and is now operated by a shipbuilding division of that company.

It was typical of Peter Donahue's sagacity that when he sold the original foundry, he refused to sell the lot on which it stood at First and Mission Streets. When the time was right he erected there a fine business block which, but for the fire of 1906, might have been the monument he had hoped it would be.

Railroad building was another of Peter Donahue's seemingly endless activities. With associates he constructed a line from San Francisco to Gilroy in Santa Clara County, and another from the town of Donahue (named for him) at the mouth of Petaluma Creek to Cloverdale in Sonoma County. Locomotives and cars for their lines were built in the Donahue foundry. The

Sonoma County line later was extended to Tiburon and, with additions, became the San Francisco and North Pacific Coast Railroad. Another project was the completion of an unfinished narrow-gauge rail line from Healdsburg to the mouth of Sonoma Creek. At both of these terminals the steamer *James M. Donahue* provided transportation to San Francisco.

All these did Peter Donahue accomplish, yet he found time to serve as director of the Hibernia Savings and Loan Society, the National Gold Bank, and the State Investment and Insurance Company, and for one year as president of the Society of California Pioneers. He subscribed $150,000 to the 4-million-dollar fund which put the Bank of California on its feet after the Ralston crash in 1875. He gained his title of "Colonel" by service on the staff of the Commanding General of the National Guard.

Sixteen of the later years of his life were spent as president of the San Francisco Gas Company. Ill health caused his resignation only a short time before his death in his sixty-third year, November 26, 1885. The family home was at Bryant and Second Streets, then a select residential district.

In reporting his death the San Francisco *Chronicle* said:

"Peter Donahue was the first man to engineer a steamer through the Strait of Magellan, the first to establish an iron foundry and machine shop in California, the first to light the City of San Francisco with gas and the first to construct a street railroad on the Pacific Coast.

"In manner he was courteous, affable and companionable. . . . The dignity of labor has never been more practically exemplified than in the life of this intelligent and industrious mechanic."

It was fitting that the monument to his memory, which stands at Battery and Market Streets, San Francisco, should bear this inscription:

Dedicated to Mechanics
By James Mervyn Donahue
In Memory of his Father, Peter Donahue

* * *

James, two years younger than his brother Peter, was a boilermaker. Ill health forced him as a young man to seek the warmer climate of Mobile, Alabama. During the Mexican War he was superintending erection of a foundry and ship-repair shop for the United States government at the mouth of the Rio Grande on the Gulf of Mexico. After peace was declared he and his brother Michael, who had served an enlistment in the Army, operated a foundry of their own but not for long.

When news of gold in California reached the Gulf ports, James lost no time in heading West. Through Mexico and Texas he rode horseback, reaching San Francisco in the spring of 1849. He arrived months ahead of Peter, but it was many months later before the brothers were reunited, each not knowing the other had joined the gold seekers.

James's first years in San Francisco were absorbed by affairs of the foundry and the gas company. The young boilermaker quickly developed a flair for business, finance, and management. Like his brother Peter, he was driven by a restless energy that was never satisfied with the accomplishment of the moment. One result of this was the Occidental Hotel which he and banker Joseph A. Donohoe, later a president of the San Francisco Gas Company, built on Montgomery Street between Bush and Sutter Streets. The hotel became one of the landmarks of San Francisco until it was destroyed in the fire of 1906.

James Donahue, however, did not live to see the hotel completed. He had supervised much of its construction, but before it was finished he was forced to retire to Laurel Wood Farm, his country home near Santa Clara. Never of robust health, he died August 17, 1862, at the age of thirty-eight.

In 13 years in San Francisco he had gone farther than most men do in a lifetime. The *Daily Alta California* said of him: ". . . a remarkable man. For the fortune accumulated by him he was indebted to no successful speculation but to his unaided energy, industry, sound judgment and integrity."

* * *

A chance meeting with James Donahue in Texas during the Mexican War gave to the San Francisco Gas Company one of

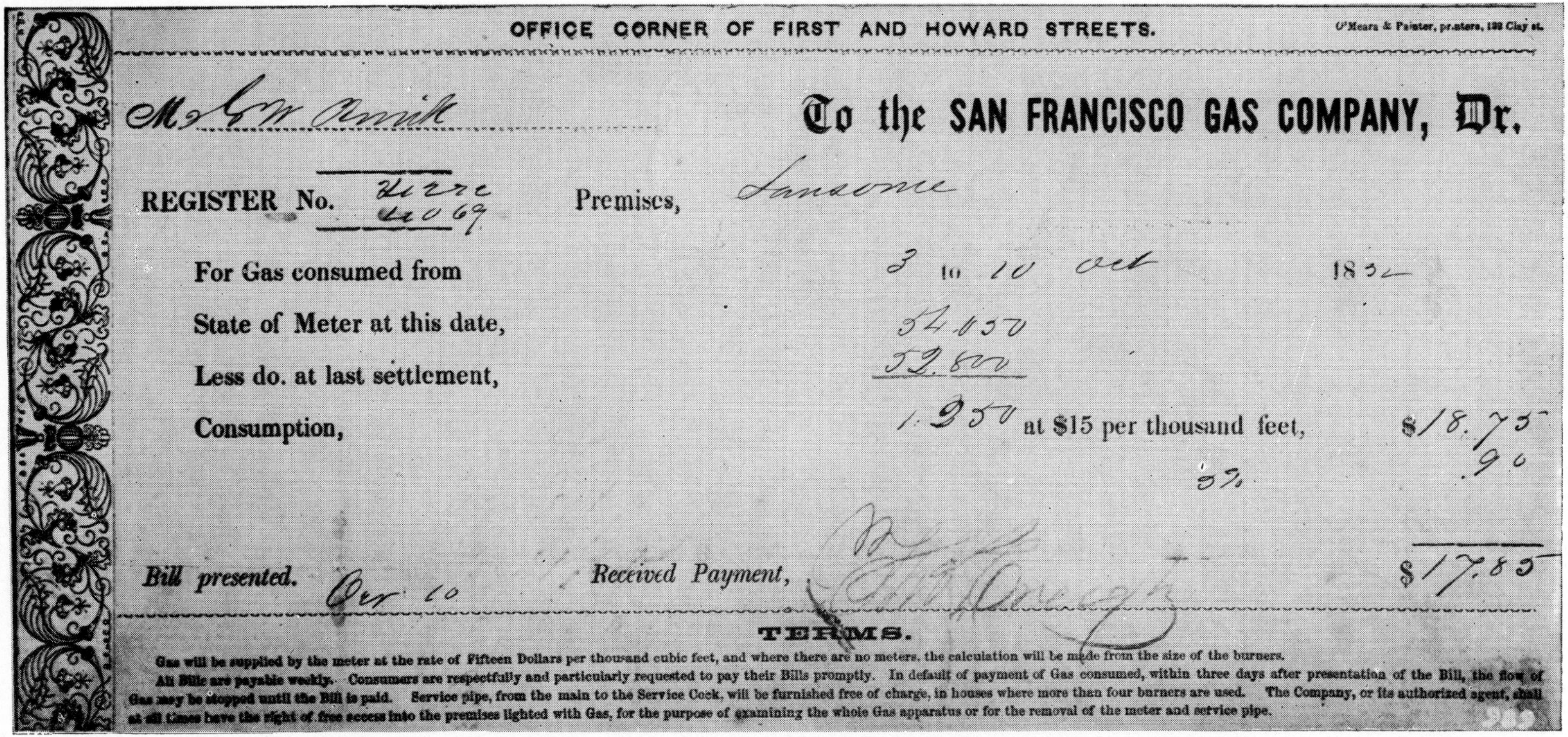
OFFICE CORNER OF FIRST AND HOWARD STREETS.

O'Meara & Painter, printers, 132 Clay st.

M G W

To the SAN FRANCISCO GAS COMPANY, Dr.

REGISTER No. Premises, Sansome

For Gas consumed from 3 to 10 Oct 1852

State of Meter at this date, 54.150

Less do. at last settlement, 52.800

Consumption, 1.250 at $15 per thousand feet, $18.75

5% .90

Bill presented. Oct 10 *Received Payment,* $17.85

TERMS.

Gas will be supplied by the meter at the rate of Fifteen Dollars per thousand cubic feet, and where there are no meters, the calculation will be made from the size of the burners.

All Bills are payable weekly. Consumers are respectfully and particularly requested to pay their Bills promptly. In default of payment of Gas consumed, within three days after presentation of the Bill, the flow of Gas may be stopped until the Bill is paid. Service pipe, from the main to the Service Cock, will be furnished free of charge, in houses where more than four burners are used. The Company, or its authorized agent, shall at all times have the right of free access into the premises lighted with Gas, for the purpose of examining the whole Gas apparatus or for the removal of the meter and service pipe.

This early bill of the San Francisco Gas Company, showing the original rate of $15 per thousand cubic feet, was in accordance with the founder's purpose to supply gas "at such rates as will make it to their [the consumers'] interest to use it."

TERMS AND RULES

—OF THE—

San Francisco Gas Company

Gas will be furnished at Eight Dollars per 1000 Cubic Feet, with the following scale of discounts.

To consumers of				[Per 1000 Feet.
200 to 500	Feet per Night,	3	per cent. being	$7 76
500 to 1000	do	5	do.	7 60
1000 to 2000	do	8	do.	7 36
2000 to 3000	do	10	do.	7 20

To consumers of more than 3000 Feet per night, 12½ per cent., being..................$7

These discounts are based upon CASH PAYMENTS, and will only be allowed upon bills which are PROMPTLY PAID.

For Laying Service Pipes, of less than 30 Feet in length from centre of Street, $10 each,
Additional lengths charged per Foot.
For placing, or re-connecting Meters..$2 each.

All Tubing and Fixtures for the use of Gas, are to be approved by the Engineer of the Com. pany, before its introduction.

The Company reserves the right to refuse to introduce Gas, without a deposit in advance, as security against loss. This rule applies especially to premises from which bills are due, by former tenants.

Consumers must give immediate notice at the Office of the Company of any escape of Gas, as no deductions will be made upon bills from the amount shown by Meter.

To prevent such accidents, no one is allowed to remove or disconnect a meter, without obtaining permission from the Office of the Company.

In default of the regular payment of its bills, the Company will discontinue the supply of Gas until settlement is made.

JOS. G. EASTLAND,
Secretary.

Office, San Francisco Gas Company,
Cor. First and Natoma Sts.
November 4th, 1857.

Soon the San Francisco Gas Company had reduced its rate to $8 per thousand cubic feet and was offering discounts for cash payments.

Businessman Beverly C. Sanders gave additional financial standing to the young San Francisco Gas Company as its first president.

J. Mora Moss, pioneer banker and businessman, was third president of the San Francisco Gas Company, serving from 1862–1865.

The busy San Francisco water front, center of commerce, had developed substantial wharves and warehouses by 1869. (*Courtesy of California Historical Society.*)

the strong characters of its formative years—Joseph G. Eastland, its secretary for 23 years. Eastland came from White County, Tennessee, and in his older years he looked the part of the Southern gentleman—white hair, sweeping mustaches and goatee; the kind of man one instinctively addresses as "Colonel." One writer described him as "a man of surpassing and unbending dignity."

Eastland had come to California in 1849 with his father, Thomas B. Eastland, who during the Mexican War had been a major in the Quartermaster Corps, at Brazos, near the mouth of the Rio Grande. It was there that the Eastlands met James Donahue, and the acquaintance was renewed in 1851 in San Francisco. James Donahue needed a clerk and bookkeeper at the foundry and offered the job to young Eastland, who then was only nineteen years old. That was what Eastland called "the turning point in my life."

Joseph G. Eastland fitted in at the Donahues' foundry and joined enthusiastically in the gas project. Given his choice of jobs, he went to the gas company in 1856 as its secretary. While the Donahues were busy with the foundry and other enterprises, he carried much of the administrative burden during the first years of the gasworks operation.

The young secretary early became a stockholder in the gas company and the Donahue ironworks. A family tradition is that funds for an interest in the foundry were obtained by purchase, "sight unseen," of a package at an express company's sale of unclaimed shipments. The box contained scarce playing cards which were sold for a substantial profit "at several dollars per pack."

Eastland was not a man, however, to be content with only a salaried job. In the sixties he obtained the first franchise for a gas plant in Oakland, incorporated a company, and placed his brother Van Leer in charge as superintendent. He served as president. He also joined a group which purchased the struggling Stockton Gas Company and placed it firmly on its feet. Another of his later undertakings was the Mill Valley Land Company in Marin County in which he joined with Lovell White and others in subdividing ranch land and creating the town of Mill Valley.

Grieving over the accidental death of a daughter, Joseph G. Eastland resigned as secretary of the gas company in 1878 but remained a member of the board of trustees. He died at his Mill Valley home November 23, 1894—a man of many interests, president of St. Luke's Hospital, director of the Donohoe-Kelly Bank and the San Francisco Savings Union, president of the Oakland and Stockton gas companies, and holder of stock in many leading industrial corporations.

* * *

The first president of the San Francisco Gas Company, Beverley C. Sanders, was well chosen by the Donahues to head their gas enterprise. He was active in the community—Collector of the Port in 1852–1853, and associated in the banking and exchange business with C. J. Brenham, reform mayor of the city in 1851–1852. Sanders was a member of the Vigilance Committee of 1851.

As president of the gas company from 1852 to 1855 Sanders gave the weight of his financial standing to the young enterprise and remained at its head until it was safely on its way as a going concern. Theodore H. Hittell, in his "History of California," relates an incident which illustrates perfectly the "free enterprise" of the men of that period. Ice, says Hittell, was a valuable commodity in San Francisco. To meet the need, five vessels were engaged in the fifties in bringing ice cargoes from Boston until one smart entrepreneur reasoned that ice could be brought at much less cost from Sitka, Alaska, then in Russian hands. So the Russian-American Commercial Company was organized for the purpose. All that was needed was permission of the czar's government to export frozen water from Sitka, and Beverley C. Sanders, one of the incorporators, was sent to St. Petersburg to open negotiations. Sanders was equal to the task. "Being a man of good presence and fine address," says Hittell, "he met with great success in his negotiations. One of the means he took to impress the Muscovites was to dress in a rich military costume and call himelf a colonel. But on a certain occasion he came near to losing his prestige. At a large party which he attended, an inquisitive lady asked him to what department of the United States Army he belonged. He was at first somewhat startled; but the next moment, recovering his equanimity, he coolly answered, 'To the Pacific, Madame'—a reply which, though perhaps not entirely appreciated, was received as perfectly satisfactory."

* * *

Another of the distinguished men who played important parts in the development of the pioneer gas company was J. Mora Moss, member of the board of trustees, vice-president during its first years, and president of the company from 1862 through 1865.

Moss was a territorial pioneer of 1850 who had come from Philadelphia in search of the fortune he found in San Francisco business instead of the gold fields. He was a member of the banking house of Pioche & Bayerque. In addition to the gas company his interests included ice and water companies and the Alaska Fur Company. Apart from business he devoted much of his time to the causes of education and charity. He was a member of the Board of Regents, University of California, and of the board of directors of the asylum for the deaf, dumb, and blind. When he died in November, 1880, at his home, Moss Avenue and Broadway, Oakland, the writer of his obituary said of him:

"California has lost one of her most prominent mainstays. A man of great public spirit, liberal to a fault, ever ready to assist the needy and deserving poor from the abundance he, by his energy and financial ability, had accumulated."

Memory of the pioneer is perpetuated in Oakland's Mosswood Park which was created on the land on which the Moss home stood.

CHAPTER 3

Tortured Streets

THE PACE was fast in San Francisco in the fifties and sixties. One of the causes was the rocketlike upsweep of population. San Francisco's handful of habitants in Marshall's year of gold discovery had grown to more than 36,000 in 1852 and nearly 57,000 in 1860. The official record gives figures down to the last digit, but no one knows how the enumerators ever managed to count the last man. The swirling tide of humans never was static in those days—in and out of the city from and to everywhere, parties off to the mines and back from the mines, shiploads arriving and other shiploads departing.

The Donahue brothers' little gas company moved ahead, extending its mains as the streets reached farther and farther into the sand hills, installing more and more street standards, lighting without favor the way of the frock-coated nabobs of Montgomery Street and the booted and flannel-shirted throngs in Portsmouth Square.

The dignified secretary of the company, Joseph G. Eastland, once solemnly said to a gas convention: "At the time of the first lighting of this city it occurred to me then, and I will repeat it now, . . . that this Company should follow the Scriptural injunction, to let your light so shine before men that they will see your good works; and I know of no better rule for gas men to follow."

The Donahues were following the rule.

The Howard Street plant had been in operation scarcely more than a year when it became necessary to enlarge its production and storage capacities. When the plant was first placed in commission, it could send out only about 70,000 cubic feet of gas daily; its two small storage holders had a total capacity of only 160,000 cubic feet. By contrast, a single industrial consumer today will use as much as 1,400,000 cubic feet in a single day, and the two largest of P. G. and E.'s many storage holders have a capacity of 17 million cubic feet each. To meet the upsurging demand, additional retorts were installed and in 1860 two steel telescopic gasholders were erected at Fifth and Howard Streets.

So general was the call for the new lighting service that the company was receiving petitions from residents of whole blocks begging that gas be supplied them. Among the first of these was from South Park where in the late fifties and sixties dwelt the aristocracy of San Francisco. In the area at the westward base of Rincon Hill, between Bryant and Brannan Streets and Second and Third, the barren sand lots had been converted in 1854 into a residential district designed to bring the atmosphere of London's Berkeley Square to the western shore of America. The builder was "Lord" George Gordon, English forty-niner who dreamed of re-creating in San Francisco a bit of his beloved London. Here lived the Leland Stanfords, the Hall McAllisters, the George Hearsts, and many another leading family in the days before Nob Hill claimed precedence.

The demand for gas lighting was not a distasteful one to the Donahues and their associates who, November 15, 1855, had inaugurated annual dividends, a practice that has been maintained by successor companies with few interruptions since that time.

The growing popularity of gas light, however, brought inevitable competition to the pioneer company. The first challenge proved not to be serious. It was offered by the Aubin Patent Gas Company which in 1857 had built a small plant at Jones and Market Streets designed to use a new patented process of gas manufacture. The project failed, and after the property had been sold by the sheriff, the San Francisco Gas Company took it over from the purchaser.

Opposition came next from the Citizens Gas Company, incorporated January 5, 1863, by A. J. Whitcomb, its president, John Benson, Calvin Paige, John Bensley, and I. K. Roberts with capital of $2,000,000. The Citizens group built a well-equipped plant at King and Second Streets which was placed in operation in 1866. Peter Donahue, who became president of the San Francisco Gas Company that year, promptly solved the problem by buying out the competitor before it was fairly under way.

Joseph A. Donohoe, banker, followed Peter Donahue as president in 1868. He was another early San Franciscan who in a few years had amassed fortune and reputation. With experience only in a New York dry goods house, he came to California in 1850. After two years of trading ventures in Sacramento and in the mining camps, he returned to San Francisco and established a dry goods firm with Eugene Kelly. From dry goods the partners turned to private banking, first in association with ill-fated W. C. Ralston. The partnership continued until Ralston and D. O. Mills founded the Bank of California. In 1864 the name of the partnership was changed to Donohoe, Kelly and Company which operated as a private banking firm until the Donohoe, Kelly Banking Company was incorporated in 1891. During the wild days of the Comstock in the sixties, Joseph A. Donohoe was familiarly called "the safe banker."

His term as head of the gas company seems not to have been disturbed by untoward events. The company was well financed by increasing its capital to $6,000,000 and its business still was on the upgrade. Donohoe long had been associated with the Donahues in various enterprises, and his high rating in the financial world made him an effective chief executive.

But in 1870, when Peter Donahue returned to the presidency to remain in charge for the next 14 years, storm clouds were gathering. Formidable new competition was threatened by the City Gas Company, incorporated April 6, 1870, with capital of $1,500,000.

The challenger was headed by powerful Montgomery Street figures, some of whom were to play important roles in P. G. and E. history. City Gas was incorporated by Alvinza Hayward,

James Ben Ali Haggin, Lloyd Tevis, C. J. Brenham, and Nicholas Luning.

Hayward was then gathering his millions from the Comstock and from California mining properties. Later he became interested in the vast water and canal system of the South Yuba Water Company which eventually served as a foundation stone of the P. G. and E. hydroelectric network.

The business interests of James Ben Ali Haggin and Lloyd Tevis were widespread—mines, railroads, banks, a principality in grain, and range lands stocked with great herds of cattle and horses. In 1872 Lloyd Tevis was to become president of Wells Fargo and Co.

Nicholas Luning, with D. O. Mills and W. T. Coleman, was a partner in "Lord" George Gordon's San Francisco and Pacific Sugar Refinery at Eighth and Harrison Streets.

The works of City Gas Company were extensive and well equipped. They were built in the Potrero on blocks bounded by Georgia, Massachusetts, and Humboldt Streets. Two holders provided storage for 1,038,000 cubic feet of gas. The plant was placed in operation in 1872. Parts of that old gasworks have survived and are included in the present Potrero manufactured-gas plant of the P. G. and E. stand-by system.

Still another aspirant for gas business was the Metropolitan Gas Company, incorporated May 13, 1863, by J. W. Stone, W. W. Montague, R. A. Swain, H. B. Williams, J. J. Felt, Josiah Belden, A. P. Brayton, and Ira P. Rankin. The incorporators were all well-known businessmen—Montague the founder of the pioneer hardware firm of the same name; Brayton and Rankin of the Pacific Iron Works, Brayton later to be the founder of the Pelton Water Wheel Company; and Swain a crockery and glassware importer. Josiah Belden was a Californian years before the gold rush, having arrived in 1841. He was the first mayor of San Jose in 1850, a merchant and large landowner.

The works at Eighth and Channel Streets were designed to produce gas from crude oil by what was known as the Gale and Lane retorting process. Metropolitan did not prove to be a dangerous competitor. There were plant troubles with the new process, and although a bid was made for customers by cutting rates, the frequent interruptions of service prevented the new company from making any real progress.

City Gas competition was different. Rates were cut, and Donahue fought back with still lower rates. With increasing gas consumption and lowered cost of coal and other operating expenses, the original gas rate of $15 per thousand cubic feet had dropped to $4.50 in 1870. The practice of granting graduated lower rates for increased consumption long had been in use by the old company. The war continued for two years until the gas rate had been reduced to $1.60 per thousand cubic feet—an unprofitable low at which neither side could win.

The result was consolidation. Peter Donahue recognized that duplication in public-utility service is costly—that two organizations, two plants, two lines of pipe in a single street could not serve the customers on that street at as low rates as could one. Doubling the expense of service was not the way to rate reduction. Consolidation, efficiency, and economy in operation were the answers. Consequently negotiations were opened and on April 1, 1873, the San Francisco Gas Light Company, representing a merger of the San Francisco Gas Company, the City Gas Company, and the Metropolitan Gas Company, was incorporated with authorized capital of $10,000,000. Peter Donahue continued at the head of San Francisco's gas lighting business. The basic gas rate was restored to its previous level of $4 per thousand.

One of the first new customers of the merged companies was the Palace Hotel which opened its ornate doors October 2, 1875. Illumination of Ralston's and Sharon's great inn marked a forward step in gas lighting. The inner courtyard into which the elite of the city, the Mother Lode, and the Comstock were driven in their victorias and landaus was lighted by 516 gas jets installed in crystal chandeliers and in standards lining the driveway entrance from New Montgomery Street. Gas light shed its radiance from sparkling chandeliers in the spacious public rooms and from white-globed standards on the galleries which rose tier on tier above the court. The lighting fixtures were so arranged that a hundred jets might be regulated by the turning of a single master key. Although electric lighting was not yet perfected, other novel electric devices were installed—electric call buttons in every room and telegraphic communication between the service pantries on each floor and the main dining room. Some 20 miles of gas pipe were needed to light the 800 guest rooms and other areas of the hotel which attained world renown for the richness of its furnishings and the quality of its hospitality.

General Phil Sheridan was guest of honor at the first formal banquet in the Palace, October 14, 1875. The *Daily Alta California* described the lighting in the resplendent banquet hall: "The main hall is lit up by twelve handsome chandeliers, in each of which were twenty-five globes or three hundred gas jets in all. . . . The head of the table was occupied by Governor Pacheco. On his right was General Sheridan, next to him sat Senator Sharon. . . . Hon. Peter Donahue proposed a toast to the memory of Admiral Farragut."

The gas rate war of 1870–1873 was to be followed by others even more bitter and more costly. It was the beginning also of the periodic excavation of streets in the business section by competing gas companies that left the underground area of the tortured thoroughfares a tangled maze of gas pipes. During that decade there was increasing discussion of gas rates and a not unnatural editorial protest against the "monopoly." Many decades were to pass before public acceptance of the principle that operation of gas and electric utilities by a single agency under proper rate regulation is more to the people's advantage than wasteful and uneconomic competition. In the early 1870s the state issued charters to new gas companies; the city government passed upon applications for franchises to operate. The state legislature in 1870 empowered municipalities to grant to *any* gas company the privilege of laying pipes in the streets and supplying gas for lighting.

Some of the public clamor bounced back upon the heads of the organizers of competitive companies. Historian John P. Young stated the case tersely in these words:

"The experience of the consumers during the Seventies was responsible for the passage of the act which gave to any corporation desiring to exercise the privilege the right to occupy the streets with gas pipes. It was thought by the author of the measure, and all the ardent reformers of that period, that the problem of obtaining cheap gas was solved by this step; but subsequent experience demonstrated that it merely helped men with the predatory instinct to profit at the expense of the old company, which had developed sufficient strength to buy out fresh competitors as fast as they appeared on the scene."

And so it came about that the state legislature in 1878 passed "an act to regulate the quality and standard illuminating power, and the price of gas, in all cities within the State of California having a population of one hundred thousand or more." At that time only San Francisco had such a population. The act provided that gas furnished must produce light of not less than 16 candle-power which it defined as "at least equal to that afforded by the combustion of 16 standard sperm candles." The maximum rate to be charged for gas services was fixed at $3 per thousand cubic feet.

The Donahue company had reduced its rate from $4 to $3.75 in 1874 and in obedience to the state law November 11, 1878, cut deeper to $3.

In 1879 a new state constitution extended the act of 1878 to apply to any city regardless of size and broadened the scope of municipal control to include other public utilities. The coming of electric service was anticipated by making the granting of franchises upon all city streets applicable to suppliers of "gas light or *other illuminating light*."

This was the start of gas rate regulation by governmental authority in California, and even as it was made effective, a new competitive threat was hanging over the heads of the gas men. Before another year, San Francisco was to have electric light—the strange new illuminant Edison, Brush, and other inventors were developing in Eastern laboratories. Meanwhile, however, it must be remembered that other parts of Northern California needed and promptly obtained the comfort of gas light enjoyed by San Franciscans.

CHAPTER 4

Gas Light Goes to the Country

THE TENS of thousands of Argonauts of the gold-rush era fell into two classes—those who came only to try for quick fortune and then, having succeeded or failed, turned homeward again and those who had cut loose their home ties and were determined to find a new life in California. The stayers were the builders of the towns and cities; they were the creators of the more substantial economy of agriculture and industry which supplanted the old order. They built lumber, grist and flour mills, carriage works, tanneries and saddleries, foundries and machine shops, and established a wide variety of business enterprises. Note how the population of the state grew—379,994 in 1860; 560,247 in 1870; and 864,694 in 1880. The hordes of fortune seekers had had their day. As trade, industry, and agriculture expanded, the new population changed in character. The newcomers came in search of permanent homes.

Not to be outdone by San Francisco, the metropolis, they built gasworks in their booming towns. After the first hysteria of the gold rush had subsided and mining had become a fairly well organized industry, useful and helpful gas light was brought to many an inland community of the Golden State.

With the spread of gas service over the state, the legislature passed a law requiring that all meters be tested for accuracy by a state inspector of gas meters. In 1876 Governor William S. Irwin appointed to the post Henry George who was then writing his classic work, "Progress and Poverty."

George held the position, which was generally regarded as a lucrative one, for four years. There were some who declared the governor was inconsistent when he handed to George a well-paid state job at the very moment the writer was blasting the conduct of public affairs and was demanding sweeping reforms. George, however, protested that he actually worked on the gas meter job, assisted by his brother John V. George. "Though my official duties were light," he said, "I never ate the bread of idleness, but was always very hard at work."

Primitive methods sometimes were used by the inland pioneer gas men. Coal for the making of gas was costly when the expense of sacking and hauling from the port of San Francisco was added to the high prices demanded at shipside—$25 to $55 a ton for imported cannel coal. The most commonly used substitute, generally mixed with coal for economy's sake, was pitch pine wood, which in the mountains was easily obtained. Resin oil was added to increase the gas production.

Iron pipe for the distribution mains was scarce and costly, but the ingenious gas men occasionally solved the problem with wooden pipe, made by boring or burning through small, straight logs.

* * *

Fire and flood checkmated the first efforts of the pioneers to build the city of Sacramento on a site below Captain John A. Sutter's historic fort at the confluence of the American and Sacramento Rivers. In 1854, however, a levee had been built, grades raised, and a thousand or more new buildings erected to house the 8,000 residents of the new state capital. Early in the same year, the governor, members of the legislature, and state officials had arrived to establish the state government in its permanent home.

Sacramento then was the focal point for trade and travel to and from the mining camps. Its people dreamed of making it the leading city of the state, and gas light was one of the first necessities.

Only a few months after San Francisco had been lighted with gas, William Glenn obtained a franchise June 5, 1854, to build and operate a gas plant in Sacramento. He sold his right to others who incorporated the Sacramento Gas Company, August 22, 1854. Angus Frierson was the first president, and N. W. Chittenden, secretary. On October 20, 1854, construction was formally started, with Mayor R. P. Johnson officiating at the handle of the first ceremonial shovel. After only a few months the river brought down a March freshet that flooded the building site in Slater's Addition, and all work was abandoned. Construction was resumed after a few months; the plant was completed and gas service was first available December 17, 1855. Peter and James Donahue of San Francisco supplied all ironwork for the new plant. The officers and directors of the company were Mayor R. P. Johnson, president; P. B. Norman, engineer; H. W. Watson, secretary; D. O. Mills, treasurer; James Murray, W. F. Babcock, and L. McLean, Jr.

Darius Ogden Mills, treasurer of the new gas company, then had not reached his thirtieth birthday. Soon after arriving from New York in 1849, he founded the banking house of D. O. Mills & Co., in Sacramento. There he established such a reputation as a banker that in 1864 the businessmen of San Francisco begged him to organize a new bank in San Francisco. The Bank of California was the result, Mills serving as president for nine years. When the bank failed in 1875 under W. C. Ralston's management, D. O. Mills returned to the presidency and in less than two months reopened the bank.

In the first year of operation, the daily output of gas in Sacramento was only 8,000 to 10,000 cubic feet, and the customers, largely hotels and business houses, numbered 113. The rate was $15 per thousand cubic feet, the same as in San Francisco. In 1863 the city entered into a contract with the gas company to install 45 street lamps to be lighted *only during the sessions of the state legislature,* a special service that must have been appreciated by the solons.

Not until 1871 did competition challenge the progress of the pioneer gas company. On March 21 the Citizens Gas Light Company entered the field under the leadership of W. E. Brown, president; Robert C. Clark, vice-president; Albert Gallatin, treasurer, and J. W. Pew, secretary. Works were built on the river front between T and U Streets, and 18 miles of street mains were laid to compete with the 10 miles then operated by the older company. The result followed the pattern established in San Francisco. On January 4, 1875, the Sacramento Gas

Company and the renamed Citizens Gas Light and Heat Company were consolidated as the Capital Gas Company, capital $2,000,000. The merged system served only gas until July 1, 1887, when a small plant built by the Pacific Thomson-Houston Electric Light Company was absorbed and both gas and electric service were provided by the single organization.

This was to become the usual process of evolution of gas and electric utilities in Northern California—first the little pioneer gas companies, then competition and merger, then merger with electric companies, then consolidation into regional systems and finally into the one integrated, interconnected system of today.

Albert Gallatin, treasurer of the Citizens Gas Company and member of the group which brought about consolidation of the Citizens and the Sacramento Gas companies, represented the interests of Collis P. Huntington and Mark Hopkins who, with Leland Stanford and Charles Crocker, had built the Central Pacific Railroad.

Gallatin was a late arrival in California, reaching San Francisco in 1860. When he failed to find fortune in mining, he obtained employment as a utility man in the Sacramento hardware store of Huntington & Hopkins. In 1868 the two railroad builders turned over their hardware business to Gallatin and four other employees in order to devote all their time to the Central Pacific. Gallatin grew in business stature. Representing Mark Hopkins, he became a director of the Capital Savings Bank and a director and vice-president of the California State Bank in Sacramento. Twenty years later he was to appear again as a powerful factor in the Sacramento gas and electric business.

* * *

Marysville, founded in 1850 and named in honor of Mary Murphy Covillaud, a survivor of the tragic Donner party, was the third California community to have the benefit of gas light. Centrally located in the Sacramento Valley, the town was a busy place in the fifties, thronged with miners from the Feather and the Yuba River diggings, and a source of supply for camps throughout the foothill country. In 1857 three different proposals to build a gas system were submitted to the city council. The Marysville Coal Gas Company was incorporated June 8,

1858, by David Edgar Knight, Charles H. Simpkins, and Adoniram Pierce. With shrewd foresight the incorporators guarded against competition by agreeing, in exchange for their 15-year franchise, to light all public buildings free of charge so long as no franchise was granted to any other gas company. The precaution was effective, for no rival company appeared until late in 1898 when the Yuba Power Company completed a small plant and began seeking gas customers. Competition lasted only five months when the Marysville Gas and Electric Company, which had absorbed the old company, reached an agreement with the newcomer.

Gas making in Marysville was costly. Coal was sacked in San Francisco and forwarded by river boats at freight and drayage rates that nearly doubled the first cost. Pitch firewood, resin, and castor beans frequently were used in the gas retorts. In 1867, when the Marysville plant was reconstructed, a new and larger storage tank was shipped around the Horn from Philadelphia on the clipper ship *Old Hickory* which was at sea 356 days before making port at San Francisco.

Marysville owed its gas service to one remarkable man, David Edgar Knight, the gas company's first president and manager. Knight was a born enterpriser, driven by restless energy to one undertaking after another. In his younger days he had been a plumber, a copper worker, and a cobbler. Before he went to Marysville he had had some experience as a gasworker in Sacramento. Then he broadened his activities. He built the first horsecar line between Marysville and Yuba City; he owned the race track; he started the first steam laundry in Marysville, was one of the owners of the Marysville Foundry, and president of the Marysville Woolen Mills. When he died in 1900 he was president of the Marysville Gas and Electric Company and a member of the county board of supervisors. Two Sacramento River boats, *Knight No. 1* and *Knight No. 2,* were named for this astonishing exemplar of pioneer enterprise.

* * *

Stockton, supply center for the Mother Lode mines of the Amador and Calaveras region, and chief city of the northern San Joaquin Valley area, kept abreast of the times by obtaining gas lighting service only five years after San Francisco had installed its first street lamps. The Stockton Gas Company was organized July 23, 1859. P. E. O'Connor was superintendent of the first small coal-gas plant, and the charter customers paid $10 per thousand cubic feet for their service. Ten years later, Joseph G. Eastland, secretary of the San Francisco Gas Company, and a group of his associates bought control of the company and Eastland became president, a post which he retained until his death.

Stockton occupies a special niche in California gas history as the scene of the earliest useful development of natural gas in the West. In 1864 workmen drilling for water on the site of the county courthouse brought in a well at a depth of 1,800 feet which supplied gas for lighting the courthouse and warming water for the Weber Swimming Baths. Other wells followed. On the Solomon Ranch, two miles south of French Camp, gas was found at 1,350 feet and for many years the ranch houses and other buildings were lighted by the flow from the home well.

The Stockton Natural Gas Company, organized in 1888 by Jerome Haas, bored a well at Lincoln and Lafayette Streets, Stockton, which produced 80,000 cubic feet daily. Encouraged by this development, the company laid mains to the business district and started gas distribution to customers. The property later became a part of the Stockton Gas and Electric Company system. Drilling continued sporadically until 1917. Property owners developed gas for their own use; among these were the State Hospital for mental cases, St. Mary's Church and Convent, the Crown Flour Mill, and the California Paper Mill.

Two separate companies were formed to serve residential areas adjacent to their wells—the Northern Natural Gas Company and the Citizens Natural Gas Company. In all, some 33 wells were drilled in the Stockton district. By present-day standards, the gas was of low heat content, and when in 1930 Pacific Gas and Electric Company began delivering gas from Kettleman Hills which was high in thermal value, use of the Stockton product gradually was discontinued. Long before that time the original Stockton Gas Company, by mergers and purchases, had

Battery Street, San Francisco, in 1856 was rough-and-ready but had its gas-lamp standard. (*Courtesy of Wells Fargo Bank Historical Room.*)

Joseph G. Eastland carried much of the administrative burden of the young San Francisco Gas Company and was its secretary for 23 years, 1856–1878.

Joseph A. Donohoe, fifth president of the San Francisco Gas Company, was also head of the banking firm of Donohoe, Kelly and Company. He was known as "the safe banker."

become successively the Stockton Gas Light and Heat Company and Stockton Gas and Electric Company.

* * *

San Jose, the Garden City, created as a pueblo by the Spanish nearly a century earlier, joined the gas-lighted cities in 1860 when its first coal-gas plant was built. The old pueblo had grown rapidly under American rule and the impetus of new gold-rush population. Following the example of San Francisco, James Hagan obtained from the town government on July 13, 1860, a franchise to build and operate a gas plant and mains.

In granting the privilege to Hagan, the city authorities reserved the right to reduce the initial gas rate of $10 per thousand cubic feet after the first five years should the cost of coal be lowered at that time. Coal then cost $53 per ton. The San Jose Gas Company was incorporated October 6, 1860, with $21,000 capital, by Thomas Anderson of San Francisco, president; James Hagan, manager and superintendent; Austin Roberts, secretary; and James K. Prior. Hagan received a salary of $100 per month.

Gas lighting service was inaugurated January 21, 1861, from a little plant that had only one wooden storage holder of 8,000-cubic-feet capacity. Seven street lamps served the needs of the town's night traffic and a total of 84 customers used gas during the first year of operation.

San Jose had no rail communication in 1860, so coal for the gas plant was shipped in scow schooners or barges to Alviso at the southern tip of the Bay. From Alviso the coal was hauled in wagons over nine miles of soggy road through the salt marshes. During the winter season when the road was impassable for wheeled traffic, pack mules were used. Occasionally a mule would lose his footing and he and his load of coal would be buried in the morass alongside the road. For many years writers and speakers have speculated on the deposit of coal and mule skeletons that must lie buried in the mud flats between Alviso and San Jose.

Partial proof of the legend was found in 1950. A crew of P. G. and E. gas men was digging a trench on Taylor Street in

Alviso at a point where a levee protects the low-lying area from the high tides of the Bay. The land had been reclaimed from the salt marsh through which the mule trains plodded nearly one hundred years ago. The diggers shoveled from the trench what they thought were lumps of hard clay until one of the chunks was broken and revealed to be a very good quality of Australian coal—without much doubt a part of a long-lost mule load en route to the gas plant.

In 1876 the company procured a perpetual gas franchise from the county of Santa Clara in order to extend its mains to the town of Santa Clara, three miles distant. To this day this is the only gas franchise under which P. G. and E. operates in Santa Clara County. When this line was completed, service began in Santa Clara to 37 customers and lighted nine street lamps.

The pioneer San Jose Gas Company met competition in a new form on June 20, 1877, when the Garden City Gas Company was incorporated by Z. P. Boyer of Pennsylvania, J. W. Walker and John H. Brucken of Oakland, J. C. Uhler of San Francisco, and W. P. Dougherty, C. B. Hensley, and Return Roberts of San Jose. The new company built a plant on San Augustine Street to produce gas by the Lowe water-gas process, a new method which was to have a profound effect on the gas business of the entire Pacific Coast.

The promoters of the San Jose Gas Company brought the San Francisco Board of Supervisors on a special excursion to San Jose. They wined them and dined them, and demonstrated the cheapness and efficiency of the new process. One San Francisco newspaper attributed a sharp drop in the price of stock of the San Francisco Gas Light Company to the threat offered by the Lowe process. In San Jose the old company met a rate reduction to $2.50 per thousand cubic feet with a rate of $1.50. The newcomer evidently was not strong enough to carry on the fight and after less than two years it was merged into the older system.

* * *

The city of Oakland was founded on the oak-studded leagues of the Peralta rancho, a part of the principality along the eastern shore of San Francisco Bay that had been granted by a Spanish governor to the Peralta family. Only a few hundred settlers lived in the little village clustered about the *embarcadero* on the estuary at the foot of what is now Broadway, when the city was incorporated May 4, 1852. Growth had lagged because of inadequate transportation to San Francisco across the Bay.

When Oakland had a population of 2,500, December 9, 1865, Joseph G. Eastland, secretary of the San Francisco Gas Company, and W. W. Beggs, its engineer, obtained from the city council a franchise to build and operate a gas plant and lay mains in the streets. This is the primary gas franchise under which P. G. and E. still operates in Oakland. The ordinance granting this franchise was amended for the first time in 1951 to provide for franchise payments to the city. After issuance of the franchise the Oakland Gas Light Company was incorporated June 12, 1866, with capital of $150,000. A coal-gas plant was built on land purchased for $3,300 on Washington Street between First and Second. The first storage holder had a capacity of only 10,000 cubic feet. When service was inaugurated December 1, 1866, just 15 customers were on the company's rolls.

Anthony (Antoine) Chabot, who had acquired a fortune in the placer mines at Nevada City, was first president of the new gas company. It was only one of his many activities. He developed the beginnings of San Francisco's first water supply from Lobos Creek, built a water system for Vallejo and San Jose and constructed Oakland's earliest water system, served first by the waters of Temescal Creek and San Leandro Creek and, later, by Lake Chabot. Chabot Observatory was the pioneer's gift to the city of Oakland a few years before his death in 1888. Other presidents of the gas company were H. H. Haight, one of California's early governors, J. West Martin, and W. W. Crane, both of whom also served as mayor of the city, and John W. Coleman, miner and financier.

Technical operation of the gas plant was in the hands of Henry Adams who had operated plants at Sacramento and Napa and later, for many years, at Stockton. He was succeeded in Oakland by Van Leer Eastland (brother of Joseph G.) who served as superintendent until his death in September, 1895.

The Oakland Gas Light Company made history in 1879 when it introduced gas cooking stoves into California and in 1877 when it established what was said to be the first high-pressure gas transmission in the United States. The cooking stoves came as a result of a visit to England by Joseph G. Eastland. They were known as Fletcher stoves, manufactured in England and a novelty in America where gas commonly was used only for lighting. Seeing a possibility of expanding the company's business, Eastland ordered a large invoice of the cookers shipped to Oakland. When they arrived, however, the housewives of the town were slow to accept them. Extreme promotional effort had to be made before the women of the day were convinced that good pies and bread could be baked in an oven fired by anything but wood and coal.

Two years earlier the Oakland company had reached out for the gas business of the growing towns of Alameda and Berkeley. Gas mains were extended to the neighboring communities and, by the use of compressors and governors, the illuminant was transmitted to storage holders erected in each town. It was one of the first attempts at interconnection of adjacent gas systems, a practice later used in the consolidation of larger and larger groups of companies for unified operation.

Not waiting for competition from electricity, the gas company built its own little electric plant in 1885 and operated the merged companies of Oakland, Alameda, and Berkeley under the name Oakland Gas Light and Heat Company, incorporated in 1884.

The consolidated company continued extending its gas and electric lines until it was merged into the California Gas and Electric Corporation and afterward into the P. G. and E. system. Gas street lighting in Oakland was not discontinued until January, 1940, when the few remaining gas lights, long since obsolete, were turned off for the last time.

* * *

Nevada City, at the hustling, bustling heart of the gold-mining country, was one of the early fields of gas lighting development. J. S. Kaneen and Adoniram Pierce built a small plant there in 1859, making the holder, retorts, and other parts with their own hands and laying some 2 miles of mains in the streets. The plant, reorganized in 1865 as the Nevada City Gas Works, was at Main and Coyote Streets. Gas was made from coal, pitch pine wood, and resin oil. Charles H. Simpkins, who had been associated with Knight and Pierce in building the Marysville plant, was interested also in the Nevada works. He went on to become one of the leading gas men in the state, serving as president of the Los Angeles Gas Company from 1875 to 1889. The Nevada City enterprise was incorporated in 1885 as the Nevada City Gas Company.

* * *

Gas lighting was available to Grass Valley residents in 1862 when The Grass Valley Gas Company was incorporated by Edward McLaughlin. The system was sold in 1865 to Adoniram Pierce who had gas company interests in Marysville and Nevada City. After passing through several hands, the property was acquired in 1885 by John Glasson.

Edward McLaughlin, founder of the company, was a successful hardware merchant who had come to Grass Valley in 1852. In 1868 he moved to San Jose where, with Judge Ryland, he established the private banking firm of McLaughlin & Ryland. Subsequently he organized the Commercial Savings Bank which was later incorporated as the San Jose Safe Deposit Bank of Savings and still later became a branch of the Bank of America. McLaughlin established in 1882 the Union Hardware & Metal Company of Los Angeles, which his grandson Edward H. McLaughlin now heads.

* * *

Gas service came early to the historic town of Vallejo, with first service supplied July 4, 1866. A small plant was built and placed in operation by M. P. Young who had been connected with the San Francisco Gas Company. Tragedy interrupted service August 21 of the following year when Young was fatally shot by John Lee, a hotel proprietor. Lee had been caught evading his gas bills by building a by-pass around his meter. When

Young attempted to obtain restitution, the hotel man shot and killed him.

General John B. Frisbie, pioneer citizen of Vallejo and son-in-law of General Vallejo, incorporated the Vallejo Gas Light Company, September 14, 1867. The plant, enlarged and improved, served the town until it was taken into the P. G. and E. system. General Frisbie, lawyer, politician, and militia officer, came to California in 1847. Settling in Vallejo and marrying the eldest daughter of General Vallejo, he attained prominence as president of the local bank, railroad builder, and member of the state legislature.

* * *

Napa was the tenth city in California to introduce gas lighting. In 1867 William W. Beggs, chief engineer of the San Francisco Gas Company, who with Joseph G. Eastland had built the first Oakland gas plant, organized the Napa City Gas Light Company. He was joined in the venture by J. H. Goodman and James Freeborn. Beggs designed and built the plant which went into operation September 1, 1867. Part of the street mains laid to serve the first 65 customers were condemned boiler tubes joined by cast-iron sleeves and lead-sealed joints.

* * *

San Rafael joined the march of gas cities in November, 1871, when Allen Lee installed a Maxim gas machine and sold gas to a few customers. With J. O. Eldridge, he incorporated the properties in 1883 as the San Rafael Gas Company, which became the San Rafael Gas and Electric Company December 8, 1887. One of the early-day gas men in San Rafael was J. S. ("Pop") Kaneen, who had started his gas career in Nevada City in 1859.

* * *

Eureka, the lumber port of the Northern California coast, did not have gas lighting until 1878 when Herbert Kraft built a small plant after two previous attempts to establish a gas utility had failed. The first was by J. W. Henderson, banker and mill operator, whose Maxim Gas Company operated only a short time. The next attempt resulted only in the granting of a franchise to promoters who later decided not to build a plant. Kraft's Eureka Gas Works was plagued by the poor quality of gas it produced, and in 1883 the system was sold to the Eureka Gas Company, which also took over the mains laid by the earlier Maxim company. The Eureka Gas Company properties later were sold to C. O. G. Miller's Pacific Lighting Company, and finally to Western States Gas and Electric Company before that system was acquired by P. G. and E.

* * *

The gas men continued to bring the boon of light to the towns of Northern California. The course of the companies followed much the same pattern—small plants serving increasing numbers of customers as rates were lowered and the quality of gas was improved, and eventually being merged with the oncoming electric systems.

CHAPTER 5

War Balloons and California Gas

BECAUSE the chief aeronaut of the Union Army needed a better gas for the observation balloons flown over Civil War battle lines, the development of California's gas utilities was vitally affected.

And the same chain of circumstances that started with war balloons was responsible for the entrance into the utility field of C. O. G. Miller of San Francisco, who at the time of his death, April 23, 1952, was the distinguished dean of Pacific Coast gas company executives, an honored veteran member of Pacific Gas and Electric Company's board of directors and member of its executive committee. Until his last brief illness, he belied his eighty-six years with a vigor of mind and body that many a younger man could not match.

The aeronaut was Professor Thaddeus Sobieski Constantin Lowe, physicist, chemist, meteorologist, inventor. In the years before the war, Professor Lowe had made scores of balloon ascensions for study of atmospheric phenomena. When civil war blazed between the North and South, the Washington government called upon him to organize and lead a balloon corps as a military arm. His search for the best gas to be used for inflation of balloons led him into exhaustive postwar study of the whole subject of gas manufacture. The fruit of his work was the Lowe carbureted water-gas process which he developed and patented at Norristown, Pa., in the years 1872–1875. His first plant was built at Phoenixville, Pa., in 1874. The new method produced an improved illuminant by the forcing of steam over incandescent carbon to obtain a mixed gas of carbon monoxide and hydrogen.

First adopted by Pennsylvania gas companies, Lowe carbureted water-gas plants spread rapidly throughout the country. The method was first employed in California in 1877 when the Garden City Gas Company, organized by Z. P. Boyer, a Pennsylvanian, built a plant in San Jose. The second Lowe plant was built two years later in Oakland by the Oakland Gas Light Company.

Professor Lowe had a genius for promotion as well as skill in the sciences. In 1882 the United Gas Improvement Company was organized in Philadelphia, chiefly to exploit the Lowe gas patents which had been purchased from the inventor. The company began an active and far-reaching campaign which was to make it one of the largest gas holding and operating companies in the world.

Among the cities which United Gas Improvement entered in search of business was San Francisco where it acquired a lease and then an interest in the Central Gas Light Company, November 1, 1883. Central Gas, under the leadership of Charles McLaughlin, had been waging a rate war against the older San Francisco Gas Light Company. The president of United was John L. Stewart, an old friend of C. O. G. Miller's father, Albert Miller, then president of the San Francisco Savings Union. Stewart came to California on an inspection tour and found his company's San Francisco affairs not to his liking. He went to Miller. "Things are in bad shape, Albert," he said. "We want you to take over." The banker demurred. He knew nothing about the gas business, but he finally consented and thereby shaped his son's career as a public-utility executive instead of the banker he might have been.

C. O. G. Miller, then in his nineteenth year, became cashier of United's Central gas company, December 1, 1883. The plant of the company was an improved Lowe carbureted water-gas installation on property bounded by Fillmore, Steiner, Bay and Francisco Streets. In the following year, October 1, 1884, Albert Miller, joined by Lloyd Tevis, Robert Watt, Senator W. A. Sharon, George D. Newhall, and Louis Sloss, formed the Pacific Gas Improvement Company which bought the California and Arizona holdings of United Gas Improvement Company, including the Central Gas Light Company's properties. The new gas company proved a troublesome competitor to the old Donahue gas system. When it was ultimately purchased in 1903 and merged into the San Francisco Gas and Electric Company, it was serving gas to 12,000 customers in San Francisco.

Pacific Gas Improvement Company was headed by Albert Miller as president. His son, C. O. G. Miller, was elected treasurer and retained that position until his father's death in 1900 when he succeeded to the presidency. From the beginning he demonstrated a talent for finding business opportunities and a capacity to make them good. In the office of Pacific Gas Improvement Company when it was starting its career, the younger Miller was associated with W. B. Cline, another youngster with ambitions. The two saw prospects for money making in the Siemens gas lamp, a German scientist's device for increasing two and one-half times the light of the old fishtail gas jet. Young Miller and Cline acquired agency rights to the lamp and built up a profitable business by buying the appliances for $60 each and renting them for $2 a week to gas users, chiefly in downtown San Francisco.

That enterprise was the genesis of the present Pacific Lighting Corporation—a $400,000,000 company in 1951. With their Siemens lamp project a success, and with the senior Miller's cooperation, the young men incorporated Pacific Lighting Company in 1886 under a charter which allowed them to enter almost any phase of the gas and electric business. They enlisted an impressive board of directors. The first president was Monroe Livingston, an investor in many California enterprises. Starting with a working capital of less than $10,000, the new company acquired small gas properties in San Bernardino, Santa Rosa, and Eureka, and in 1889 obtained control of the Los Angeles Gas Company.

W. B. Cline went to Los Angeles to take charge, and achieved a distinguished place in utility management. Pacific Lighting Corporation, as it is now known, was one of the earliest of holding companies. Through the years it has expanded until today, through its operating subsidiaries, Southern California Gas Company and Southern Counties Gas Company, it serves in Los

Angeles and other southern counties a total of more than 1,644,000 customers.

When death ended his career, C. O. G. Miller was chairman of the board of directors of Pacific Lighting Corporation. His son, Robert W. Miller, had succeeded him as president. When his Pacific Gas Improvement Company was merged into the San Francisco Gas and Electric Company in 1903, he became a director of that company and from 1912 served for 40 years on the board of its successor—P. G. and E.

Professor T. S. C. Lowe, who invented the gas-making process that caused the organization of United Gas Improvement Company, which induced Albert Miller to enter the gas business and so was indirectly responsible for C. O. G. Miller's entry into the utility field, also became a notable figure in California gas history. In 1887 the inventor moved his family to Pasadena. Two years later, his son Leon P. Lowe, then living at Lynn, Mass., was granted a basic patent on a process for manufacturing gas from oil. He came to California and organized the California Light and Fuel Company to build gas plants under his new patent. With his father, he also formed a gas company in Los Angeles and built an oil-gas plant there.

After a bitter battle between Lowe and the Los Angeles Gas Company, control of both properties was bought by Pacific Lighting and the two consolidated as the Los Angeles Lighting Company.

Professor Lowe's zest for new projects led him to other ventures. Expecting (mistakenly) that Pasadena's business center would move to the south, he built a grand opera house on what proved to be the wrong site. He erected a Lowe gas plant in Pasadena. But his major undertaking was the Mount Lowe Railway, completed in the early nineties. Up the steep and rugged face of the Sierra Madre range which rises above Pasadena to altitudes between 6,000 and 7,000 feet, he constructed a cable railway on a hair-raising angle to a mesa part way up the mountain. There he built a comfortable view-hotel and an observatory. From that point a trolley railway carried travelers to an alpine tavern nestled under the shoulder of the summit, Mt. Lowe, altitude 6,000 feet. For many years the spectacular trip was on every tourist's itinerary, but fires, rising costs, and receding revenue eventually caused abandonment of the railroad.

With his son Leon, the inventor continued his promotion of the Lowe gas processes. A dozen or more plants in the northern area were converted under the son's direction from the old coal-gas method to Lowe process equipment. In 1899 Leon P. Lowe and his inventor-father returned to San Francisco to incorporate the San Francisco Coke and Gas Company for production of coke by a Lowe patent process. The residual gas was sold to the San Francisco Gas and Electric Company.

CHAPTER 6

Dawn of the Electric Day

SAN FRANCISCO was the first city in the United States and, so far as is known, the first in the world to have a central generating station for distribution of electricity to customers.

The California Electric Light Company, incorporated June 30, 1879, was the first electric utility for public service. Its little pioneer plant began operation for arc lamp lighting in September of the same year. This was just a few months before Thomas Alva Edison applied for a patent on his first incandescent lamp, and three years prior to the opening of Edison's Pearl Street station in New York City to supply current for incandescent lighting. In England the first central plant, Brighton Station, London, was not opened until September 4, 1882. Dynamos and arc lamps had been operated earlier than 1879 in California and in eastern American cities but only for private use on the premises where they were installed.

Electric light, miraculous as it was to a generation accustomed to gas illumination, was not unknown to San Franciscans in 1879. All during the 1870 decade when Edison, Gramme, Brush, Farmer, Weston, and Thomson were seeking practical means of producing electric light for the people's use, another scientist was hard at work in San Francisco. He was Father Joseph M. Neri, S.J., professor of natural philosophy in St. Ignatius College, forebear of the University of San Francisco. Father Neri had come to America from Italy where he was born January 16, 1836, the brilliant son of a noble Italian family.

When the priest-scientist-inventor came from Santa Clara College to join the faculty of St. Ignatius College, then situated on Market Street between Fourth and Fifth where the Emporium department store now stands, he plunged into a long series of experiments and studies. He built a storage battery for demonstrations during his classroom lectures and carried on intensive research in electric lighting. His work had progressed so far by 1871 that he was able to install an electric light in a college window facing Market Street as a part of the illumination of the building in honor of Pope Pius IX. The occasion was the Silver Jubilee of the Pontification of the Pope which was celebrated by a night parade in which 20,000 San Franciscans marched. The historian of St. Ignatius College noted the light as follows:

"The parlors, halls and rooms facing Market Street were bright with gas jets, while from the largest of the windows the electric light sent forth its beams, lighting up Market Street and the adjoining buildings."

Three years later, in 1874, Father Neri received from the Compagnie L'Alliance in France a large electro-magneto generating machine that had been used by the defenders in the siege of Paris. The apparatus was a gift to the college from Tiburcio Parrott, son of John Parrott, founder of the banking firm which bore his name.

The Jesuit priest at that time was delivering a series of public lectures on electricity, but ill health had compelled him to suspend his platform appearances. In place of speaking, he arranged for a public demonstration of the light his French generator would produce. On the bell tower of the college buildings, 95 feet high, he installed an arc lamp equipped with a "light regulator" for lighthouse use, a spherical mirror and Fresnel lens, all mounted on a revolving platform. The published accounts of the display declared the searchlight was "such as to be seen at a distance of two hundred miles" and that cost of the apparatus "represents over $5,000."

Father Neri's lighting demonstration was given April 9, 1874. During the Centennial parade July 4, 1876, he illuminated Market Street in front of the college with three arc lights which shed a startling white radiance upon the marchers below. In the same year, St. Ignatius College installed an elaborate exhibit at the Eleventh Industrial Exhibition, conducted by the Mechanics' Institute in Mechanics' Pavilion. The newspapers published long descriptions of the lighting equipment. The *Mining and Scientific Press* said: "The exhibitions given by Father Neri with this light are very interesting—the immense pavilion being completely flooded with light so strong that people at some distance are compelled to shade their eyes."

Father Neri went on with his research until in 1903 he lost his eyesight. He died November 17, 1919, at the University of Santa Clara. His prediction of years before that electricity would revolutionize the lighting of the world long since had come true.

After Father Neri had made his successful demonstrations of arc lamp lighting, Charles de Young, one of the editors of the San Francisco *Chronicle,* returned in 1878 from a visit to the Paris Exposition with a Gramme generator and two Jablochkoff candles, a form of arc lamp which the Russian inventor had induced him to introduce in America. The following year the equipment was installed in the *Chronicle's* new building at Bush and Kearny Streets where the generator was operated by the same engine that ran the presses. The *Chronicle* corner was described as "one of the brightest as well as handsomest in the city by reason of the five electric globes that stand like sentinels along the curbstones." John P. Young in his history of San Francisco, however, reported: "Owing to the irregularities of the engine and other imperfections the light produced was very unsatisfactory but the *Chronicle* was insistent in proclaiming that electricity would be 'the light of the future.' "

George H. Roe, a young money broker, was the organizer and for many years manager of the first San Francisco electric company. Like Peter Donahue, who built the earliest California gas plant without prior experience in gas manufacture, he started with neither technical knowledge nor training in electrical operations.

Roe came to San Francisco in 1875 from Ontario, Canada, when he was twenty-three years old. One of his first acts was to deposit in the Bank of California a draft for his savings. When he went to the bank a few days later to collect the proceeds of his draft (the date was August 27, 1875), he found the doors closed and a worried, milling crowd outside, clamoring for return of their deposits. Learning from bystanders that the bank had suspended payments, Roe elbowed his way through to the entrance and somehow gained admittance. The paying teller refused his demand that he be given a certified check for the amount of his draft, but he persuaded attendants to take him to W. C. Ralston, president of the bank who sat alone in his office, a broken man, his resignation in the hands of his directors. When Ralston heard Roe's plea for relief, he called a clerk and ordered a check drawn and delivered to Roe. It was possibly his last official act. Later in the day the banker gave up his life, the victim either of suicide or accident in the chill waters of the Bay, where he had gone for his customary swim.

Roe's check was worthless at the moment but it did help him establish his credit with the keeper of his boardinghouse, and when the bank reopened he recovered all of his small funds.

The young Canadian had been on his own resources since he was thirteen when his father died. With limited education and little actual business experience, he looked about for a doorway to a career in San Francisco. He made friends quickly. Among them was W. P. Plummer who joined him December 7, 1876, in establishing an office on Steuart Street near the water front under the partnership name of Roe & Plummer. The firm discounted notes and dealt in exchange.

Then on a day in 1878 chance led George H. Roe to his opportunity. The express company had received a C.O.D. shipment of a Wallace-Farmer dynamo and lamp. Lacking the cash to meet the bill, the consignee applied to Roe & Plummer for a loan, offering two endorsers on his note and the apparatus as security. When the due date passed without payment, the money brokers found themselves in possession of a dynamo with no prospect of recovering the money they had loaned.

Weeks passed. The Wallace-Farmer machine gathered dust. Then the firm of Roe & Plummer decided to retire from business. In the division of the partnership's assets George Roe drew the apparently useless electrical equipment as a part of his share. He began asking questions, wondering whether there was money to be made in the new electrical business.

C. O. G. Miller, whose career in utilities spanned almost 70 years, was a director of Pacific Gas and Electric Company from 1912 until his death in 1952.

Joseph B. Crockett, starting his utility career as a gas engineer, served as president of the San Francisco Gas and Electric Company and predecessors from 1885 to 1902.

Gas standard at Market Street and Third, San Francisco, in 1865, where the lamplighters made their rounds at dusk. (*Courtesy of California Historical Society.*)

Roe tried the Wallace-Farmer dynamo and lamp which were among the first produced for commercial use. The lamp was unsatisfactory and he had a new model made. He employed such technical help as he could find in a city where few knew anything about electricity. In the end he decided the Wallace-Farmer apparatus could not be operated profitably but nevertheless he determined to go ahead.

The time was propitious. Arc light generators and lamps were being offered for commercial use. In Cleveland, Ohio, Charles F. Brush, an electrician employed by the Cleveland Telegraph Supply Company, obtained a patent in 1877 on his first dynamo and followed that with improvements of the design of both generator and arc lamp. The Telegraph Supply company began manufacture of the Brush equipment early in 1878.

An exhibition of the light produced by the Brush dynamo and lamp was given at Mechanics' Pavilion April 11, 1878, when the public was invited to witness the machine in action. Thanks to the enterprise of Senator W. A. Sharon who was determined his new Palace Hotel should outshine all others, San Francisco was among the first of American cities in which the Brush system was installed. When Senator Sharon learned that the Brush generators could be obtained, he ordered two arc lamps hung in the picturesque courtyard of the hostelry. He was so pleased with the effect that he ordered a larger dynamo and more lamps.

The arc lamps displaced 1,085 gas jets which had been used to illuminate the hotel's public rooms.

At about the same time the Union Iron Works installed Brush lights and generators.

Introduction of electric lighting by the Palace Hotel was followed by events that were to result in the establishment of the city's pioneer electric utility. The Cleveland manufacturing company was represented in San Francisco by the San Francisco Telegraph Supply Company, William Kerr, president. When in 1878 the Brush arc lighting system appeared to offer bright prospects of success, Kerr obtained from the Ohio factory a contract which gave to him exclusive Pacific Coast selling rights to its products. Six months later the Cleveland Telegraph Supply Company secured from Charles F. Brush the right to manufacture under all his patents and changed its corporate name to Brush Electric Company.

Kerr began promoting the new electric lighting apparatus. His advertisement in the *Mining and Scientific Press* December 14, 1878, announced: "Electric Light, Brush Patents, The Best, Cheapest, Cleanest and Most Powerful Light in the World."

One of the first of Kerr's customers outside San Francisco was a Yuba County mine where adequate light meant greater production of gold. The *Mining and Scientific Press* of May 10, 1879, quoted the Nevada City *Transcript* as follows:

"The first electric light ever introduced in a mining claim was placed on the Deer Creek Claim of the Excelsior Water Company (near Smartsville) on the 10th of last month. A 12,000 candlepower Brush machine was put in operation and three lights of 3,000 candlepower were placed in prominent positions upon the claim. . . . Although the night was very dark, the lights shed a brilliant light around and enabled the miners to work as readily as during the day. . . . The company's daily cleanup is from $500 to $1,000 and by running nights also, the yield of the mine can be doubled."

While Kerr was exploiting the Brush arc lighting system, George H. Roe was continuing his experiments with generators. He had a notion that he could build a workable generator and he did have a small machine constructed. Purely for decorative purposes the mechanics had added to the design a polished iron band around the armature. When all was ready for the test run, the friends he had interested in his project were called in to observe the performance of the new machine. Not a spark! Although the machine revolved at its rated speed of 1,200 revolutions per minute, no electricity was generated. All the tests failed. It was not until sometime later, when they had become better versed in the workings of electric generators, that the builders learned the fancy iron band around the armature had caused the trouble by diverting and neutralizing the magnetic forces generated by the machine.

Despite his failure to develop a dynamo and arc lamp of his own, Roe held to his belief that lighting current from a central generating plant could be distributed successfully to customers.

His next step was the incorporation June 30, 1879, of the California Electric Light Company with offices at 427 Montgomery Street. Associated with him as incorporators and directors were John Bensley, O. F. Willey, J. R. Hardenbergh, and R. A. Robinson. Hardenbergh became the first president and Roe, secretary and manager.

John Bensley appears to have been the most prominent of the company's directors. Coming to California in 1849, he had operated a mercantile and freighting business in Sacramento. Moving to San Francisco, he acquired interests in industrial, shipping, and utility enterprises. He had been one of the incorporators of the Citizens Gas Company in 1863 and for a number of years prior to 1875 had been a stockholder and director of the Black Diamond Coal Company. Although he was listed as subscribing for four-fifths of the authorized $5,000,000 stock issue of California Electric Light Company, how much money he or any of his associates actually invested is unknown. Judging by the modest initial expenditures of the infant enterprise the amounts must have been small.

Of the remaining incorporators, J. R. Hardenbergh was a pioneer of the gold-rush years, had been one of the proprietors of the Russ House in 1861, and in 1872 had held the government position of U.S. Surveyor General for California. His grandson, Percy B. Hardenbergh, joined the P. G. and E. staff many years later and retired in 1945 after 42 years of service. O. F. Willey was an importer and dealer in carriages and wagons. R. A. Robinson was a deputy superintendent of streets.

San Francisco's first electric utility company was organized, but there remained the question of what generators should be installed. In the articles of incorporation the founders declared: "The purpose for which said corporation is formed is to manufacture, use and sell the Titzell Electric Generator and Lamps and any and all other appliances and inventions necessary to successfully maintain and put the electric light in successful operation in the State of California and all the states and territories of the United States."

The "Titzell generator" was unknown. It may have been the name given the dynamo George H. Roe had built and which had proved to be a failure. He may have hoped eventually to perfect the machine. Search of the records of electrical inventions of the period has failed to reveal any "Titzell."

What then happened was that William Kerr, holder of territorial rights to the Brush dynamo and lamps, joined forces with the budding electric utility. In exchange for a large block of stock and a directorship in the California Electric Light Company he turned over to the company his contract with the Brush Electric Company. Obviously, Roe and his associates must have known all about the Brush equipment, for it had been in operation for many months at the Palace Hotel and the Union Iron Works. The story of the negotiations that led to the agreement and the details of the bargain which induced Kerr to relinquish his valuable contract in exchange for stock in an undeveloped corporation remain buried in the ashes of the 1906 earthquake-fire.

With generating equipment assured, the California Electric Light Company lost no time launching its project. It erected a small frame building to house the Brush machines in the rear of the corner where the Pacific Building now stands at Fourth and Market Streets. Additional machines and lamps were ordered shipped from Cleveland.

With a sure advertising instinct the new company arranged to install generators and lamps in the Fourteenth Industrial Exhibition at Mechanics' Pavilion August 5 to September 15, 1879. The *Mining and Scientific Press* of September described the illumination of the great central nave of the Pavilion, 441 feet long by 100 feet wide, as equal to the light given by 1,000 gas jets. In addition to the 16 lamps installed in the pavilion, two others, powered by a smaller dynamo, were hung outside over the main entrance. The press declared the cost of operating the 18 lamps was 8 cents per hour for each lamp.

The first generating plant was experimental. In a letter written years afterward to the editor of the *Journal of Electricity,* Roe explained why:

"Being unable to obtain any information regarding the business of electric lighting because no electric lighting had been done, we determined to ascertain whether the business of renting lights could be made profitable; and for the purpose built a station, if station it could be called, for the purpose of ascertaining: first, whether it was practical to distribute lights throughout the city . . . ; and second, whether the people would take these lights and pay a price for them that would show a profit.

"Naturally, the cheapest building was constructed, simply 4 x 4 uprights, a wooden floor laid on the ground, the sides of the building covered with sheet iron. The boiler, engine, dynamos, oil house, coal pile, and everything was huddled together in this one enclosure. . . . We realized that the expenditure we were making was merely experimental and would be of no value if the business amounted to nothing."

The electric installation consisted of two Brush arc light dynamos, one with a capacity of 16 lights and a smaller machine that would supply only five lamps.

When the plant at Fourth and Market Streets was ready to serve customers in September, 1879, the new company immediately reached out for business. It would provide light to a customer from sundown to midnight for a charge of $10 per lamp per week. No service was given on Sundays or holidays. Or, as agent of the Brush Electric Company, it would sell the customer a generating machine, the necessary lamps, and a supply of carbons. The company's prospectus declared the new arc light "is not offered for domestic purposes, because in dwellings it is not as cheap as gas or oil and is not yet adapted to such uses."

Among the first customers were the Hastings clothing store at Sutter and Montgomery Streets and Andrews Diamond Palace, Montgomery between Sacramento and California Streets. In a letter dated August 21, 1879, J. R. Hardenbergh, president of the company, offered service to Collector of the Port Thomas Shannon. He wrote:

"We will furnish the Post Office at San Francisco with 6 electric lights of 2000 candlepower each sufficient to light the office and entrance which will make a very fine light not trying to the eye as gas light for the sum of $450 per month, and when the Appraisers building is complete you will need additional light and if we are correctly informed you will be provided with an engine and boiler in that building then the extra expense of power will be done away with. We will sell the Government this

6 light machine that we propose to light the Post Office with for $2500 with all the lamps complete or in case you conclude to light both buildings we will sell you a large machine of 35,000 candlepower to use in lighting both buildings with 16 lamps complete for $4000 this price includes the expense of placing the lamps in position and we guarantee that they will work satisfactorily. We also furnish you with 100 carbons. Remember that in the foregoing estimate we intend to furnish double lamps that will burn 16 hours without attention. The single lamps burn 8 hours and there is no other electric lamp giving a good light, except ours (The Brush Lamp) that will burn longer than one hour and a half."

That demand for the lighting service was immediately created is proved by the fact that two 16-light generators were added to the Fourth Street plant in December, 1879, and in the next few months two more with an aggregate capacity of 100 lights.

Something of the light hunger of a generation that had known only candles, kerosene lamps, and flickering gas jets is discernible in newspaper accounts of Gen. U. S. Grant's visit to San Francisco when the former President of the United States was given a gala reception September 20, 1879. The *Daily Alta California,* with evident exaggeration of the number of lights installed, fairly underscored the lighting features of the celebration: "The grand event was the parade accompanied by numerous torch bearers and pyrotechnics. Electric lights in many places rendered the scene brighter and lighter than the sunniest noon. . . ."

An editorial commented: "He [Grant] had left this state more than a quarter of a century ago when it was but a crude country. We noticed him as he rode through the streets last night over solid pavements, which he left as little better than sand and mud, as if his eyes were seeking some well-known and remembered shanty or adobe of ancient construction. But, instead they followed up the façades of palace-like structures, their windows brilliant with illumination of gas light, electricity and ladies' eyes."

Misfortune came April 24, 1880, when the uninsured plant was destroyed by fire. The loss threatened to become disastrous when, a few days later, the Brush factory in Cleveland also was burned and the damaged generators could not be sent there for repair. Even though no mechanics trained for generator work were available, the fire-scorched machines were reconditioned and made ready for service again. A new plant was built on leased ground at 117 O'Farrell Street and lighting service was resumed.

While the struggling little electric company was operating its small O'Farrell Street central station, Pierre B. Cornwall first publicly became associated with its affairs. At the July, 1880, annual meeting he was elected vice-president and treasurer, evidently advancing to the presidency in 1881. From then on for more than a decade he was an influential factor in San Francisco's pioneer electric utility, as president of the corporation.

Pierre B. Cornwall was one of the many vivid personalities that emerged from the hurly-burly of the gold-rush period. Arriving from New York State in 1848, he entered into a mercantile business at Sutter's Fort in Sacramento. He bought city real estate when land was cheap. When Sacramento's city government was organized in 1849 he was elected a councilman. He and his partners erected a hospital to care for the sick. With his partner, Barton Lee, he established an active real-estate and banking house and in 1850 he sold his interest and two-thirds of his real estate to Lee for $640,000. He had made a fortune only 18 months after his arrival in California, in debt for $8,000.

Cornwall was elected from Sacramento to California's first legislature. Resigning that post, he changed his residence to San Francisco in 1858 and from that time on his activities multiplied—he was one of the organizers of the first stock exchange, president of the Mechanics' Institute and the Society of California Pioneers, university regent, San Francisco school director, in addition to his varied business enterprises. These included the Black Diamond Coal Company, which operated mines at the base of Mt. Diablo in Contra Costa County in California and in Oregon and Washington, and a ship line operating coal carriers from northwestern ports. He was president of both.

Cornwall had been closely associated with John Bensley, one of the incorporators of the California Electric Light Company, through the years when Bensley was a director of the Black Diamond Coal Company, and he knew William Kerr, territorial agent for the Brush patents. Through his long association with the Mechanics' Institute as trustee and president he had developed a keen interest in the progress of the electrical arts. Possibly as a stockholder he was interested in the California Electric Light Company some time before he was elected its treasurer and vice-president.

By the end of 1881 the demand for electric light in the stores and factories of downtown San Francisco had increased to the limit of the O'Farrell Street plant's capacity. A plot of land on Jessie Street between Third and Fourth was acquired in October of that year and a new and larger plant was erected. Two years later the plant was enlarged, and in 1888 a second powerhouse, known as Station B, was built at Townsend Street and Clarence Place. Its capacity was 1,000 lights for a single machine of 960 kilowatts. The engineers were beginning to rate generating capacity in kilowatts instead of numbers of lights. Additions were made to both plants as the roster of customers mounted.

The original Jessie Street plant, known then as Station A, was enlarged twice, the second time in 1892 when an extension named Station C was erected, with a smokestack rising 175 feet above its boiler room. The plant was partly destroyed by fire in February, 1906, and two months later its towering stack went down in a rubble of brick when the earthquake started wrecking and burning downtown San Francisco. Rebuilt, Station C still is operated by P. G. and E. as a switching point in its distribution system.

In 1951 an old memorandum found among historical documents revealed the existence of an unexplained marble tablet in the pavement of the Station C yard. When the spattered asphalt and dirt were cleaned from its surface, this inscription was found cut deep in the 14-inch square block of marble: "E. L. & P. Co. 1892." The letters stood for Edison Light and Power Company which succeeded the original corporation. Workmen with a jackhammer uncovered below the marble a leaden cylinder in which were packed moisture-soaked newspapers bearing 1892 dates and containing architects' drawings and descriptions of the new building erected on Jessie Street 60 years ago. Tablet and cylinder had marked for posterity another step in the growth of the city's electric system.

The first electric street light in San Francisco was erected in 1883 in front of the City Hall on a high mast carrying four 4,000-candlepower lamps. Gradually the system was extended. In 1888 the company was awarded a two-year contract by the city to erect and maintain 21 masts 150 feet tall each with 16,000 candlepower and 102 masts 40 feet high with lamps of 2,000 candlepower. Rates for the lighting service were fixed at $4.40 per night for each of the 150-foot masts and 55 cents per night for each of the 2,000-candlepower installations. Street lighting experts of the day held to the theory that lights of great power placed high aloft would serve as artificial moons, spreading their illumination over areas many blocks in extent.

The new electric lighting was placed in the business section of the city. Gas light continued to be used in the outlying residential areas, and in 1888 the municipal government renewed its contract with the San Francisco Gas Light Company to maintain the 5,100 street standards then installed at 12 cents per night for each lamp. Gas lamps had a light rating of 17 candlepower. Street lighting contracts and rates continued to be a bone of contention between the gas and electric companies. Because both were under control of the Board of Supervisors the utilities almost constantly were embroiled in political contests.

Although Thomas A. Edison had perfected his first incandescent lamp late in 1879, the new lamps did not become available in quantity on the Pacific Coast until the early eighties. In 1883 the Oregon Navigation Company lighted its dock at the foot of Spear Street with 240 16-candlepower incandescent lamps shining from the rafters and powered by a generator installed on the dock.

The first store to adopt the little Edison lamp was the Rosenthal shoe store on Kearny Street which in 1887 installed in each of its two display windows a series of eight incandescent lamps fed by an arc circuit. Forty lamps arranged in five series from an arc circuit were installed in the Bush Street Theater in 1888. The current show was *The Little Tycoon.*

The first dynamo for incandescent lighting service was installed in 1888 by the California Electric Light Company in its new office building at 227–229 Stevenson Street between Third and Fourth. The new machine had a capacity of 150 kilowatts. In addition to the company's offices, it served the nearby Café Royal, the Bijou Theater, and the People's Bank. The first incandescent lighting rate was 20 cents per kilowatt hour.

In its first years the pioneer electric company had been beset with obstacles. The utility was carrying on a dual business, supplying lighting to its customers in San Francisco and selling Brush dynamos, lamps, and other equipment to buyers in other parts of California, in Nevada, Oregon, and Washington. The supply business, which was continued until 1891, occupied much of Manager Roe's time. William Kerr, original owner of the Brush territorial rights, served as president the second year and remained a director of the company throughout its active existence.

The experiment of electric utility operation had proved successful. Despite frequent mechanical troubles with the first crude equipment, the company had maintained its financial integrity and had steadily increased its revenue. Its $100 par value stock which, upon its first stock exchange listing, ranged in price from $4.37½ to $9.25 in 1882–1883, was quoted at $21.50 in 1890.

During the first years of electrical development the crying need was for men who knew. The colleges had not yet begun to turn out electrical engineers. There were no handbooks for guidance of those who installed the strange equipment shipped from Eastern factories.

In 1886 Roe found an invaluable technical aide. He was Frank E. Smith, native Californian, young, a tireless student, who had learned and kept on learning by study and experience. Smith had started his electrical career only 10 years before, when he was twenty years old, as a lineman for the American District Telegraph Company in San Jose. From there he came to San Francisco to become an electrician and later chief inspector for John I. Sabin, who was then establishing the first circuits of the Pacific Bell Telephone Company. He returned to

San Jose to become chief electrician for the San Jose Brush Electric Company. It was there that George Roe met Smith and appointed him electrical engineer of the California Electric Light Company in San Francisco.

During the years he served the company and its successors, Smith established a lasting reputation as an electrical engineer. He installed the first Edison three-wire underground system in San Francisco. To prepare for this task he went East and consulted Thomas A. Edison. One of his notable accomplishments was the building of a 450-kilowatt hydroelectric underground plant in the Chollar mine at Virginia City, Nevada. George Roe had sold the Brush generators and equipment for the project. Generators and Pelton water wheels were placed in a cavern carved out of solid rock at the 1,680-foot level of the Chollar shaft where it was drained by the Sutro tunnel. Water was dropped in pipes from the surface and, with that high head, 450 kilowatts of electric energy were produced deep in the bowels of the earth for operation of the mine's 60-stamp mill above ground. The feat attracted world-wide attention.

In 1899 Frank E. Smith resigned his position as electrical engineer of the recently formed San Francisco Gas and Electric Company to establish his own laboratory for repair and adjustment of electrical instruments. There, as consultant, and Western representative of the Weston Electrical Instrument Company, he spent more than 30 years in continued research and expert accomplishment until his retirement and subsequent death in 1935.

It was Smith who was responsible for the preservation of the crude Wallace-Farmer lamp which started George Roe on his electrical career in 1879. When he joined the California Electric Light Company in San Francisco and started clearing the station of discarded equipment, he found the dust-covered Wallace-Farmer apparatus. Not knowing its history, he placed it in his office as an interesting relic and there it remained until one day George Roe noticed it and told him its origin. Smith kept the curio and later presented it to the museum of the Edison Institute in Dearborn, Michigan, where it is now on display in the Henry Ford collection.

The California Electric Light Company had the electric field to itself during its earlier years, until 1887 when a contender appeared under the name of the Electric Improvement Company of San Francisco. The newcomer, incorporated March 21, 1887, was headed by Augustus J. Bowie, mining engineer, and among its leading stockholders were Fred Sharon of the Palace Hotel family, Louis T. Haggin, J. B. Randal, Fred Butterworth, and capitalist William H. Howard of San Mateo. The company announced its intention to serve lighting customers at low rates, to undertake wiring jobs for new installations, and to deal in Wood and Slattery arc and incandescent generating machines for which it held territorial selling rights. The generating plants were small—one on the water front at Vallejo, East, and Davis Streets and another in the Hendy machine shop on Fremont Street.

The battle between the California Electric Light Company and the Electric Improvement Company was a fierce one while it lasted. Having no city permit to erect their own poles, the Electric Improvement people attempted to string wires on the poles of the older system. When that failed they ran their circuits over building roofs and through basements of friendly building owners. Rates were cut and free wiring offered to new customers.

The invasion appears to have been a costly one to the Electric Improvement Company. Some of the stockholders became dissatisfied and dropped out; those who remained paid one assessment after another.

The new company, having Fred Sharon as a stockholder, obtained a contract to wire the Palace Hotel and supply the power for lighting the entire building from a separate adjoining plant. The contract was on a cost-plus basis. After more than two years of struggling with the "battleship" construction of the hotel, running wires through its sturdy walls, and encountering many difficulties, the Improvement company turned the contract back to the Palace management. John R. Reagan, its electric superintendent who had been in charge of the wiring, resigned and took over the task of completing the Palace job. Two more years passed before it was finished at a total cost of $225,000.

Power for the Palace lights was supplied by six Slattery generators, each with a capacity of 1,000 lamps, in a plant at New Montgomery and Mission Streets.

The Electric Improvement Company continued its losing fight until 1892 when it sold its San Francisco properties to its competitor. For several years the company continued operating systems in other parts of the state, notably San Jose and Los Angeles, which finally were absorbed in utility consolidations.

In midyear of 1890 the California Electric Light Company was threatened with the most powerful competition it had faced. The Edison General Electric Company of New York, which held the rights to the great inventor's patents, including the new and vital Edison three-wire underground conduit system, sent men to San Francisco to investigate the possibility of establishing a competing utility company there.

Here was an opponent to be feared. Edison equipment was supplanting the older machinery in many cities because of its greater efficiency. The Edison companies were backed by the Wall Street house of J. P. Morgan & Co.

George H. Roe recognized the danger and went to New York to open negotiations. He was accompanied by Charles R. Lloyd, a promoter who through all the early years of electric development was apt to be found involved in deals where commissions were to be made. Nearly a year passed before the New York negotiations resulted in an agreement. By its terms, the Edison Light and Power Company was incorporated in San Francisco July 1, 1891. It was to have exclusive rights to the Edison patents within a radius of 100 miles of the city. The New York Edison company was to be paid with bonds to be issued by the new San Francisco company which was to purchase the business and properties of the original California Electric Light Company by exchange of stock.

Roe obtained approval of the plans from the directors of the old company and its provisions were carried out. Having been for 12 years manager of the enterprise which he initiated in 1879, Roe became president of the new company when it was organized. The original California company in which Charles and Gustav Sutro, Alvinza Hayward, and many others of the city's financiers had become stockholders was not dissolved until 1905, when final distribution of its assets was made. Charles Sutro was its last president.

Pierre B. Cornwall withdrew late in 1892 from the company which he had headed for so long, and two years later he established a competing electric utility, the Mutual Electric Light Company. Cornwall's departure from his old company appears to have been the result of a number of untoward conditions. He and other directors felt that Roe had exceeded his authority in his handling of the Edison deal. The last straw, possibly, was the loss of the contract held by his Black Diamond Coal Company for supplying fuel to the electric company. The contract yielded an average annual gross revenue of $150,000 to the coal company, and when the new Edison management awarded the business to a rival coal firm, Cornwall withdrew and arranged for a new customer to replace the lost coal contract.

At about that time W. R. Summerhayes, a jeweler, had come into possession of some old arc light dynamos under circumstances similar to those which had plunged George Roe into the electric utility business. Failing to find a buyer, Summerhayes decided to launch a utility venture of his own. Pierre B. Cornwall and Alvinza Hayward agreed to provide financial backing, and the Mutual Electric Light Company was incorporated December 15, 1894.

Cornwall became president of Mutual, which built a well-equipped plant on the site of the Church of the Advent on Howard Street at the foot of New Montgomery. The engine and parts of the machinery installed came from the powerhouse that had supplied electricity for lighting the Midwinter Fair in Golden Gate Park. The plant's generating capacity was 1,270 kilowatts, the largest single station in the city. When Mutual sought a franchise to erect poles and run its distribution lines through the city, its troubles began. The Board of Supervisors refused to grant permission. The question became a political issue. A Supreme Court decision finally gave to the Mutual company the right to erect pole lines. The strongly entrenched Edison company, however, held territorial rights to the Edison underground system and this forced its competitor to devise its own conduits built of grooved redwood planks.

The San Francisco *Call* in its issue of June 20, 1895, predicted another rate war when Mutual entered the field, but its competition did not develop the rate-cutting tactics of other contests. The company, however, gained considerable business and in 1905 built a new plant at Spear and Folsom Streets which served an extensive area south of Market Street.

This powerhouse, its capacity raised to 4,000 kilowatts, survived the earthquake-fire of 1906 without serious damage and was a helpful point of electric supply during the reconstruction period. One of its important customers was the San Francisco *Examiner* which occupied temporary one-story buildings on Folsom Street opposite the Mutual plant until the Hearst Building at Third and Market Streets was rebuilt. Mutual retained its identity as an independent operator for nearly two decades. In 1911 it was merged into the P. G. and E. system and the plant was closed down.

Pierre B. Cornwall continued as president of Mutual until his death, September 26, 1904.

During the first decade of its operation the pioneer California Electric Light Company had met little competitive opposition except from what the utility men call isolated plants. These are generators installed in factories, office buildings, and similar establishments for private, not public, service. Just as the Palace Hotel had done, E. J. (Lucky) Baldwin, who took great pride in his glittering Baldwin Hotel at Powell and Market Streets, built his own lighting plant. It was erected on Stevenson Street between Fifth and Sixth, and in July, 1888, the famous inn blossomed with thousands of lights, powered by a Westinghouse alternating-current generator. In the nineties isolated plants were installed in the Mills Building, the California Hotel, the Claus Spreckels and Phelan Buildings. Some of them challenged the utility company for business by extending their wires to serve customers in the neighborhood.

Isolated plants were to be a thorn in the side of the major electric companies for many years while the utilities were striving to build their customer load. Years of missionary work, increased efficiency, and lowered rates finally persuaded the majority of manufacturers, hotels, and other private plant owners that electric service from an interconnected company system was more to their advantage than the maintenance of individual generating equipment.

In 1893 another contender for electric customers appeared under the name Western Light and Power Company, led by Alfred Bouvier, Allan St. John Bowie (brother of the mining engineer), and Charles Hyland. From a small plant in the General Keyes Building at Stockton and O'Farrell Streets, the company battled for business, but the older Edison Light and Power Company was too strong. It first gained stock control, and in 1897 the properties were deeded to its successor, San Francisco Gas and Electric.

Harbor Light and Power Company was incorporated in 1894 when a group of commission merchants installed a small plant near the sea wall at the foot of Vallejo Street. It served a few customers, but stock control eventually was gained by the Edison company and in 1897 the San Francisco Gas and Electric Company acquired the property.

The Central Light and Power Company had a more pretentious location and stronger financing. Incorporated in 1897, its officers were attorney Charles L. Ackerman, president; clothier Frank Pauson, vice-president; J. W. Pauson, secretary; and Samuel Napthaly (superintendent of San Francisco Gas and Electric Company in 1906), manager. Central's plant was in the Parrott Building on Market Street near Fifth, now the Emporium. It had been in operation a year before the company was incorporated. With a generating capacity of 1,080 kilowatts, Central's competition was more aggressive than that of some of the other companies. Only a few days before the 1906 earthquake the just-formed P. G. and E. purchased Central's business and property. It never operated the plant, which was destroyed in the April 18 holocaust.

Another little powerhouse operated at Fremont and Mission Streets by the Martell Power Company but owned after 1902 by J. W. Pauson and his associates of the Central company, also was destroyed by the earthquake-fire. It was never rebuilt.

George H. Roe founded California Electric Light Company in 1879, earliest electric predecessor of P. G. and E. Rates were $10 per lamp per week—sundown to midnight.

Pierre B. Cornwall, wealthy businessman, was president of the California Electric Light Company from 1881 to 1893, later founded Mutual Electric Light Company.

The Palace Hotel, San Francisco, was lighted with 10 arc lamps in 1878 from the hotel's
own generating system. Two of the lamps can be seen in the picturesque courtyard

The Martell company had acquired some 200 customers in the south-of-Market Street area. By using wastepaper, sawdust, and nearly anything else that would burn under the boilers, the company had been able to show a profit even at the low rates it offered. In 1908 the Martell company was purchased by the City Electric Company which wanted its underground distribution lines, its only tangible property to survive the fire.

In the first years of the 1890 decade, George H. Roe had seen the fruition of all his hopes. His little lighting company of 1879 had become a strong operating utility. Roe had won a place in the business and social world, with fortune and power at his command. Study and an enormous capacity for work had given him his education. He had become a patron of the arts and a student of political economy and government.

But, unsuspected, time was running out. Roe fell ill. After two months spent in Brooklyn, where he had gone for medical treatment, he died there December 10, 1894, only forty-two years old.

The Edison Light and Power Company maintained its identity only two years after his death. In 1896 it was merged with the San Francisco Gas Light Company to form the new San Francisco Gas and Electric Company.

CHAPTER 7

Arc Lamps in the Sky

WITH the successful launching of electric lighting in San Francisco, George H. Roe became a Missionary of Light throughout the northern part of the state. He did not forget that his California Electric Light Company controlled territorial agency rights to the Brush electrical equipment. The growing interior towns of the area were quick to use the new light for illuminating their streets, factories, and stores, and then their homes as incandescent lamps came on the market.

Acting either as one of the incorporators or as the vendor of generators and lamps, Roe had a hand in the establishment of some 17 electric companies in Northern California towns and cities, all operating their generators by steam power. He sold more than 50 small electric plants for private operation in mills, mines, and other industrial establishments.

* * *

Probably in no other city in California were there more spectacular contests for lighting supremacy than in San Jose. The early gas companies fought for business; then struggled valiantly against the invading electric utilities, which in turn battled among themselves for contracts and customers. Competition eventually ceased there, as elsewhere, when the advantages of consolidation and unified management were realized.

San Jose's first electric lighting won the city world-wide fame. The light came from a cloud-piercing wrought-iron tower 237 feet high to the tip of its 30-foot mast. Under the platform at the top, which served as a reflector, six 4,000-candlepower arc lamps were hung in a circle. The builders believed they had the solution of the street lighting problem; that from the single point in the sky their 24,000-candlepower beacon would make every part of the city as bright as day. It was a pretty theory but it failed.

The tower project was the result of an editorial written by J. J. Owen, editor of the San Jose *Mercury,* May 13, 1881, suggesting that a light tower, higher than ever had been built, be raised at a midtown street intersection. The idea pleased the *Mercury* readers and they began sending in cash contributions. Soon there was a fund of $3,500 available and construction was started. The structure, built of tubular wrought iron, stood at the intersection of Market and Santa Clara Streets. Each foot of its straddling four-legged base was planted on a street corner at the curb and from the ground level the iron lattice tapered to a small platform 207 feet above. The tower was completed at a cost of $5,500 and first cast its light over the city on the evening of December 13, 1881.

San Jose's light tower gained widespread publicity. A Paris publication, *La Lumière Electrique, Journal d'Electricité,* published a description of the project, bemoaning meanwhile the backwardness of French electric street lighting. Testimonials were published to prove the far-reaching power of the tower's lights. One farmer in the city's foothill suburbs declared he could read his newspaper at night by towerlight. Nevertheless, as a street lighting plant the tower proved sadly lacking. Twelve 150-foot masts equipped with arc lamps were erected later to supplement its deficient illumination. The project also proved a financial white elephant. To satisfy contractor's liens it was sold for $5,000 the year after it was built to the San Jose Brush Electric Light Company, which had been established by George H. Roe in 1882.

When street lights were brought down to earth and the old "high light" theory was discarded, Editor Owen's light tower became just a striking landmark. Sometimes it blazed with strings of incandescents for a gala event, but most of the time it remained a darkened monument to the past. For more than a quarter of a century it stood, until in December, 1915, its crystallized joints weakened by age and insufficient bracing, the structure collapsed during a violent storm.

The Brush Electric Company was San Jose's first electric utility. Roe had installed the generator which supplied current to the tower lights and he capitalized that advantage into a company for general electric service. The prize was the city contract for street lighting, then held by the San Jose Gas Company. The fight dragged on for years until, under the leadership of Charles W. Quilty, the San Jose Light and Power Company was formed by merger of the San Jose Gas Company and the Brush Electric Light Company. This was accomplished June 21, 1889.

Competition might have ended there had it not been for a difference arising between Quilty and Harry J. Edwards, then general manager of the Light and Power Company, which resulted in Edwards' leaving the company. Four months later, the San Jose Electric Improvement Company entered the field. Three-quarters of the stock was held by the Electric Improvement Company of San Francisco and the remaining quarter by Edwards; De Witt Teasdale, banker; Charles M. Shortridge, editor of the *Mercury* and brother of Samuel Shortridge who later was elected United States Senator; James W. Rea, property owner and active in politics; and W. P. Dougherty, lumberman. Edwards became manager of the new company and the old bitter fight for business and the city lighting contract was renewed. The motto on Edwards' office door was "We Never Sleep," and there was evidence that he told the truth.

The Electric Improvement Company finally won the city street lighting contract, but the San Jose Light and Power Company, which had bought the tower, refused to permit its rival to restore its long darkened lamps. Edwards persuaded the city council to give him official permission, the tower was rewired, and the lights were turned on February 25, 1891. Keystone cops-and-robbers comedy followed: men cutting wires and removing arc lamps in the dead of night; court injunctions; process servers; disputants fined $50 each; W. W. Gillespie, secretary of the Light and Power Company, arrested for brandishing a revolver to drive an Edwards crew off the tower. The tower again was lighted but only for a short period.

Competition between the two companies provided page one news for the next decade until in 1902 the United Gas and Electric Company was formed to consolidate all the utilities of the peninsula south of San Francisco to and including San Jose.

* * *

The merchants of Oakland were reluctant to accept the blessings of electric light. George H. Roe discovered this in 1883, four years after he had launched his California Electric Light Company in San Francisco, when he attempted to sell the new service to the East Bay community.

For demonstration purposes, Roe set up a Brush arc dynamo in a woodyard on Eleventh Street between Broadway and Franklin. From that point he ran wires under the wooden awnings sheltering the store fronts on Broadway between Twelfth and Ninth Streets and for a month illuminated the street from dusk until ten o'clock. The attempt failed, and Roe abandoned the project.

The following year Samuel H. Taylor, representing the Thomson-Houston Electric Manufacturing Company, was more successful. He leased for the night hours the steam plant of a flour mill at Fourth and Washington Streets and installed a 25-light arc dynamo. The Oakland Gas Light Company, alert to this threat of electricity's competition, decided to forestall a battle by purchasing the Thomson-Houston plant and offering its customers the choice of gas or electric lighting.

Thus the first electric plant in Alameda County was built adjoining the Oakland Gas Works on Second Street near Washington. The installation consisted of steam engine and four 25-light arc dynamos. First operation, serving 50 lamps, was on January 2, 1885. Distribution wires were stretched on poles and under awnings along Broadway and Washington from First to Fourteenth Streets. In three years the business had grown so fast that in 1888 a new plant was erected at First and Grove Streets, equipped with a 1,300-lamp Westinghouse alternating-current generator. In order to consolidate its gas and electric business under one management, the Oakland Gas Light Company reincorporated July 18, 1884, as the Oakland Gas Light and Heat Company.

* * *

In his interesting history of the college village that grew to city stature, William Warren Ferrier credits the initiative of J. L. Barker as responsible for Berkeley's first electric lighting. Barker was a pioneer citizen who once owned 40 acres of land in what is now close to the heart of the city. In the late eighties he led a movement to organize a company by public subscription to light the town's streets. As a result, the East Berkeley Electric Light Company was incorporated November 4, 1887, and on March 17, 1888, light burst forth from arc lamps placed on five 100-foot towers and five 60-foot masts. The project was more nearly a community than a commercial enterprise and the following year a $24,000 municipal bond issue was voted and the electric system bought by the city. The local newspaper, commenting upon the result, declared, "The rapid growth of our town . . . is without question due in great measure to the electric light," a fact which hundreds of Northern California communities have found to be true.

Electric lighting up to this time had been by arc lamps for street and commercial purposes. When agitation began for incandescent lighting of homes, the municipal management was unwilling to undertake the expense of building a residential distribution system and increasing its generating capacity. The result was the leasing of the city plant about 1892 to the newly incorporated Berkeley Electric Light Power and Heat Company and the subsequent intervention of the Berkeley Improvement Company and the San Francisco Electric Company which organized the Berkeley Electric Lighting Company. These varied interests and properties and the leasehold interest in the city's street lighting system were all transferred by sale to the Oakland Gas Light and Heat Company about 1907 and the physical properties merged into the Oakland company's system.

* * *

Electric lighting came to Sacramento, the state capital, in 1884 when two companies entered the field against the long-established gas company. The Sacramento Electric Light Company, having paid $20,000 for exclusive city rights to the Brush machines, was organized February 15, 1884, and promptly opened a campaign for street lighting contracts. Two months later, April 26, 1884, the Pacific Thomson-Houston Electric Light and Power Company, Western representative of the manufacturers of Thomson-Houston machines, installed arc generators.

For three years the struggle for business between the three companies continued, with little profit to any one of them. Then on July 1, 1887, the competitors saw the light of consolidation, and the two electric systems were brought into unified operation by merging with the older Capital Gas Company.

In these days of advanced knowledge of electrical mechanics it is difficult to realize the trouble the early arc machine operators encountered. The following excerpt from the daily log of a Sacramento station operator gives just a hint. It is dated December 18, 1891:

"Nun of the Controllers on Arke machines wont work had to pull the wire out of Big machine and couldn't run city lites all night the Arke Lamps in station wont burn."

* * *

Stockton citizens saw their first electric lights about 1884 when the Stockton Gas Company installed two arc dynamos in the P. A. Buell planing mill to serve arc lamps hung in a few downtown stores. When the mill closed at sundown its steam engines drove the generators until midnight. In 1886 the company was granted a franchise to light the city streets and built a small plant on Center Street. By 1889 a new powerhouse was erected by the Stockton Gas Light and Heat Company for operation of the city streetcars, and in 1895 two gas engines, operated with natural gas from Stockton's pioneer wells, supplied the primary power to drive the generators.

* * *

The Vallejo Electric Light and Power Company was organized in 1897 by Kaskill Casper, a merchant who two years earlier had come from Nevada City, after experience there as builder of a small hydroelectric plant. Casper built a steam-operated plant in Vallejo and a distribution system which he and succeeding members of his family operated successfully until December, 1949, when all the stock of the company was acquired by Pacific Gas and Electric Company. Since 1901 the Vallejo Company had purchased its power supply from the Pacific Gas and Electric Company and its predecessor companies. P. G. and E. for many years had owned 45.8 per cent of the company's stock.

* * *

Humboldt County's widespread lumber industry was responsible for the early introduction of electricity into the northern county. Lumber mills on Gunther's Island off Eureka in Humboldt Bay were first lighted by arc lamps November 10, 1883. This started agitation for better street lighting in Eureka, and John Vance, owner of the Vance Hotel, showed what could be done by installing eight arc lights in the neighborhood of his hotel October 24, 1885.

The Eureka Electric Light Company was formed May 17, 1886, and March 21, 1894, the Eureka Lighting Company brought under one management the gas and electric utilities of the city. The convenient steam engine facilities of the lumber mills made possible the installation of electric generators for lights throughout the Humboldt region. In the nineties the towns of Arcata, Fortuna, Ferndale, Loleta, Rohnerville, Alton, Hydesville, Carlotta acquired electric lighting facilities, first for their streets and then for their homes.

Today, the Eureka and Humboldt County area is served by the Pacific Gas and Electric Company transmission system and two steam plants within the city. The latest of the steam plants is the Donbass, a unique installation among electric powerhouses throughout the country. The Donbass plant is contained in the salvaged afterhalf of a wrecked Russian tanker which was towed to Eureka and beached on the water front in 1946.

The *Donbass III* was an electrically propelled American-built ship turned over to the Russians on lend-lease during the war. The tanker had cracked apart during a storm while carrying a cargo of aviation gasoline and a deck load of planes and tanks to Vladivostok. All its officers and crew were lost. Five days after the disaster the S.S. *Puente Hills,* an American tanker, found the wrecked ship still afloat and after a 21-day struggle brought her safely to Port Angeles, Washington. The War Shipping Administration paid the salvagers $110,000 to regain possession of the ship.

Pacific Gas and Electric Company bought the stern half of the ship and had it towed from Puget Sound to Eureka, where the Humboldt County area, booming with postwar lumber orders, needed more electric power than could be supplied quickly.

The wrecked half-ship still contained its 4,800-kilowatt generator in good condition and the necessary steam plant for operation. Resourceful P. G. and E. engineers converted the marine power plant to land purposes, and December 16, 1946, the novel generating station began feeding its power into the system to meet the emergency. Donbass plant continues in commission, serving stand-by and peak-load requirements.

The spread of electric lighting throughout the Northern California area was rapid following the success of the early plants established in San Francisco, San Jose, Oakland, and Sacramento. Little steam plants operating arc lamp circuits were installed in one town after another. Everywhere the people adopted the new light to supplant kerosene lamps and flickering gas jets.

CHAPTER 8

Gas against Electricity

THERE were prophets of doom in the gas utility field in the uncertain years following the introduction of electric lighting in California in 1879. As the arc lamp and the Edison incandescents gained in popular favor, the gas companies began looking to their defenses. There were gloomy predictions that the day of gas was done.

Few of the gas men realized their own strength. It was too early in the 1880 decade for a clear view of the future which would disclose both gas and electricity occupying an important position as complementary providers of light, heat, and power to industry and agriculture as well as to commercial establishments and residences.

The gas cooking range at that time was a new gadget, something of a luxury and not yet accepted as a superior substitute for coal and wood stoves. The gas water heater and the gas furnace had not been perfected. Industry still was to learn the virtues of gas as a fuel for an endless variety of uses.

Another difficulty was the "flat rate" system of charges used by the electric companies—a fixed amount for each lamp served or for a given period of service, without measured limitation of the amount of electricity used. The gas companies, billing their customers on quantity rate by meter, found that many persons were attracted by the opportunity to use electric lamps as much as they wished without extra charge. They liked their freedom from the restrictions a meter imposes.

In 1879, to meet the threat offered by the new electric light, the San Francisco Gas Light Company introduced the Argand lamp, a new device to increase the light capacity of gas street lamps. The Argand lamp, equipped with a three-ringed burner with a light rating of 210 candlepower, consumed 50 cubic feet of gas per hour. It proved to be an expensive improvement, however, and was not generally adopted.

While the gas and electric utilities were arguing the merits of their respective lighting systems, a reprieve for gas lighting was being drawn up. The author was Carl Auer von Welsbach, an Austrian who in 1884 announced his invention of the Welsbach gas mantle to increase the illumination produced by the standard gas jet. The Welsbach mantle was a lacy asbestos hood which became incandescent when attached over a burning gas jet. It increased the candlepower sixfold with a white light far superior to the yellowish flame of the bare jet.

The Welsbach light was brought to the United States in 1887 by United Gas Improvement Company of Philadelphia, holder of the Lowe process patents. Through the Welsbach Incandescent Light Company, a subsidiary of United, a factory was established at Gloucester, Mass., and the new mantle went into service all over the country.

The Welsbach mantle, improved by many changes in the original design, extended the life of gas lighting nearly half a century. It sustained the gas utilities while they were discovering other productive uses for gas which would permit them to give up the struggle against electric lighting. The Welsbach Street Lighting Company of America, an independent organization founded in 1896 to service gas street lamps, helped keep gas on the streets of San Francisco and many other cities long after electricity had usurped the indoor lighting field. The last gas street lamps in San Francisco were not extinguished until 1930. Gas jets still exist and are connected for emergency service in many old homes in San Francisco and in public buildings in various cities.

Its existence almost forgotten, the Welsbach Company went out of business in 1940.

One effect of the threat against the gas utilities was to draw them together in an association for mutual discussion of their problems. The Pacific Coast Gas Association was created at a meeting held in San Francisco July 11, 1893. Joseph B. Crockett, president of the San Francisco Gas Light Company, was the association's first president. Its early convention programs were spiced with debates on ways and means to meet and defeat electricity, the invader. The ultimate decision in nearly all cities and towns proved the wise one: "If you can't beat the enemy, embrace him." Consolidation of gas and electric companies solved the problems of competition and effected economic savings by joint operation. Managements began promoting the advantages of gas fuel for cooking and heating and the benefits of electricity for light and power. As time went on and appliances were improved and multiplied, gas and electricity each found its place in the service of mankind.

* * *

In San Francisco, where gas and electric competition continued long after it had been smothered by consolidation in many inland towns, the merger of the two services did not take place until December 11, 1896. On that day the San Francisco Gas and Electric Company was incorporated by merger of Peter Donahue's San Francisco Gas Light Company and George H. Roe's Edison Light and Power Company. Capital stock was authorized for a total of $20,000,000.

Two considerations had hurried the two corporations into consolidation. One was the encroachment of the electric company upon the long-established business of the gas company. The gas men saw that they must have electric resources to meet the competition successfully. They went so far as to send President Crockett East and to Europe to inspect the newest electric plants there and they let it be known they intended to go into the electric business. A second impelling reason for the merger was the imminent expiration of street and public-building lighting contracts. Neither utility wanted the other to get the larger half of that juicy plum. When the savings to be effected by consolidation also were weighed, agreement to join the two utilities was reached without further delay.

The first board of 11 directors of the consolidated company included representatives of the solid financial strength of the city. They were:

Adam Grant—Member of the dry goods importing firm of Murphy, Grant & Co. and in 1897 president of the Donohoe, Kelly Bank.

Levi Strauss—Founder of Levi Strauss & Co.

George W. Prescott—Director, Union Iron Works.

J. Downey Harvey—Capitalist and railroad builder.

Capt. A. H. Payson—Vice-president of San Francisco and San Joaquin Valley Railway Company, predecessor of the Santa Fe in Northern California.

James B. Stetson—President of Edison Electric Light and Power Company after the death of George H. Roe; president, California Street Cable Railway Co. and North Pacific Coast Railroad Co.

Charles E. Green—Secretary, Charles F. Crocker and Crocker Estate Co.

William F. Whittier—Vice-president, San Francisco and San Joaquin Valley Railway Company.

Daniel T. Murphy—Capitalist.

Peter J. Donahue—A son of James Donahue, one of the founders of the first gas company.

Joseph B. Crockett, who had been president of the San Francisco Gas Light Company since 1885, was named president of the new consolidated organization.

The pioneer Peter Donahue had died in 1885, only two years after he had resigned the presidency of the San Francisco Gas Light Company. He had been succeeded by Eugene P. Murphy, stockbroker and financier, who remained at the helm only during the year 1884. He was followed in office by Crockett, a chief executive of a different character than any of his predecessors. For the first time, the company had a gas engineer as its president.

Joseph B. Crockett, born November 12, 1850, was a son of Joseph Bryant Crockett, who had served 10 years as a justice of the state supreme court. Young Crockett served his gas apprenticeship as an engineer for the City Gas Company in 1873. When that system was merged with the San Francisco Gas

Company, he worked and studied under William and James Beggs, veteran engineers and superintendents under Peter Donahue. From there he was advanced to assistant and then chief engineer of the company, a position he retained when he became president in 1885 at the age of thirty-five. One of the great works of his regime was construction in 1891 of the North Beach gas plant on a site on Bay Street between Laguna and Webster. Built under the supervision of Engineer E. C. Jones, the new plant embraced the latest and best in design and was regarded as one of the finest in the United States. Its gasometer or storage holder was then the largest west of Chicago.

As president, Crockett was to need all his stamina and youth for the battles that were to come. C. O. G. Miller and his Pacific Gas Improvement Company had been cutting deeply into the old company's gas business, and both before and after organization of the combined gas and electric company the city experienced a veritable rash of gas and electric competition. Inevitably the battling utilities became involved in local politics because the Board of Supervisors still controlled both gas and electric rates. Periodically there were charges and countercharges of misused political influence, an unsavory condition that continued until state regulation of utility rates was instituted in 1912.

In 1901, despite the absorption of some of the smaller competitors by the San Francisco Gas and Electric Company, there were still eight electric systems striving for business. Not for two more decades was consolidation to be complete in San Francisco, although throughout the period the San Francisco Gas and Electric Company maintained its dominance of the field.

The spread of electric street lighting was rapid in the 1890–1900 period. In 1896 the San Francisco *Call* published an editorial under the heading "The Corner Gas Lamps Must Go" in which it said: "The work of lighting up the dark byways of this city goes splendidly ahead and one street after another, where a few gas lamps twinkled dimly through the fog and gloom, is being strung with electric lamps." A large part of the work was done by the Merchants Association and neighborhood improvement clubs which provided the cost of the installation and initial service until the municipal government should be ready to assume the burden, which eventually it did. One street after another was lighted with arc lamps in this fashion. There were parades, fireworks, and music to celebrate the coming of the brighter lights.

* * *

Topping the new companies that challenged the San Francisco Gas and Electric Company were the Independent Electric Light and Power Company and the Independent Gas and Power Company, incorporated March 29, 1899, and January 5, 1901, respectively, by Claus Spreckels and his sons A. B. and John D. Spreckels. And thereby hangs an oft-told tale but one never fully confirmed.

The day is early in 1899 or possibly late in 1898. The scene is the Pacific Union Club at luncheon time. The actors, Claus Spreckels, sugar magnate and head of the millionaire clan whose multiple interests reached far in those days, and Joseph B. Crockett, president of the San Francisco Gas and Electric Company. The meaning of what followed is better understood when it is recalled that Crockett was a super-club man—once president of the Pacific Union Club and of the Burlingame Country Club, charter member of the University Club, and long a member of the Bohemian Club. The colloquy when the two met was said to have been something like this:

MR. SPRECKELS: "Mr. Crockett, what are you going to do about that smoke from your powerhouses? The soot is blackening the walls of my building and filling my tenants' offices. It's a confounded nuisance." (The Jessie Street electric generating station, the stack 175 feet high, stood west and south of the Claus Spreckels Building, now the Central Tower Building at Third and Market Streets. The Stevenson Street plant was almost directly behind the Spreckels Building.)

MR. CROCKETT: "Sir, I make it a rule never to discuss business at the club. If you will take the matter up with me at my office, I shall be most happy to consider it."

That did it. Mr. Spreckels, never known to take kindly either to a rebuff or opposition, muttered something about seeing Mr.

Crockett next in an attorney's office and ended the conversation. He rushed back to his office and in two hours had started Engineer A. M. Hunt on plans for a new electric plant.

The smoke dispute was an old one. For many months Spreckels had complained to Crockett and to the company's directors. The question had been debated in board meetings and after long delay mechanical stokers had been installed in the powerhouses but they failed to abate the noxious fumes.

Whether Claus Spreckels started his competitive warfare in anger because of Crockett's lofty attitude or whether, as was doubtless true, he was moved also by a canny belief that there was profit to be made from his investment of millions in the utility business is not disclosed in the records. Crockett is said to have denied that the encounter occurred, but Rudolph Spreckels, who at that time was not on speaking terms with his father but had opportunity to know the facts, confirmed the story of the Pacific Union Club incident during a conversation with the writer in 1951.

"Yes, it is true," he said. "My father was very proud of the Claus Spreckels Building. It was the finest and tallest in the city. He deeply resented Crockett's reply to him and his failure to stop the smoke."

The two Spreckels independent companies were capitalized for a total of $15,000,000. Under the supervision of Engineer Hunt, who became general manager of the new company, a well-equipped electric generating plant was rushed to completion on a site in the Potrero adjoining the Western Sugar Refining Company's plant. Its capacity was 5,000 kilowatts. That same plant, many times enlarged and modernized, is at this writing the P. G. and E.'s Station A, capacity 150,000 kilowatts. When the Independent Gas and Power Company was formed in 1901, Spreckels built a down-to-date gas plant adjoining the powerhouse. When all was ready a supercharged rate war was declared.

Competing gas and electric companies in San Francisco in previous struggles for business had effected a pseudo truce by tacitly respecting each other's service zones, but now all restrictions upon extensions of line were removed. Although the contest in-

Smoke from this generating plant started the dispute that caused Claus Spreckels, sugar magnate, to organize competing gas and electric companies in San Francisco.

Dynamo room at the Jessie Street generating station of the Edison Light and Power

cluded both gas and electric business, it appears to have been hottest in the gas field. Four gas companies were involved—the Spreckels gas corporation, the San Francisco Gas and Electric Company, Pacific Gas Improvement Company, and the Equitable Gas Light Company which had started a "dollar gas" campaign of its own after it was established February 21, 1898.

Equitable had been promoted by A. J. Chisholm, who had come from the East with the so-called Hall process of gas manufacture. Attorney Charles L. Ackerman and clothier Frank Pauson, who earlier had organized the Central Light and Power Company, were the principal stockholders. The Hall process proved to be faulty and Chisholm left the company. Equitable replaced its equipment with a standard carbureted water-gas plant and opened its assault upon the older companies. Running its mains through the districts where the need for gas service was greatest, seeking the cream of the business, Equitable was accused of offering gas at even less than $1 per thousand cubic feet when the prospect was a large consumer.

In defense of their customer list in the residential districts the Pacific Gas Improvement Company and the San Francisco Gas and Electric Company agreed to offer contracts to consumers, good for two years or more, under which they would serve gas at $1.25 per thousand feet. It was stipulated, however, that any rate made by any other company would be met. Later, gas was sold by the contending companies at $1, 75 cents, and even 50 cents in some zones at a time when the established rate was $1.40. Rates varied in different parts of the city. Solicitors were everywhere trying to switch customers from one of the other companies to their own.

Ironically, the costly rate war resulted in unprecedented consumption of gas by the San Francisco Gas and Electric Company's customers. The low competitive rates induced unrestricted use of gas, and the company found itself doing the greatest volume of business in its history but at a considerable loss in revenue. In December, 1901, its gas sales reached an all-time peak of 4,256,000 cubic feet.

Spreckels' competition brought the contest to white heat. The attack was centered upon Crockett and the San Francisco Gas and Electric Company. C. O. G. Miller and his Pacific Gas Improvement Company, although striving for a share of the city's gas patronage, had remained on friendly terms with Crockett's company and with the Spreckels interests but they were inevitably drawn into the contest. Earnings of all the participants fell off and stock quotations dropped sharply. Banker I. W. Hellman and capitalists Antoine Borel and James M. McDonald backed Pacific Gas Improvement Company with a loan to save it from levying an assessment upon its stockholders.

The competitive warfare had stirred the conservative San Francisco Gas and Electric Company more than any other of its long list of struggles for maintenance of its leadership. Before Claus Spreckels had completed his first plant, the directors had begun to seek ways to strengthen their position. The executive committee probed the company's affairs for weaknesses. Reduction of the capitalization from $20,000,000 was debated, and a bond issue to extinguish the floating debt and provide for plant modernization was considered. Reduction of the 5 per cent annual dividend was predicted.

When old customers began drifting to the Spreckels pasture, President Crockett would report lugubriously to the directors the number of deserters for the week and sometimes their names. Market quotations on San Francisco Gas and Electric shares, which in good times were not far under $100 par, dropped as low as $30.

Efforts to reach an agreement with Claus Spreckels, under which some sort of peace might be established, all failed. Late in 1901 Captain A. H. Payson, a director of San Francisco Gas and Electric Company, and Robert Watt of Pacific Gas Improvement Company interviewed Spreckels on a peace mission and failed. At another time Adam Grant and Levi Strauss sought unsuccessfully an agreement to stop the rate war. Spreckels was adamant to all proposals.

In the midst of the contest an odd conflict of the Spreckels family interests was revealed when Rudolph Spreckels, son of Claus, was elected to the board of directors of the San Francisco Gas and Electric Company, against which his father was fighting. Although he was not at the time on friendly terms with his father, Rudolph Spreckels later insisted that he joined the San Francisco Gas and Electric Company's defense against his parent solely for business reasons. He had sold control of the Hawaiian Commercial Company in 1898 and invested the proceeds in San Francisco Gas and Electric stock. He said that his motive in seeking election to the board was merely one of investment protection.

Rudolph Spreckels and C. Osgood Hooker were elected directors of the company January 22, 1901. Hooker was said to represent W. B. Bourn, then a powerful figure on Montgomery Street who had amassed a fortune from the Empire and North Star mines in the Grass Valley district. Almost immediately the fur began to fly. Director Spreckels, alarmed by the drop in value of his investment, began asking questions and enlisting support among the other members of the board.

When, in the summer of 1901, the directors voted to offer to purchase the Claus Spreckels properties and so end the war, Rudolph Spreckels was the only one to vote a positive "No." He continued his attacks on the company management. Only a month later he was appointed chairman of a committee of five directors to investigate the affairs of the company. When President Crockett made the appointments he virtually signed his resignation. Engineers and accountants were employed to make the examination. The report was critical. Methods of management were antiquated. Plants and equipment needed overhauling. Crockett promptly submitted his resignation which became effective January 15, 1902. His death followed less than two years later, December 24, 1903.

Drastic changes followed Crockett's resignation. W. B. Bourn, on Spreckels' nomination, was elected president of the San Francisco Gas and Electric Company. New directors were elected from the top echelon of the city's financial community. They included Frank B. King, William J. Dutton, George H. Collins, E. J. McCutcheon, and Louis F. Monteagle. Harvey, Hooker, Spreckels, Murphy, and Payson held over from the old board.

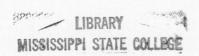

W. B. Bourn, the new president, was a native San Franciscan. In his later years he was president and chairman of the board of the Spring Valley Water Company and engaged in numerous civic and cultural activities. Under his leadership the gas and electric rate war with Claus Spreckels was fought out. Gradually the old company gained strength, and in 1903 decision was made to end the battle by resorting to the old tactic—consolidation.

Negotiations to purchase their properties were opened with the Equitable Gas Light Company, the Pacific Gas Improvement Company, and the two Spreckels independent companies. After some months of discussion the three deals were closed, and by September 1, 1903, all three competitors had laid down their arms and joined the camp of the San Francisco Gas and Electric Company. The purchases were made upon the basis of exchange of stock and assumption of bonded debt.

The Equitable Gas company purchase was preceded by an interesting financial byplay. Early in 1903 meetings were held with Charles L. Ackerman and Frank Pauson, who controlled the Equitable, in an effort to reach a price agreement. The Equitable men held out for $100,000 more than was offered and the negotiations failed. Then Frank G. Drum, who in a few months was to be a vice-president of the de Sabla and Martin California Gas and Electric Corporation, stepped in. An astute negotiator, Drum succeeded in obtaining an option from Ackerman and Pauson for more than two-thirds of the Equitable's stock. This he promptly offered to the San Francisco Gas and Electric Company, upon the condition, however, that he be paid the $100,000 which previously had been refused to Ackerman and Pauson. The directors agreed and the purchase was completed.

Claus Spreckels fared well financially when he finally yielded to the offer to purchase his two utility systems. The Independent gas and electric plants were new and efficient. They were desirable additions to the production facilities of the old company. When negotiations were concluded Spreckels had received as a part of his price $5,000,000 in San Francisco Gas and Electric bonds. The records show also that he had made a clear profit of $1,214,000 as recompense for the coal smoke that had smudged the walls and windows of his office building at Third and Market Streets.

Thus ended perhaps the most destructive and wasteful of the gas and electric rate wars. There were to be others before rate regulation by the state would protect utilities and customers alike from the abuses of competition. It had been proved that unrestrained competition between utilities operating in the same service area was costly and did not result in lasting benefit to the customer.

In postscript, Rudolph Spreckels, the value of his investment in San Francisco Gas and Electric stock restored, resigned from the board of directors September 30, 1903. It was not his last utility campaign, as later events proved.

CHAPTER 9

Hydro's Heritage of Water

NORTHERN CALIFORNIA owes its early preeminence in water-powered generation of electricity to two primary factors—highly favorable topography and the vast water works built by the gold miners.

When prehistoric upheavals raised the Cascades and Sierra Nevada mountain ranges along the eastern boundary of the state, the stage was set for hydroelectric development. The snow-crested peaks of the two ranges rise to elevations topped by Mt. Whitney's 14,500 feet in the south and Mt. Shasta's 14,161 feet in the north. The wide watersheds formed by glacier-scoured heights feed scores of tumbling streams in the gorges that slice through the western slope of the escarpment. Deep-packed snow and ice fields are water storehouses from which the summertime flow is drawn.

The falling waters of the Sierra move fast in their descent to the broad Central Valley which extends nearly 500 miles north and south between the eastern mountain bastion and the Coast Range close to the ocean shore. Their drop in elevation is abrupt —96.4 feet to the mile in the south fork of the Yuba, 92.2 feet in the middle fork of the American, and 133 feet in the north fork of the Stanislaus, compared to the 14-foot fall of the Hudson or the 17-foot slope of the Missouri. The steep descent of the California rivers makes it possible to build not one but sometimes as many as six generating plants on one stream.

The gold miners were the first water-system builders in the foothills of the Sierra. Water was the lifeblood of the placers. Without its help to wash away the sand and gravel in which the gold lay buried there could have been no placer mining. As the stream-side claims were quickly exhausted, the miners began prospecting gravel deposits far from the creeks. They found rich ground and in some places laboriously packed the gravel on muleback to the creeks for washing. Ditches to bring water to the dry diggings became a necessity. Water was nearly as valuable as gold.

The first canal of considerable length was completed in Nevada County in December, 1850. It was built by the Rock Creek Water Company, organized by Charles Marsh, a civil engineer whose name appears in many an account of later ditch enterprises, William Crawford, John and Thomas Dunn, and C. Carol. The Rock Creek ditch ran for 9 miles to Gravel Hill near Nevada City (some historians say Coyote Hill was the terminus). The precious stream that filled the ditch was sold to claim owners along its route at rates that in six weeks repaid to the builders the $10,000 they had spent for its construction. Two other companies completed ditches the following year. They were the Coyote and Deer Creek Water Company and the South Yuba and Snow Mountain Ditch Company.

Disputes over water rights between the rival ditch builders resulted in consolidation of the competitors in 1854 into the Rock Creek, Deer Creek, and South Yuba Canal Company. Under that name the little miners' ditch company of 1850 appears on P. G. and E. records as the earliest of the 520 corporations which have been welded into the present system. It was the parent organization of what later became the South Yuba Water Company.

With successful demonstration in Nevada County that water could be transported profitably to the mining claims that mushroomed on every canyon side, ditch and flume building spread like wildfire north and south. In Nevada, Placer, and Eldorado, in Amador, Calaveras, Stanislaus, and Tuolumne Counties, water grew into big business. Millions of dollars were spent for storage reservoirs and conduits to meet the miners' demand for more and more of the indispensable flow. Langley's "Pacific Coast Directory," published in San Francisco in the early sixties, said: "There are 5,328 miles of artificial water courses for mining purposes constructed in this State at a cost of $15,575,400 . . . , numerous subsidiary branches, the aggregate length of which is estimated at over 800 miles, and several hundred miles of new ditches in the course of construction." At the zenith of hydraulic mining, the total probably had reached 8,000 miles.

When surface mining waned and hydraulic mining received its death sentence by the Federal court's permanent injunction forbidding the washing of silt from the mines into the rivers, the great aqueduct systems stood ready and waiting for the oncoming hydroelectric industry.

* * *

The South Yuba Water Company was the most extensive of all the mining water properties that eventually became a part of P. G. and E. At the peak of its activities it operated 450 miles of conduits of various types in Nevada and Placer Counties. It owned 20 storage reservoirs in the upper reaches of the Sierra with a total capacity of 14½ billion gallons and 15 lesser reservoirs. The company sold water to mines, to towns for domestic use, and to farmers for irrigation. Through a subsidiary it operated three hydroelectric plants. The seed of this mighty growth was the little Rock Creek ditch built by the miners in 1850.

From 1854 to 1870 the company held to its original name, Rock Creek, Deer Creek, and South Yuba Canal Company. The owners were enterprising and daring. In the first 12 years they spent $1,000,000 in building water works or purchasing those built by others. Their feats of construction were spectacular. They carried timber flumes across deep canyons on trestles 100 feet and more above ground. They did unheard-of things with iron pipe carrying water under high pressure. In places where gulches could not be bridged they ran the water pipe in inverted siphons, the head or elevation at the upper end forcing the flow down one side and up the steep opposite bank.

They built a main canal 16 miles in length from the gorge of the South Yuba below the present Lake Spaulding. Seven miles of this canal were wooden flume, sometimes on high trestles and sometimes on a shelf blasted out of the granite canyon wall. For a mile and a half of this construction along the rock walls of the South Yuba, the workers drilled holes for blasting while sitting in slings held by ropes secured at the top of the precipice.

A half-mile-long tunnel west of Bear Valley carried the waters of the South Yuba through the ridge into Deer Creek. Two branch ditches, each 18 miles long, served the historic mines of Chalk Bluff, Red Dog, You Bet, Gold Hill, and Blue Tent.

By the middle sixties the company had developed water storage in five lakes lying under the Sierra summit where the spring runoff could be caught and held against summertime needs. Dan A. Rich, a famous figure in the early history of the South Yuba Water Company, explored the region as agent of the company and made many of the legal locations, among them Lake Fordyce and Meadow Lake.

Meadow Lake is about 1,000 feet higher in elevation than Fordyce into which it drains. This was the site of Summit City where 4,000 persons lived in the gold-rush days until, in 1866, a devastating storm drove them out in a panic of fear that they might be snowed in for the remainder of the winter. They left without attempting to move their possessions. Bread was found in the ovens of abandoned kitchens. Most of the inhabitants never returned, and Summit City soon became just another ghost town, its flimsy buildings falling into ruins.

Lake Fordyce, an artificial reservoir, lies cupped in a green valley at 6,500 feet altitude, 7 miles from the station of Cisco on the Southern Pacific railroad. It drains into Fordyce Creek, a tributary of the south fork of the Yuba. Dan Rich found the spot in 1853 when he visited Jerome Fordyce in his homestead cabin there. He recognized the storage possibilities of the place and filed a claim upon the site for his company. Twenty years passed before Rich returned to the valley to superintend the building of Fordyce dam.

The project called for construction of the largest dam yet built in California. It was to be of the rock-fill type, the material to be quarried from the gorge that funneled the lower end of the meadow. As the dam rose in height, engineering difficulties slowed its progress, and then into the picture came John Spaulding and Alvinza Hayward, the same ubiquitous capitalist and mine owner whose financial operations had threaded the early history of San Francisco.

Hayward owned the Polar Star and the Southern Cross, two of the largest hydraulic mines of the Dutch Flat district. He operated mines in Shasta County and on the Comstock Lode in Nevada. He controlled the water system of San Mateo where he had his home.

John Kilbourne Spaulding was a man of different sort. He had come West by steamer in 1853 from his birthplace in Canton, New York, when he was only twenty-two, going first to the mines at Thompson Flat near Oroville. The miners were crying for water and the need appealed to the youth's practical mind. It must have been only a short time after his arrival when he wrote home, February 5, 1853: "As soon as the snows melt, I plan to leave here and go back into the mountains about 100 miles. There a group of us plan to build a canal to carry water to some mines." Other letters evince the same early interest in water.

From mining, John turned to stage driving. He was in Nevada City in 1856 driving for the California Stage Company to Sacramento and from Folsom to Dutch Flat until 1862. In that time he acquired a reputation as an expert reinsman. In 1862 he tooled a Wells Fargo Concord stage between Placerville and Virginia City, and three years later was placed in charge of Wells Fargo's operations between Sacramento and the Comstock in Nevada. When completion of the Central Pacific rail line in 1869 started the stage business on its downhill course, Spaulding's friend, Alvinza Hayward, whom he had met during a prospecting trip to Siskiyou County, appointed him superintendent of the San Mateo water system. From there he returned to the mountains to take charge of his employer's mines near Dutch Flat and for a time to superintend the Hayward mining properties in Virginia City. It was while he was at Dutch Flat in 1874 that Spaulding was loaned to the South Yuba Company to complete Lake Fordyce dam.

The South Yuba water system continued to expand. The original corporate name had been changed in a reorganization in 1870 to the South Yuba Canal Company. Hayward had not been wholly unselfish when he agreed to send Spaulding to Lake Fordyce to solve the dam construction problems there. For some time he had cherished the thought that if he could control the water company, he could then be assured of a constant supply of water to his mines.

With John Spaulding's assistance, a plan of purchase at last was worked out, negotiations were concluded, and a contract was signed in October, 1876, for sale of the South Yuba system to Alvinza Hayward. Then came dry seasons when mines were forced to close down because of water shortage and one hard winter when ice and snow and floods wreaked costly damage on ditches and flumes. Hayward, although in nominal control, was unable to make the stipulated payments to the water company.

Despite financial difficulties the water company during this period made one notable improvement. While every foot of its canal system was patrolled, communication between the headquarters office at Nevada City and its scattered lake tenders and ditch tenders was slow and undependable. In 1878, only two years after Alexander Graham Bell had received his first telephone patent, the South Yuba Canal Company obtained a supply of the new instruments, strung wires along 184 miles of its waterways to its headquarters office, and thus established a complete telephone system. With the better known Ridge telephone line built the same year by the North Bloomfield, Milton, Eureka Lake, and other ditch companies serving the mines of the North San Juan district, this was one of the earliest long-distance telephone installations in the United States.

In the meantime Alvinza Hayward, still desperately trying to purchase the South Yuba Canal Company's system, went to New York hoping to interest Eastern capital in the deal. He won the attention of Warner Van Norden, who later became president of the National Bank of North America in New York, and who in 1877 came to California for a firsthand examination of the system. The result was the incorporation of the South Yuba Water and Mining Company, a New York corporation which took over control of the properties of the South Yuba Canal Company and Hayward's mines which operated under the name Nevada Hydraulic Mining Company.

After many delays and discouragements, Lake Fordyce dam was completed in 1881 to a height of 96 feet. Rebuilt and raised to 140 feet in 1914, the old dam still is in service, one of the important sources of water supply of the present P. G. and E. system.

John Spaulding took over the maintenance and operation of the far-flung South Yuba network of canals and reservoirs. He knew every foot of the system. He fought for repairs and extensions. Every mountain family knew him. He held his men to a strict discipline but sometimes revealed a sly sense of humor. Once a ditch tender reported that a man whose home was directly below a South Yuba flume irrigated his garden and orchard by violently shaking the boarded side of the flume until water dripped from the loosened seams. Spaulding's response was to send the offending householder a brace and a half-inch bit with the request that after he had obtained sufficient water from the flume, he should plug the hole he had bored.

John Spaulding's memorial is splendid Lake Spaulding, created by a massive dam 275 feet high across the gorge of the South Yuba at a point below Emigrant Gap. He first recommended the building of the original dam and waited impatiently 12 years before the New York office of the company would approve its construction in 1892–1893. W. A. Englebright superintended its construction. In 1912 and 1913 the lake was enlarged to its present size by construction of a great new dam below the old and much smaller structure. Three powerhouses, each bearing the Spaulding name, today also honor the memory and the foresight of the veteran water master who knew a good reservoir site when he saw one. And the Spaulding saga is not yet finished. The present general superintendent of P. G. and E.'s extensive water systems is John N. Spaulding, grandson of the revered elder John.

Under the management of the New York company, the South Yuba system continued to grow. Although by 1880 the hydraulic mines which were the greatest users of South Yuba water had begun to close down, the Van Nordens held to their faith in the future earning power of their properties. Spaulding built the Boardman ditch in 1893 from the end of Big Bear Valley to a point south of Clipper Gap where it joined the Bear River Canal.

Dr. Charles Van Norden, brother of the New York banker

and the company's California representative, had been a prominent clergyman and former president of Elmira College, Elmira, New York. Ill health had forced him to take up residence in California. He believed that in irrigation lay the solution of the Yuba company's problem, should the mine's business fail. It was not long before his belief was put to the test.

Early experiments had proved that in the foothill country of Placer and Nevada Counties only water was needed to produce profitable and bountiful fruit crops. Lands in the vicinity of Newcastle, Loomis, Auburn, Colfax, and other mountain towns were transformed into blooming orchards.

With irrigation in prospect, the South Yuba company in 1890 acquired the properties of the Bear River and Auburn Water and Mining Company from their owner, Frederick Birdsall, which enabled it to extend its service to the towns of Auburn, Newcastle, and Lincoln. The Bear River ditch was one of the oldest in Placer County, having been built in 1852 from a point below the junction of Greenhorn Creek with the Bear River to the area just north of Auburn. Dr. J. R. Crandall and James Neal located the water rights in 1851.

The name of the Van Norden corporation again was changed April 4, 1890, and it became simply the South Yuba Water Company. One other expansion was made in 1893 when the Fall Creek Water Company system was added to the long list of South Yuba holdings.

Before this there was little question that the South Yuba Water Company had lost its greatest customer—the hydraulic mining industry. Irrigation and domestic water supply replaced some of the vanished income but not enough. The Van Nordens and their associates turned then to the new hydroelectric development as a lifesaver. They organized a subsidiary, the Central California Electric Company, and built three power plants supplied with water from the ample ditches of the system—Newcastle in 1896, Auburn in 1898, and Alta in 1902. Newcastle Powerhouse was closed in 1914 and Auburn in 1912. Alta is still in commission, a part of the P. G. and E. hydro system.

Rudolph W. Van Norden, son of Dr. Charles Van Norden, joined the South Yuba company after he finished his college training in engineering. When its three powerhouses were built, he had much to do with their design and operation. He later resigned to become a consulting engineer.

Newcastle powerhouse at first served electricity, for lighting only, to the towns of Rocklin, Loomis, Penryn, and Newcastle. With completion of Auburn powerhouse, a transmission line was built to Sacramento and an aggressive campaign for business was waged. Surplus power was sold to the Capital Gas Company which at that time was in close competition with the Sacramento Electric, Gas and Railway Company.

Sitting in his New York office, Warner Van Norden became an enthusiastic proponent of electric power. Early in 1903 he wrote to his brother:

"The belief here is that electricity is going to crowd out every other form of power. A bill is now before the legislature to prohibit the use of steam locomotives on the Island. An excellent authority predicts that within ten years horses will be prohibited and that everything will be run by electricity or other mechanical power."

The banker urged extension of Yuba's electric system to Nevada City and other points in its territory. "I am delighted with the outlook," he wrote to his brother, "and feel that it justifies all that you have said and done in the past. Strain every nerve to sell the current [electric] while there is a demand for it and prepare for new construction if necessary."

In 1903 there was talk of selling the properties of the water company, a suggestion to which Warner Van Norden evidently was not opposed. "I think we should mark up our asking price for the stock to at least $5,000,000," he declared in one letter. Negotiations for the purchase of the South Yuba Water Company system were opened in 1904 by the California Gas and Electric Corporation. Eugene de Sabla went to New York to discuss the proposal with the banker. After long negotiations which frequently bogged to the point of failure, a purchase price of $2,000,000 was agreed upon. At one stage of the discussions, de Sabla telegraphed his directors: "VAN NORDEN AND HIS SON ARE HARD NUTS," a discouraged opinion of his opponents which might well be regarded as a tribute to their horsetrading abilities. Sale of the South Yuba water properties to California Gas and Electric Corporation was closed January 4, 1905.

The far-reaching South Yuba water works, grown to giant's stature from the pygmy Rock Creek ditch of 1850, went on to a new and more lasting career by supplying water power for production of electric power. Dr. Van Norden's vision of irrigation as the destiny of the South Yuba has been realized. Today, the waters his company developed drive the generators in many powerhouses and then continue on their course to serve the domestic and irrigation requirements of the valley.

The history of the South Yuba is the history of water development up and down the Sierra. The miners of the Feather, the American, the Mokelumne, the Stanislaus, the Tuolumne and their tributaries also left their heritage to modern economic development. Some twoscore of their aqueduct systems—rebuilt, improved, and adapted to present-day needs—are still in service. The hydroelectric ditch tender of today must see many a red-shirted, booted ghost as he patrols the ditches and flumes of early days—the Butte Creek, the Miocene, the Boardman, the Bear River, Cedar Creek, Fiddler's Green, Angels, Utica, Race Track, Dutch Ravine, and all the other waterways of gold-rush days that still are in use.

CHAPTER 10

Kilowatts from Falling Waters

WHEN Edison and Brush and their brother inventors brought the electric generator to the point of commercial usefulness, they laid a Midas gift in the lap of the water-minded West. It was a gift that was to produce an endless flow of electric energy from water-powered plants—energy that was to transform arid and semiarid lands into bountiful sources of agricultural wealth—energy that was to give to industry and commerce the means of production in regions where the high cost of coal fuel had retarded growth.

Two European experiments encouraged the early Western development of water-powered generation of electricity. In 1886 power had been transmitted from the Cerchi, Tivoli, plant in Italy to Rome, a distance of 17 miles. This was regarded as the first transmission of alternating current. The plant was steam-driven and was equipped with two 150-horsepower generators, transmitting at 2,000 volts. Its significance in California, where transmission was the chief problem, was that power actually had been carried a substantial distance. The second historic foreign achievement was in Germany in 1891 when electricity was transmitted from a water-powered station at Lauffen to Frankfort, about 100 miles away. Transmission was three-phase at 30,000 volts, far above anything attempted in earlier trials.

No sooner had the utility of the electric dynamo and motor been demonstrated than the engineers, the water men, and the miners of California began studying the possible use of water power instead of steam to drive electric generators. Taking a long but surprisingly accurate look ahead, the editor of the *Mining and Scientific Press* made this prediction October 8, 1887:

Office of Coyote and Deer Creek Water Company, early 1850s. This was one earliest of the 520 corporations later to become part of P. G. and E.

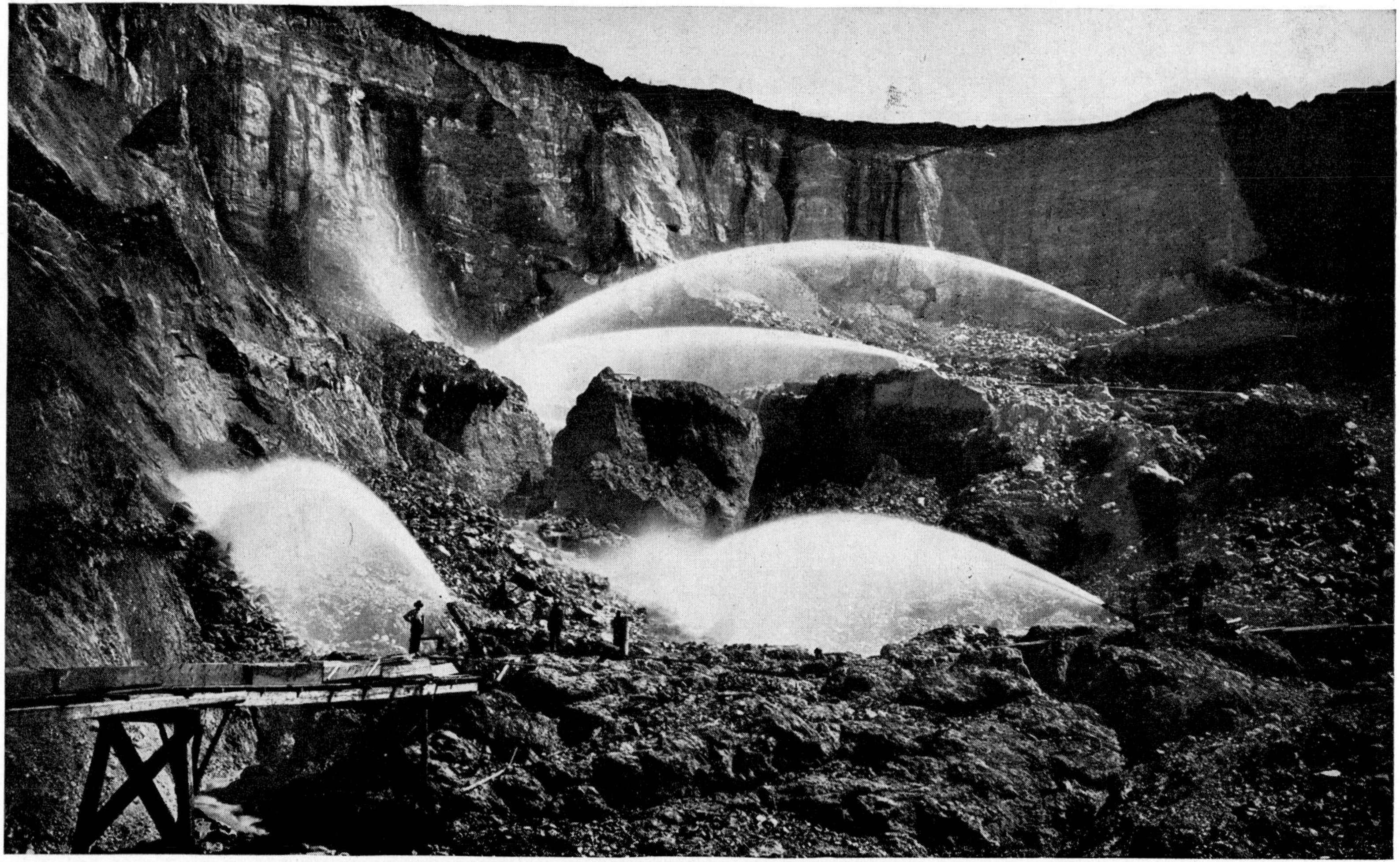

Four hydraulic monitors bombard the gravel bank at Malakoff Mine, Nevada County.
(Courtesy of Bancroft Library, University of California.)

Miles of flumes—like Bald Rock, part of Upper Standard Canal, Mokelumne River—carried water to the early hydroelectric powerhouses.

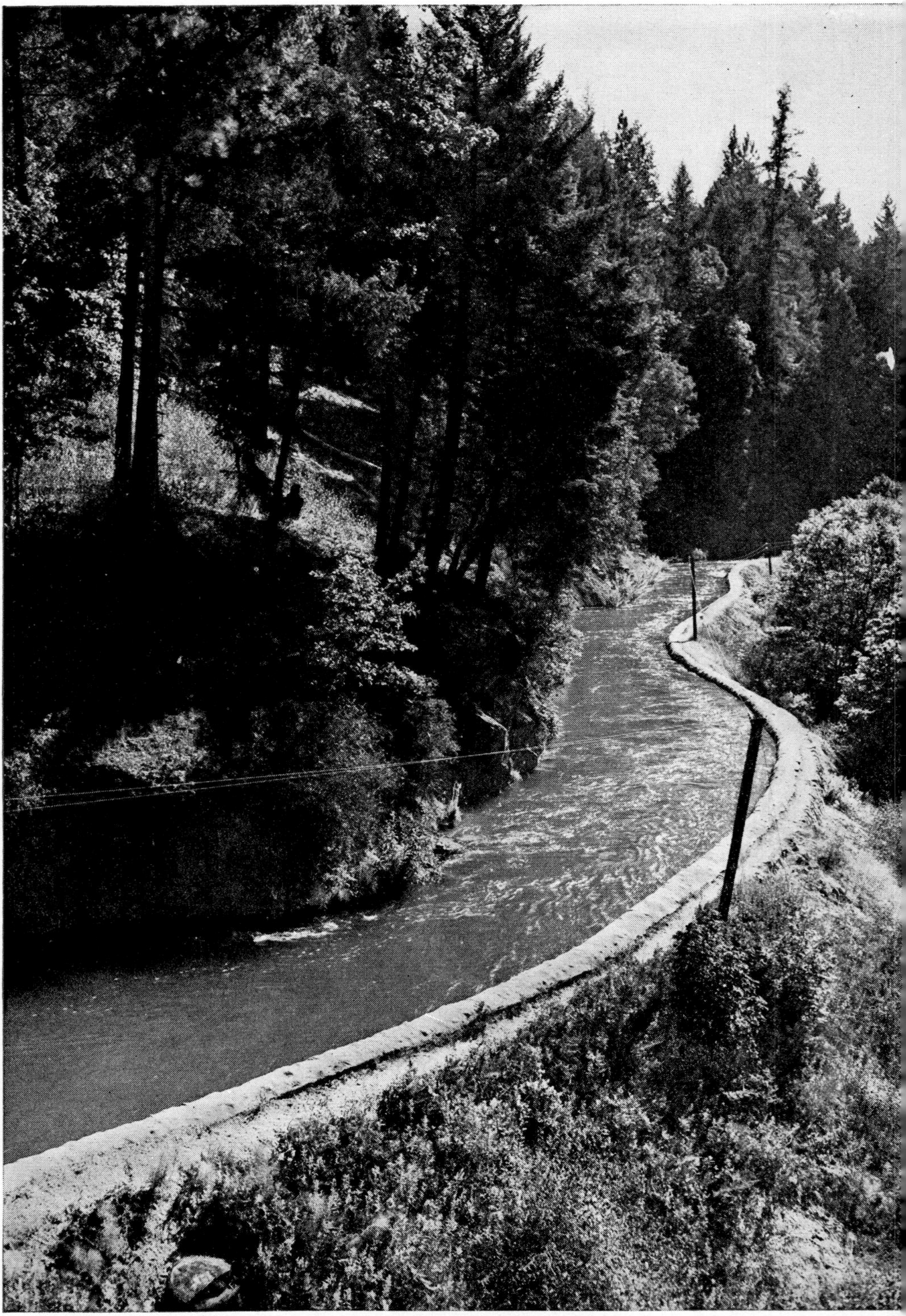

Bear River Canal, Placer County.

"If the expectations of the electricians [regarding hydroelectric power] shall come to be realized, as is altogether probable, there is no calculating the effect it will have on the industries of this State. The horsepower that could be generated here may be estimated by the hundreds of thousands. It would be ample to drive all the machinery in the New England States, and if utilized only in part would make California a great manufacturing country. . . ."

The location of the first hydroelectric plant in the state is not fully established. There is evidence that a little direct-current generator installed at Highgrove near Colton in Southern California was placed in operation in June, 1887, to supply San Bernardino, 8 miles away. The plant was placed on the ditch system of the Riverside Water Company at a point where a fall of 40 feet was obtained. The installation was made by the San Bernardino Electric Light and Power Company, which in 1888 was absorbed by C. O. G. Miller's Pacific Lighting Company.

But the always alert citizens of Nevada City and Grass Valley were not far behind the Southern Californians. Early in 1887 franchises to install electric street lamps in the two mining towns had been granted to representatives of one of the many electric manufacturing companies then competing for business.

Commenting upon the coming of electric lighting, the *Grass Valley Tidings* printed this gem of early day journalism:

"Woodland, Chico, Marysville and other towns smaller than Grass Valley are lighted by electricity, and Grass Valley, the Quartz-Crowned Empress of the Temperate Fruit Zone, should not be behind the Mud-Hen Infested Villages of the Valley in point of enterprise and progress."

The Grass Valley Electric Light and Motor Company, with a capitalization of $15,000, was incorporated by E. L. Campbell, William Boericke, Charles F. Burrell, A. A. Osborn, and A. H. Clough. The incorporators were all of San Francisco, where the articles were filed August 4, 1887. The *Weekly Tidings,* published in Grass Valley, described the coming of electricity to Nevada City:

"Nevada City, the county seat of the county of the same name, was in a state of the wildest excitement last night. The people of the town were all on the streets and the men shouted themselves hoarse and the ladies waved handkerchiefs. . . . The cause of this ebullition of feeling was that two electric lights were put in operation. One was suspended at Broad and Pine streets and the other near the bridge at the foot of Broad Street."

Lights also were placed in the National Hotel and in several stores.

Grass Valley celebrated its first electric illumination August 27, 1887. The circuit extended from the generating plant at the Charonnat Mine to Nevada City, thence to Grass Valley and to the county fairgrounds at Glenbrook, a reported circuit length of 14 miles. The initial generating installation appears to have been a 15-lamp arc dynamo, quickly followed by a 40-lamp machine, both operated by a Pelton water wheel. The plant later was moved to a more favorable site near the city reservoir. In succeeding weeks, after much discussion, contracts for electric street lighting were granted by the trustees of both towns.

The old established gas companies in the meantime were annoyed and disturbed by the new-fangled lighting. They had enjoyed a monopoly in street lighting for too many years. At first they tried open opposition. In one of a series of advertisements in the Nevada *Transcript* the gas company declared:

"The time is here when the gas works is to lose support, but if the consumers of this town will consider their own interests and the hazardous and precarious nature of electricity as a light, and let ordinary prudence be their guide, they will make no change."

When these warnings failed and attempts to influence the town trustees were of no avail, John Glasson, head of the gas company, took the obvious course and bought the intruding electric companies.

Nevada County achieved another triumph with its new electric lighting. During the District Fair at Glenbrook Park, midway between Nevada City and Grass Valley, there were two nights of horse racing by electric light. Arc lamps were installed around the race track, in the grandstand, and on the connecting road between the two towns. While far less brilliant, the illumination was an early forerunner of the floodlighting in today's sports arenas where nighttime baseball has become commonplace.

Incandescent lighting in homes as well as on the streets followed soon after introduction of arc lights in the mountain towns. In 1892 Kaskill Casper (the enterprising merchant who later built Vallejo's first electric plant) began operating a small water-powered generator to serve Nevada City. He obtained a contract with the city to provide street lights. After a few months Casper sold out to John Glasson, head of the older gas and electric companies. A new and enlarged hydro plant was built on Deer Creek to meet the growing demand for electricity. In 1896 the plant was sold to the Nevada County Electric Power Company, which continued it in operation until 1899, when it was abandoned as obsolete.

Use of electric power to operate the mines of the Sierra naturally followed the use of water power to run the generators. There is fragmentary indication that the Banner Mine at Nevada City contracted for power from the hydro plant there after its installation in 1889. The Empire, the Idaho, and the North Star were reported also planning to install their own generators for lighting their works and later to operate hoists, stamps, and pumps.

At the Dalmatia and the Gopher-Boulder quartz mines, Eldorado County, a hydroelectric plant was placed in operation in May, 1889. These two quartz mines, near Kelsey on the American River, were old claims taken over in the eighties by an English syndicate. George Cullen Pearson, a former British consul in Japan, was resident manager. When he decided to install electric power, he purchased the water rights of the partially abandoned Tom Williams ditch, built a new diversion dam, and at the end of the ditch on Rock Creek set up a Pelton water wheel and a 126-horsepower generator. Power was transmitted 3 miles to the Gopher-Boulder mine and 1½ miles to the Dalmatia. The two mines employed electric motors and electric lighting until they were closed down three years later.

Another early use of electric power was at the Standard Consolidated mine at Bodie, Mono County, August 18, 1892. On that day the Standard placed in operation a 112-kilowatt single-phase generator and transmitted current 13 miles to the mines.

The lure of electric lights spread to old Sonora in Tuolumne County. The citizens of that historic town threw away their kerosene lamps and their candles in 1892 when Otto Kanig built a small water-powered plant at Brown's Flat on Wood's Creek and ran copper wires to the town, a mile distant. Business places and residences were lighted by 16-candlepower incandescents. Kanig's single generator served Sonora until 1898 when the Tuolumne County Water and Electric Power Company placed its new Phoenix plant in operation.

And so the use of water power for the generation of electric power had its small beginnings in the mountain towns of Northern California. Transmission was the bar to further progress. The electrical engineers had not yet learned how to carry electricity by wire for any considerable distance from the generator without costly loss of power.

The first commercial hydroelectric plant in the nation was built in 1882 at Appleton, Wis., but power was transmitted only a short distance. On the Pacific Coast the earliest hydroelectric installation probably was at Spokane Falls, Washington (now Spokane), where in 1886 the Spokane Falls Water Power Company, headed by George A. Fitch, lighted the village streets with 10 arc lamps. The generator, a Brush machine, had been removed from the coastal steamer *Columbia* and installed in the basement of a mill. A hurdy-gurdy water wheel provided the primary power.

Then came the first important advance in transmission. At Oregon City, Oregon, on June 3, 1889, the Willamette Falls Electric Company completed a hydro plant to serve the city of Portland, 14 miles away. The initial installation consisted of three small dynamos with a total capacity of 60 arc lamps. The problem of transmission was solved by running individual customer circuits on the pole line, thus making the use of transformers unnecessary. As the load increased, there were as many as 36 wires strung on the poles from the Willamette Falls station to the customers' lamps in Portland.

California was not far behind Oregon in attempting long-distance transmission. Solution of the problem in the Golden

State was imperative because the larger cities and towns were nearly all many miles from the water sources. In Southern California, a college president, Dr. C. G. Baldwin of Pomona College, organized the San Antonio Light and Power Company, and after countless difficulties and long negotiations with reluctant Eastern manufacturers of electrical equipment, built the Pomona hydro plant on San Antonio Creek. Capacity of the plant was 150 horsepower. Transmission at 10,000 volts, single phase, started November 28, 1892, to Pomona, 13¾ miles, and a month later to San Bernardino, 28¾ miles. Another milestone! The first hydroelectric installation in California for long-distance transmission of alternating current at high voltage.

The electrical engineers, however, were not yet in agreement on the question of transmission. In 1893 a delegate to the International Electrical Congress at St. Louis rashly declared: "I wish to say definitely that to the investor in California today, the successful machine for long-distance transmission of power exists only in the minds of the inventors and promoters, or in some beautiful advertisement." Even as he spoke, disproof of his statement was in the making.

In an editorial, June 1, 1895, the San Francisco *Call* said:

"The air of California and the whole Pacific Coast for that matter, has all at once become filled with talk about setting up water wheels in lonely mountain places and making them give light and cheaply turn other wheels in towns miles away . . . two or three years from now airy copper lines may be running from the Sierras to half the towns of the Sacramento and San Joaquin Valleys."

Though the financial depression of 1893 made capital for electric projects extremely cautious, the era of hydro construction definitely had been opened. Its progress was aided and speeded by two factors—the devices developed by hydraulic miners to handle water under high pressures and the water wheel improvements initiated by Pelton, Dodd, Moore, and others.

* * *

It is a black, icy midnight at one of the big hydraulic mines high in the Sierra in the early 1880s. A battery of "giants" or "monitors" is bombarding the 100-foot gravel bank with thick streams of water that shoot from the nozzles with cannon-ball velocity. The "pipemen," lone figures in slickers and boots, stand by the monitors, directing the streams to the target, undercutting the bank, boring into the "face" until tons of "pay dirt" fall into the flood that washes the rubble down the slope.

The giant or monitor is a cannonlike pipe mounted on a ball-and-socket joint that permits its movement in any direction. On its nozzle is a deflector device with which the pipeman controls the rushing stream of water.

The giants are fed by big riveted iron pipes that deliver the water under high "head" or pressure from the supply canal. The nozzle may be 3, 6, or 9 inches in diameter.

The mass of gravel is washed into bedrock sluices and then perhaps into a debris tunnel where riffles of iron blocks or the cross sections of logs catch the heavy particles of gold in the crevices between them. The torrent of rolling boulders and gravel sends up a rumbling undertone to the steady swish of the water rocketing from the giants. Day and night during the season of plentiful water, the bombardment and the flood continue. Periodically the water is shut off, the riffles are lifted from sluices and boxes, and the gold held there is recovered. In the heyday of hydraulicking, a fortune—$50,000–$100,000—might be taken in a single "cleanup."

The earliest known approach to hydraulic mining occurred in April, 1852, when Antoine Chabot, French-Canadian owner of a claim at Buckeye Hill in Nevada County, tried using a hose to wash the loosened gravel into the sluice box (this is the same Anthony Chabot, builder of water systems and philanthropist, who in 1866 became the first president of the Oakland Gas Light Company). Chabot attached a length of canvas hose to a small flume bringing water from a point above his claim. He used the hose to wash the gravel into his sluice boxes and found the method a great laborsaver compared to the slow process of hand shoveling.

In the same year, Colonel William McClure, mining a gravel claim at Yankee Jim in Placer County, set up a small open flume above his gravel bank, attached so that the lower end could be moved back and forth on a log. Through this he released a flow of water with sufficient volume and velocity to wash great quantities of gravel into the sluice boxes below.

Then came Edward E. Matteson (sometimes spelled Mattison), a Connecticut Yankee mining at American Hill in Nevada County. In 1853 he tapped a ditch high above his claim with a rawhide hose to which he attached a tapered nozzle carved from a block of wood with a hole bored through its center. With this he played a sharp stream against the gravel bank's face and washed masses of pay dirt into his sluice boxes with considerable saving in time and labor costs. Matteson used the basic method of hydraulic mining, and early writers generally credit him with a "first."

Hydraulic mining spread through the gold country as the placer claims were worked out. It grew more rapidly when rich gold deposits were found in the alluvial gravels of ancient river channels running through ridges high above existing streams. Then began the building of longer canals and flumes, tapping water sources at ever higher elevations. Year after year hydraulic mining gained momentum. At the peak period there were 425 hydraulic mines operating in the mountain regions, dumping millions of cubic yards of debris "tailings" into the creeks and rivers each year.

Right there was the catch that marked the doom of hydraulic mining. Silt and gravel from the mines were carried in muddy streams to the rivers of the valleys below. The level of river beds began to rise; resultant floods caused heavy damage to the farms through which they passed. After a bitter fight between the farmers and the miners came the decision of Judge L. B. Sawyer of the United States Circuit Court, January 23, 1884, which granted a perpetual injunction against the North Bloomfield Mining Company of Nevada County, forbidding the discharge of debris into the rivers. The Caminetti Act of 1893 followed, setting up the State Debris Commission and permitting hydraulic mining only after construction of debris-impounding dams under official sanction. The miners launched a campaign to persuade the state legislature to lighten the restrictions. The controversy went on for many years, and in the end the farmers won. The day of hydraulic mining, in which $100,000,000 was said to have been invested, was done.

A few attempts were made to continue operations by erecting legally approved dams and catchment basins for the mountains of gravel and sands washed down by the monitors. At two of these dams Pacific Gas and Electric Company today operates small hydro powerhouses where electric power was at first produced as a by-product of the mining activity.

One of these is at Bullard's Bar on the north fork of the Yuba in Yuba County. After a first small dam proved inadequate, the present larger structure was built in 1923–1924 by a group of Eastern capitalists headed by Harry Payne Whitney, who owned mining properties upstream in Sierra County and planned to impound their mining debris in the lake, 7 miles long, created by the dam. Under a lease agreement the Pacific Gas and Electric Company built a powerhouse at the base of the dam with an electric capacity of 7,500 kilowatts. After passing through the powerhouse, the water from the storage lake is diverted from the stream and again drives a hydroelectric generator at Colgate Powerhouse some 8 miles downstream. After a few years the mining company ceased operating and the electric company purchased Bullard's Bar Dam.

A second debris dam is at the Narrows on the Yuba River near Smartsville. Here in 1942 a P. G. and E. powerhouse was built. The generator at the Narrows has a capacity of 12,000 kilowatts.

At Gold Run in a canyon just off the highway south of Dutch Flat, James D. Stewart, veteran hydraulic engineer, dwells in retirement on the spot where he, and his father before him, saw the rise and fall of hydraulic mining. James Stewart the elder came to Gold Run in 1867 and his son was born there, destined to follow in his father's footsteps.

At the peak of its prosperity there were 45 hydraulic mines at Gold Run within a radius of 1½ miles, recovering gold from the deep gravel deposits at the rate, sometimes, of a million dollars a year. The Gold Run Ditch and Mining Company, formed in 1870 by Alan Towle, J. L. Gould, and their associates, became the dominant company. The canyon, where in the early days nearly a hundred separate claims were being worked, gradually was brought under control of the single company. At the height of activity, operations were on a grand scale. With tons of explosives to break down the cemented gravel, the floods of water from the monitors washed out a vast chasm 400 feet to bedrock.

The beginning of the end came in 1881 when the Gold Run Ditch and Mining Company was enjoined by the court from dumping debris into the north fork of the American River through the drainage tunnel from the mine. By the time he reached manhood and had become superintendent and manager of the Gold Run properties, Jim Stewart was convinced that hydraulic mining could be saved. After the Gold Run workings were closed down, he moved to Auburn and practiced his profession as consulting engineer. Meanwhile he battled for years for legislative relief. He organized campaigns for the mine owners. He wrote and spoke whenever and wherever an appeal to public opinion could be made. In the end, as before, the miners lost.

After many years in Auburn, Jim and Mrs. Stewart returned to Gold Run where they live within a stone's throw of the idle mine shops and compressor building. From the porch of their comfortable home they look across the deserted mine workings where 100 million cubic yards of pay dirt were washed through the sluices and tunnels. Almost an equal yardage of gold-bearing gravel remains untouched, waiting for the time when its golden treasure can be recovered without filling the river channels with silt. Jim believes that time will come.

The Gold Run Ditch and Mining Company was sold in 1897 to Joseph D. Redding who in turn sold to Gold Run Gravel, Ltd., an English corporation. In 1907 the United Water and Power Company succeeded to ownership and in 1913 sold to the Pacific Gas and Electric Company its water rights, the Miner's and Extension ditches and connected storage reservoirs. Today the sign over the gate at Gold Run reads: "STEWART GRAVEL MINES."

Today the great hydraulic mines of the north country are idle, deserted wastes. The second-growth pines and firs that dot the deep gashes in the mountainsides mutely measure the half century that has passed since the pits were seething centers of activity. The Malakoff, the Cherokee, Gold Run, the Polar Star, the Joubert, and most of the others have become only names in the history of a long-gone but still vibrant and dramatic period of California's story of gold.

* * *

An obscure millwright, living in one of the isolated mountain towns of the gold country, gave to the hydroelectric builders the primary motive power they needed for their generators—the Pelton impulse water wheel.

Water power had been used in California from the beginning. The first wheels were the cumbersome overshot wooden models the gold miners had known in their Eastern and Middle Western homes, not much improved in design over the type favored by the Pilgrim Fathers when they set up their grist mills on the banks of New England's rivers. California settlers built similar wheels to run lumber mills, flour mills, and pumps. In the mining regions where water under high pressures was available, a new type of wheel, called the "hurdy-gurdy," somewhat more efficient, was evolved.

Lester Allen Pelton came to California in 1850, a quiet, studious youth of twenty who was more successful with carpenter's tools than with the miner's pick and shovel. In Camptonville, high in the mountains of Yuba County, he labored in the mines and then turned to carpentry and the work of a millwright. He built homes, a schoolhouse, mine structures, mills, and water wheels. The water wheels attracted his interest, and he began to study the force that made them revolve. With an inventor's curiosity and imagination he sought a way to increase the speed and power of the hurdy-gurdy wheel.

Differing accounts have been published regarding the circumstances that led the inventor to discovery of the "splitter" principle of the Pelton wheel design. By splitting the stream of water from the nozzle into two parts and changing the angle of the impact against the buckets attached to the wheel he multiplied its speed, power, and efficiency.

On July 13, 1910, a Sacramento newspaper published a full-page article on the Pelton wheel written by Harry P. Bagley and based upon the firsthand story of Mrs. Margaret Groves, at whose home in Camptonville Pelton boarded. Bagley is at present a member of the Stockton *Record* staff. The inventor, Mrs. Groves said, had built a shack workshop in the rear of her home. Using such tools and materials as were available, Pelton made a miniature wheel with buckets and a tiny nozzle. He persuaded Mrs. Groves to let him connect the wheel to her prized sewing machine, and the toy contraption worked.

Pelton, however, had not yet found the improvement he sought. He built a larger model, using a wagon wheel and axle, with tin cans for buckets. One day while testing the action of the new wheel under a stream of water from a garden hose and nozzle, the jet accidentally was split into two separate impacts upon the buckets. Pelton observed an immediate increase in the speed of the wheel. In that moment, it was said, originated the "splitter" principle of the Pelton water wheel and the introduction of twin buckets on the wheel instead of the single line of cups formerly used. This was in 1878.

Dr. W. F. Durand of Stanford University gave a different version in his monograph, "The Pelton Water Wheel," published in the magazine *Mechanical Engineering* in 1939. Dr. Durand's statement, based upon a conversation of engineer friends with Pelton himself, was that the discovery of the splitter principle was made during an experiment with a Knight wheel used to drive a stamp mill. While the wheel was running, the key that secured the wheel to the shaft became loosened and the wheel shifted on the shaft so that the jet of water struck the buckets on the edge instead of at the bottom of the cavity. Pelton observed that the speed of the stamp mill instantly increased, and that fact led him eventually to the splitter principle. Both incidents easily could have happened.

Pelton went on with his experiments. He obtained instruments to measure the efficiency of the wheel. He tried 40 or more different shapes of buckets, and at last, on October 26, 1880, patented his invention. He began making wheels of the new design at Nevada City for quartz stamp mills and for other power uses in the mines. The miners had been using steam power to operate their hoists and pumps and stamps. The Idaho-Maryland, the Empire, and the North Star were among the first to change to water power. Pelton's wheel was selected by the Idaho-Maryland mine after an efficiency contest with other types.

Not satisfied with the inadequate manufacturing facilities available in the mountains, Pelton moved to San Francisco and knocked at the door of A. P. Brayton, general manager of the machine works of Rankin, Brayton & Company. The result was the incorporation of the Pelton Water Wheel Company in 1888.

Introduction of the Pelton wheel was followed by protesting assertion of priority by Knight, Colman, Dodd, Moore, and other inventors, but in the end the Camptonville millwright maintained his claim to originality. In its perfected form, the Pelton wheel was manufactured for a surprising diversity of uses. Wheels were made up to 20 feet in diameter to produce many thousands of horsepower. They were also made as small as 4 inches in diameter, weighing only 20 pounds, for the operation of sewing machines and dental and other small appliances.

In the mountain hamlet of Camptonville, on the site of the inventor's workshop, stands a granite shaft, erected in 1929 by Gravel Range Lodge No. 59, Free and Accepted Masons. At the top is mounted one of the earliest of Pelton's splitter wheels. On the face of the shaft is a bronze plaque inscribed, "On this spot, in 1878, Lester Allen Pelton invented the Pelton Water Wheel."

Production of a water wheel designed to produce maximum driving power under the high static heads characteristic of Northern California water sources was timely. It came just as the hydroelectric engineers were laying plans for the first water-powered generating plants. Almost simultaneously with production of the Pelton wheel, other models came on the market and a choice of prime movers was available. In a recent publication of the California State Division of Mines (*The Mother Lode Country,* Bulletin 141, 1948) C. A. Logan wrote:

"Pacific Gas and Electric Company has acknowledged its debt to the California miners and the tangential water wheel.

It is not too much to say that this Company owed its origin to the hydraulic miners and the Pelton wheel."

Mr. Logan's conclusion perhaps is more sweeping than he intended. The Pelton wheel, however, did an enormous service to the cause of hydro. It is to be found in numerous P. G. and E. plants. Its original design refined and improved, it is to be found also in hydro plants all over the world.

Another contribution to the cause of hydro was handed down by California's miners. This was the nozzle perfected by the hydraulic men. From the time Matteson first carved his crude nozzle from a wooden block in 1853, constant experiments were made by Craig, Hopkins, Perkins, and others to find means of controlling the water jet that shot from the hydraulic monitor. The jet deflector, which made the operator master of the giant stream and which gave maximum effect to the rushing water, was the result. The principles developed by the hydraulic miners were passed on to the designers of the Pelton and other water wheels and turbines and to the hydro engineers. Regarding this, Dr. Durand of Stanford University said:

"In order to meet the momentarily varying demands for power, the effective operation of a water wheel of this type requires at least one further essential element and that is, suitable means for regulating the mass of water in the jet which impinges on the bucket. . . .

"Apparently the first [water wheel nozzle] in point of time, brought in during the 'eighties of the last century, was a form of deflecting nozzle hinged in such a way as to admit of bringing the jet from full on the wheel to full off. This method of control was a natural, we may even say an inevitable, application of the method employed in moving and directing the stream of the 'hydraulic giant,' then in common use in the gold mining fields of California."

CHAPTER II

Folsom—Grandfather Hydro Plant

On THE granite bank of the American River at the town of Folsom, northeast of Sacramento, is Folsom Powerhouse, ancestor and first of the present P. G. and E. family of 58 hydroelectric plants. Folsom occupies a special niche in the Company's history. Its completion and first operation July 13, 1895, marked a new achievement in long-distance transmission at high voltage. Its story began nearly half a century before the plant itself became a reality.

In the summer of 1895, Folsom's generators began producing electricity for transmission at 11,000 volts to the state capital, 22 miles distant. By October the plant's four generators were in operation, with a total capacity of 3,000 kilowatts. The dream of high-tension transmission lines delivering power at low cost to San Francisco and Oakland, to the industries clustered around the Bay, was approaching realization.

The citizens of Sacramento recognized the importance of their new source of electric power. A Grand Electrical Carnival celebrated the event September 9, 1895. A salute of 100 guns greeted the dawn of the electrical day. The Capitol was outlined with thousands of incandescent lamps. A night parade of illuminated floats mounted on electric streetcars passed through streets festooned with lights. The engraved invitations, with typical Western fear of understatement, described Folsom as "the greatest operative electrical plant on the American continent."

Engineers came from distant cities to inspect the installation. The editor of the *Journal of Electricity* referred to Sacramento as "the first American city to demonstrate the practicability of long distance transmission at high voltage." The Sacramento *Bee,* following the Carnival display, said:

"In Sacramento has been first practically solved the grave problem of the long transmission of electric current for power and light purposes. Not only is this the longest power transmission line but also the largest electric power plant in the world, in the sense of power actually developed."

The writer is reluctant to endorse these claims. Assertion of "first" in electric achievement is dangerous without detailed technical specifications. It is enough that the Folsom system marked a momentous advance in the commercial application of electricity.

The output of Folsom Powerhouse was employed in Sacramento by the electric street railway system and by industries and commercial establishments.

Within a short time, when more power was needed, another 750-kilowatt generator was installed in a building erected below the Folsom plant to take advantage of an additional 26-foot fall in the stream that dropped from the forebay. The main plant operated under a head of 55 feet. The smaller plant is notable now chiefly for its curious rope drive, a museum piece which still is in place. Instead of the customary belting, rope was used to connect the revolving shaft of the water turbine to the shaft of the generator which was on a platform high above the turbine. Twenty-two hundred feet of hemp rope were threaded in 26 strands over large grooved drums attached to each shaft, with an ingenious overhead device to take up the slack. The powerhouse operators assure present-day visitors that the novel drive worked effectively. The little supplementary plant, long since obsolete, is unused, but the main Folsom plant still is in operation, its original generators running as smoothly as they did when they were installed more than a half century ago.

* * *

The Folsom story started more than a hundred years ago at Georgetown, in the mountains of Eldorado County, with the arrival in 1850 of Horatio Gates Livermore. The newcomer, an immigrant from Livermore, Maine, saw his future in the magnificent stands of sugar pine that forested the Georgetown divide. He was a public-spirited citizen and in 1854 was elected to the state senate. In his travels to the state capital he was impressed by the possibilities of the American River for logging purposes and for development of water power to operate sawmills and other industrial plants. He dreamed of an industrial city at Folsom like Lowell, Mass., where water wheels long had been used to operate the New Englanders' mills and factories.

Livermore went to work. He became interested in the Natoma Water Company, organized in 1851 to obtain water rights and auriferous lands on the American River. The name was changed in 1853 to Natoma Water and Mining Company. The flow of the river was diverted at Salmon Falls, and at a cost of $200,000 a ditch system was built to serve the mining claims at Red Banks, Mormon Island, Willow Springs, Rhodes Diggings, and a number of other placer camps.

The pioneer's two sons, Horatio Putnam and Charles Edward Livermore, joined their father in 1856 but at first they remained in San Francisco. Horatio, then in his twenties, obtained employment at the western branch of Redington & Company, a wholesale drug firm for which he had worked in Boston. In later years he was to be managing partner of the Redington San Francisco branch.

By 1862 the Livermores had obtained control of the Natoma Water and Mining Company. They acquired for the company some 9,000 acres of land that had been a part of the Rancho de los Americanos granted to W. A. Leidesdorff by a Mexican governor. Much of it contained deep gold-bearing gravel deposits. In the foothills the elder Livermore planted 500 acres in orchards and vineyards to demonstrate his faith in the agricultural future of the region. A fruit-drying plant and winery were built at Folsom.

The pioneer had clung to his dream of making an industrial city at Folsom and his plan for logging down the American. The first necessity was a dam above Folsom where the granite banks of the stream form a narrow gorge at Stony Bar. From the dam a canal was to be built on each side of the river to the town of Folsom, one for the development of industrial water

A maintenance railway ran along the top of this flume that carried water 16 miles to operate Stanislaus Powerhouse.

The early builders had no high-powered trucks and tractors. Here part of a generator is being hauled by a [illegible] horse and mule team to De Sabla Powerhouse in [illegible]

Horatio Gates Livermore's dream of an industrial city on the American River resulted in the building of Folsom Powerhouse 40 years later by his son.

Horatio P. Livermore built Folsom Powerhouse and founded the Sacramento Electric, Gas and Railway Company in the State Capital.

Folsom Powerhouse marked a new achievement in long-distance transmission at high voltage. In 1895 it transmitted power at 11,000 volts to Sacramento 22 miles away.

power under a total fall of 80 feet and the other for west-side irrigation. Only the east-side canal was constructed.

Work on the dam was started in 1867. Then for 26 years there were heartbreaking delays caused by shortages of capital, lawsuits, political bickering, and other obstacles. The dam was not completed until 1893.

The Natoma Company built the foundation and the first 30 feet of the granite and concrete dam and constructed 2 miles of railroad from Folsom to the dam site, but financial help was needed to finish the project. After long negotiations a contract with the State Prison Board was signed under which, with later amendments, the state agreed to supply $30,000 worth of convict labor at 50 cents per day per man in exchange for 484 acres of land near the dam site where a new penitentiary was to be erected. Building of the new prison was interminably delayed. The state sued the company and lost the case by a supreme court decision.

At last, in 1888, a new agreement was drawn and on July 1 of that year work on the partially constructed dam and canal was resumed. Under the new contract the state was to provide 60,000 man-days of convict labor annually for five years and was to receive, in addition to the land, water to operate a small electric generating plant in the prison, water for prison use as a perpetual right, and other lesser concessions.

Despite the inefficient convict labor and the constant interference of state machine politics, the dam at last was completed and water was turned into the canal in January, 1893. Construction had cost the state 520,349 man-days of convict labor and $24,508 for free labor to finish the lagging job. It had cost the Livermores and their associates heavy losses in income from their invested capital during the unproductive years, plus unestimated losses caused by disruption of their original plans. Folsom Dam is today a massive tribute in granite to the Livermores and to its designer, H. T. Knight, the company's engineer, who drew the original plans and supervised the job to its completion.

H. P. Livermore, a man of inexhaustible energy and persistent enthusiasm, had gradually assumed leadership of the enterprises started by his father. He was assisted by his brother Charles.

In 1881 the original plan to create a factory town at Folsom was still held to be feasible. In order to clear away corporate complications, a new company, the Folsom Water Power Company, was incorporated October 18, 1881. Charles E. Livermore was its president. The new organization took over from the Natoma Water and Mining Company all its properties and rights that were related to water power. The older company retained its mining canals and mining lands. Stockholders of the two corporations were identical.

But conditions were changing. The electric industry was making its first faltering steps. In the late eighties, H. P. Livermore began to see that by the time the dam was finished, water power as a direct motive force for the wheels of industry would be superseded by electric power. He had kept abreast of electrical developments. He had read of the early application of electric power in California mines. He had studied reports of transmission experiments in Germany and Italy. It was obvious that the water power developed at Folsom Dam should be used for production of electric power, and that the market for that power was in Sacramento. But the capital was 22 miles from Folsom, and he could find no one who would say that electricity could be transmitted such a distance economically.

Livermore learned of the advances made by Frank J. Sprague in the development of a direct-current motor for operation of electric railways. This gave him an idea. Folsom power could be used to operate the Sacramento street railways. Confident that a way could be found, he went ahead. To arm himself with a negotiating weapon, he obtained personally a franchise to build an electric railway system in Sacramento, regardless of the fact that the Central Electric Railway Company had been operating its cars by electricity for the past year. Livermore actually built a stretch of double track on H Street. Next he wrote to Sprague, who had installed electric streetcars in Richmond, Va., stating his problem in detail. Sprague offered to design a workable system.

Convinced, then, that he was on the right course, Livermore incorporated the Sacramento Electric Power and Light Company, November 5, 1892, and assigned to it his street railway franchise. He renewed his correspondence with Eastern manufacturers who had been lukewarm to his proposal that they plan a transmission system from Folsom to Sacramento and a method for conversion of alternating current to direct for delivery to the streetcars. Finally, the Westinghouse Company sent Engineer L. B. Stillwell to California to investigate. Armed with all the data, he returned to Pittsburgh and eventually his company submitted a plan, explaining meanwhile that the whole problem was theoretical and their suggested solution experimental.

When the General Electric Company heard of the the Westinghouse activities, it also developed a new interest in the Folsom project and sent Engineer F. O. Blackwell and Professor Louis Bell to study the problem. General Electric, on the basis of its experts' reports, followed its competitor with an offer to build the Folsom system.

Livermore had won his point. He had in hand two sets of plans and specifications for construction of the Folsom plant and transmission system. The new Sacramento Electric Power and Light Company was to build and operate the system, taking its water on lease from the Folsom Water Power Company. There remained the financing of the project, no small task in the depression years of the early nineties.

H. P. Livermore was to find the needed funds through one of those fortuitous circumstances which so frequently came to the rescue of utility enterprises of the past century. Dr. Thomas Addison was Western representative of the recently formed General Electric Company. His offices in San Francisco adjoined those of the hardware firm of Huntington, Hopkins & Co., which in 1886 had moved from its original home in Sacramento. Albert Gallatin, president and general manager of the hardware company, had risen to the high command after Collis P. Huntington and Mark Hopkins had turned over operation of their hardware business to their employees when building the Central Pacific railroad required all their attention.

Gallatin knew the Sacramento picture. He had been an officer of the board of trade there when that body had tried to hasten the building of Folsom prison. During the years since, he had been an officer of the Citizens Gas Company and had helped organize the Capital Gas Company. When he learned from his friend Dr. Addison about the financial needs of the Folsom Water Power Company, he decided to act.

Gallatin started negotiations into which were called J. Dalzell Brown, vice-president of the California Safe Deposit and Trust Company; George H. Roe, president of the Edison Electric Light and Power Company; and Charles R. Lloyd, a promoter and stockholder in the Edison company. Gallatin, Addison, and Lloyd went East for conferences with Charles A. Coffin, president of General Electric, and with officers of the Electrical Securities Company of Boston, an underwriting firm with which General Electric had close financial relations.

An agreement was reached after many conferences and much maneuvering. The Electrical Securities Company agreed to underwrite a block of the Livermore company's bonds. General Electric was to build and install equipment for the electric system. The contract was signed early in 1894. Albert Gallatin became a large stockholder in the Sacramento Electric Power and Light Company and also its president and an enthusiastic worker in its behalf.

Work on the powerhouse began immediately. The canal was extended 1½ miles from its terminus at the prison generating plant to the site of the new plant at the town of Folsom. A twin cedar-pole transmission line to a new substation at Sixth and H Streets in Sacramento was completed. The substation was equipped to deliver direct current to the street railway system.

While all this work was being rushed to completion, Livermore and Gallatin had concluded an agreement with the Central Electric Railway Company for purchase of the street railways. The new Sacramento Electric Power and Light Company had its first large power customer. Merger of the Central Electric Railway properties into the Livermore project was concluded in 1894, upon payment of $250,000 in cash and $265,000 in bonds of the Power and Light Company.

The generators, turbines, and all the other required equipment were received early in 1895, and after severe tests Folsom

Powerhouse was ready for operation. The impossible had been accomplished.

The new company started operations with Albert Gallatin as president; J. W. Hall, manager; T. A. W. Shock, superintendent; and C. W. Hutton, who had been electrical engineer for the Capital Gas Company, assistant superintendent. The first solicitations for business uncovered powerful opposition from the Capital Gas Company which for years had enjoyed a monopoly in both the gas and electric fields.

The old company lowered its rates and was accused of using its political influence with the city government to prevent the newcomer from obtaining needed franchises. There were charges, also, that the same influences were blocking the sale of power to the Southern Pacific, a large potential customer.

At times the Livermore company was hard pressed to meet its financial obligations. Sale of its bonds became increasingly difficult, and cash contributions from the stockholders were necessary.

Reorganization of the related Livermore companies was accomplished April 4, 1896, when the Sacramento Electric, Gas and Railway Company was incorporated to bring under one ownership the Sacramento Electric Power and Light Company, Folsom Water Power Company, and the old Natoma Water and Mining Company. A bond issue of $1,500,000 was authorized. The consolidation, however, did not cure the ills that beset the enterprise. The General Electric Company began to assert an increasing influence upon the financial operations of the company to protect its large holdings of bonds taken in payment for the Folsom plant equipment.

Piling trouble on trouble, a new competitor appeared January 1, 1897, when the Central California Electric Company, wholly owned by the powerful South Yuba Water Company, began delivering electric power to Sacramento from its Newcastle and Auburn plants in Placer County. The Placer County company, strong financially and operating at low cost, not only offered still lower rates but contracted with the gas company to supply it with its surplus power, thus strengthening the opposition to the struggling Livermore enterprise.

The fight for existence went on. The years 1897 and 1898 were "dry" years and the need for more electric power resources became acute. Help came in 1899 when the Yuba Electric Power Company operating Colgate plant on the middle fork of the Yuba River completed a 61-mile transmission line to bring more power to Sacramento under a contract with the Livermore company. Strengthened by the new source of power, the Sacramento Electric, Gas and Railway Company renewed its fight for leadership. The old Capital Gas Company, whose electric plant had become virtually obsolete and which had lost much of its gas lighting business to the electric competitor, was taken over by the Livermores in 1899. The South Yuba Water Company's electric subsidiary did not attempt to expand its business. The pendulum had swung in favor of Gallatin and the Livermores.

Financial problems, however, continued to be pressing. At one time the General Electric Company, still concerned over the payment of its bond holdings, placed Charles R. Lloyd in virtual control of the Sacramento company's finances. Lloyd was the promoter who had taken part in the original financing of the Folsom project and earlier had helped George H. Roe organize the Edison Light & Power Company. During the period in which he was active in Sacramento he disposed of $500,000 in bonds to capitalist L. P. Drexler. The funds relieved pressure upon the company, at a cost, however, of a considerable stock bonus to Lloyd.

Business continued to grow, and for a few years around the turn of the century the company paid a monthly dividend of 15 cents. But the battle had been a long and grueling one for the Livermores and Gallatin and their associates. They were ready for the offer of purchase which came from Eugene de Sabla and John Martin and their new company, the California Gas and Electric Corporation which was a consolidation of all the previously organized de Sabla-Martin companies. An option agreement was signed and in March, 1903, the Sacramento Electric, Gas and Railway Company and its properties were merged into the larger system, the immediate predecessor of P. G. and E.

* * *

When the Folsom Dam was nearing completion in 1892, H. P. Livermore plunged into a plan to utilize the flood waters of the American River for irrigation. He organized the Sacramento County Water Company and had surveys made for canals through the rich rolling country between the foothills along the American westward to the Sacramento.

Again Livermore was a generation ahead of his time. The farmers still clung to grain as the best crop for valley lands, and the Sacramento County Water Company and its ambitious plans came to nothing. Fifty-six years later, Norman B. Livermore, son of the pioneer, stood on a hillside in the foothills above Folsom and watched the ground-breaking for a great new $50,000,000 Folsom Reservoir which, on a gigantic scale, will confirm the soundness of his father's first plan. In 1948 U.S. Army Engineers started work on the mighty project which, in addition to its initial purpose of flood control, is designed to provide water for an extensive system of canals to irrigate the lands of the valley.

* * *

Horatio Gates Livermore, the sturdy man from Maine who in the late fifties planned a water-powered industrial city at Folsom and great lumber mills to be fed by logs floated down the American River, did not live to see any of his visions materialize. He died January 13, 1892, in Rockridge Park, Oakland, just as the Folsom Dam was nearing completion. The water power he had planned to develop was to be used to drive electric generators instead of industrial machines in a water-powered factory town. His hope of transporting by river the logs from the Georgetown divide was yet to be fulfilled and he never knew that his plan was to prove only partially successful.

The lumber enterprise was launched in 1888 when George W. Cummings, a stranger, came to H. P. Livermore with a timbering plan that differed little from the ideas formulated by the elder Livermore more than 40 years earlier. It seemed feasible to H. P. Livermore, and on March 30, 1889, he incorporated the $1,500,000 American River Land & Lumber Company. Some 9,000 acres of forest land lying between the south and middle forks of the American River were purchased. Construction of a 40-mile logging railroad was started.

The boulder-strewn river was cleared of its largest obstructions. At Folsom Dam a massive boom enclosed a pool for the logs. At Folsom town a down-to-date sawmill was erected. Difficulties were encountered, however, when the log drives started in 1897 and 1898. The river had not been sufficiently cleared of obstructions, and logs were hung up on midstream rock shelves. They arrived at the pool broken and splintered from the beating they had taken in the fast-running stream. Although a stock of some 6,000,000 board feet of lumber was stored at one time at the mill yard, operations were continued only a few years. They proved too costly. River transportation was abandoned and the mill was moved to a point near the logging operations.

* * *

The Maine man's grandson carried on the family traditions. Norman Banks Livermore, who in 1951 celebrated his seventy-ninth birthday, is at this writing a veteran director of Pacific Gas and Electric Company. Elected to the board in 1916, he has served the Company with only one interruption of two years, in 1918–1919, when he was an officer in the U.S. Army Engineer Corps on active duty in France. Returning from the war in 1920 with rank of lieutenant colonel, he resumed his directorship and has served continuously ever since with a knowledge of the Company's system and its origins few men have acquired.

But the greater part of the son's financial interest in P. G. and E. did not come to him by inheritance. When his father, H. P. Livermore, died in 1916, he left no great fortune. He was essentially a builder, looking to the future, more concerned with the success of his undertaking than with personal profit. Financing Folsom Powerhouse and the Sacramento Electric, Gas and Railway Company had cost him much of his stock holdings, and his irrigation and lumber projects had taken more.

Norman Livermore was educated as an engineer at the universities of California and Cornell. He spent a postgraduate year at General Electric Company's shop school in its Schenectady works. When he returned to Sacramento he assisted his father in the electric power company and the lumber operations and made an exhaustive survey of other hydroelectric plants in the state. When control of the Sacramento electric company was virtually taken over by those who had financed the bond issue, the young Livermore decided he must strike out for himself. For a short time he worked as an engineer on a government project in Florida. Then he returned to California and established his own business, dealing in heavy machinery and representing the American Locomotive Company.

As he prospered, Norman Livermore added to his original small P. G. and E. holdings. In memory of his father's early years with the Coffin-Redington drug company, he bought stock in that company and later became its president. He bought bonds and became a director of the Natomas Company which had succeeded to the properties of his grandfather's old Natoma Water and Mining Company. Refusing the ease of retirement, he still maintains an office and an active interest in business affairs.

CHAPTER 12

Two Daring Enterprisers

ELECTRIC arcs were flashing in California in the last decade of the century. While the Livermores were struggling to complete their powerhouse at Folsom, other minds and imaginations were at work in Southern California, in the San Joaquin Valley, and in the mountains of Northern California. Water power and electric power had sparked the enterprisers into action.

Among them were Eugene J. de Sabla, Jr., and John Martin who were to take leading roles in the drama that reached its climax when Pacific Gas and Electric Company was created.

Eugene de Sabla's background was storybook romance and adventure. His ancestors had been given noble rank and made guardians of a sandy section of frontier (*de sable* means "of the sands") by a French king in reward for valor in battle. His great-grandfather was in charge of the Tuileries, the king's Parisian palace, when the fall of the Bastille in 1789 forced him to flee with his family and not inconsiderable fortune to Martinique in the West Indies.

Eugene's grandfather—Jacques Joseph Sylvain de Joly de Blazon de Sabla—grew to manhood on the island of Guadalupe, French West Indies. On a voyage to the Isthmus of Panama, then under the government of New Granada (Colombia), he conceived a plan for a canal across the isthmus through which ships might pass between the Atlantic and the Pacific. He brought a party of engineers and sappers to the wilderness and spent two years surveying a route. When he returned to Guadalupe, he found his home and much of his large estate destroyed by a devastating earthquake.

Joly de Sabla, as he was known, obtained a concession from the Granadian government and organized a syndicate in Paris and London to build a railroad first and then a canal. Again disaster interfered when the French revolution of 1848 disrupted the syndicate. Under a new concession the Panama railroad was built by an American-English group headed by Aspinwall, Stephens, and Chauncey. De Sabla refused to join the new venture because he could not agree with its engineering plans. One of his sons, Theodore J. de Sabla, later was associated with Ferdinand de Lesseps in his canal enterprise and became a director of the Panama railroad.

Eugene de Sabla, senior, son of Joly, acquired plantations in Colombia and Guatemala. Eugene, junior, was born in Panama, January 20, 1865, and was brought to San Francisco in 1870 when his father decided to open an importing and exporting house there. After he had finished his preparatory schooling at Trinity School and the Boys High School, his father urged him to go to Harvard or some other Eastern college. Impatient to make his start in the world, he won permission instead to take a course in assaying at the laboratory of William Irelan. There he met Senator George Hearst and others of Comstock and Mother Lode fame.

When he had finished his training in assaying, Eugene was sent to a copper mine in Arizona of which his father was a part owner. The mine was the Planet, 90 miles from the railroad. A. A. Tregidgo was superintendent. The detail is important because the Cornish mine boss will appear later as a principal character in the P. G. and E. story.

The young descendant of the French royalists worked hard at the mine, sometimes from six in the morning until midnight for a wage of $1 per day. When the low price of copper forced the mine to close, Eugene returned to San Francisco and entered his father's office. On his twenty-first birthday he was made a full partner in Eugene de Sabla & Co. and managed the business during his father's long absences in Central America. The firm's office was in the first block of California Street near Davis and a short block from the present General Office of P. G. and E.

Then came the panic of 1893. The house of de Sabla found

itself overextended with a top-heavy list of uncollectable accounts. In his father's absence and against his friends' advice the young manager chose to liquidate the business rather than seek legal refuge. A trip to Central America followed in an attempt to collect sufficient money from debtors there to pay the firm's San Francisco creditors in full. Eventually this was done.

Meanwhile, A. A. Tregidgo, the Planet mine superintendent, had come to California and had acquired a part ownership in the Peabody mine in Grass Valley. He renewed his contact with de Sabla in San Francisco, and in time, through cash advances, de Sabla had acquired an interest in the Peabody mine.

Alfonso Adolphus Tregidgo was a Cornishman, born in England in 1858. His father was a captain in the Royal Navy and his brother an admiral, but defective eyesight prevented Alfonso's following the family tradition. He joined the merchant marine and in 1878 landed at Vallejo from the sailing ship which had brought him across the Atlantic and around Cape Horn.

Most Cornishmen are natural miners by inheritance from the generations who spent their lives in the tin mines of Cornwall, so it was natural for the young sailor to turn to mining, first at the St. John's quicksilver mine near Vallejo and then in the copper mines of Arizona. It was not long until he had worked himself up to the rank of mine superintendent.

In the Grass Valley mines, Tregidgo had been troubled by the high cost and inefficiency of steam power for pumping and other machine operations. He had read of the early experiments in California with hydroelectric plants, and his friend, Augustus J. Bowie, the engineer, had told him of the successful application of water power and long-distance transmission in a hydroelectric project in Italy. Tregidgo decided to build a hydro plant on the South Yuba River to serve not only his own mine but others in the Grass Valley and Nevada City district.

After water rights had been secured, the Nevada County Electric Power Company was incorporated September 22, 1892. Tregidgo was elected president and Eugene J. de Sabla, Jr., vice-president. Dr. Hulbert H. Clark, who served as mayor of Santa

Cruz from 1896 to 1898, was made general manager and treasurer. There is no evidence that any of the incorporators had more than elementary knowledge of the technical problems of building and operating a hydroelectric plant. A powerhouse site on the South Yuba, 4.2 miles by pole line from Nevada City and 7.6 miles by pole line from Grass Valley, was purchased and rights of way for transmission lines were secured. The plan was to divert water from the river 3 miles above the powerhouse and carry it by flume to obtain a fall of 190 feet to the Pelton wheels driving the generators.

Preliminary expenditures had nearly exhausted the funds advanced by the company's original stockholders, but Tregidgo started construction of a small diversion dam regardless of the discouraging outlook. Investors at that time were difficult to find. People were skeptical. Producing electricity by water power on a large scale was an untried venture; making it pay was doubtful. Before the diversion dam was finished, a flash flood carried the log structure away, and with it, seemingly, all hopes that work on the project could be continued.

Then came the financial depression of 1893. Mines were closed down. There was much unemployment and little money in Nevada County. Those were hard days for the Cornishman and his family. His friend, de Sabla, also was having his troubles in San Francisco, his attention wholly absorbed in the enforced liquidation of his father's importing business. When he returned in 1894 from his trip to Central America, however, conditions were changed. De Sabla needed an outlet for his energies and he turned again to the suspended project of the Nevada County Electric Power Company.

After conferences with Tregidgo it was decided to attempt to refinance the company by selling bonds instead of stock. De Sabla felt that bonds could be more easily disposed of than highly speculative stock.

The young Frenchman, not yet thirty, had made many friends during his brief business career in the city. He had the social grace, the flashing personality, and the ready wit of his Gallic ancestors. His physique was impressive—6 feet tall, well muscled, strikingly featured, with the pointed beard of the *boulevardier*.

De Sabla called on E. W. Hopkins, a nephew of Mark Hopkins of the Central Pacific. Hopkins owned the Gold Hill mine in Grass Valley and was interested in cheaper power. De Sabla sold him $15,000 in bonds of the Nevada County Electric Power Company. He persuaded W. E. Brown, a vice-president of the Crocker-Woolworth bank and operator of the Omaha mine in Grass Valley, to invest $10,000 in the power project. Brown had been president of Citizens Gas Light and Heat Company in Sacramento before coming to San Francisco. He had been private secretary to Governors Stanford and Low, president of Pacific Improvement Company, and a director of the Southern Pacific. His support was important to de Sabla.

"I rang every doorbell in the financial district," said de Sabla in later years. "I sold bonds in small lots or large, but at last we had enough money to start again on building our power plant." From that time Eugene de Sabla devoted himself to the development of electric power in Northern California. Work was resumed on the Nevada power project in 1895.

* * *

At about this time, John Martin appeared on the scene, a newcomer in the hydroelectric field. He had come to California in 1891, his chief assets inexhaustible energy, an indomitable will to succeed, an alert and facile mind, and a powerful physique. Born in Indianapolis in 1858, he had spent his boyhood in Brooklyn and since he was thirteen had fended for himself. Real-estate experience in Alabama and employment by the Armours in Chicago preceded his arrival in California. In San Francisco he was associated for a time with a coal importing firm and then established his own business as the John Martin Company, dealer in pig iron and agent for the U.S. Cast Iron Pipe Company.

In 1894 Martin had become acquainted with Charles C. Lindner, an electrician who held a letter from the Stanley Electrical Manufacturing Company of Pittsfield, Mass., authorizing him to sell its products on a commission basis. One of Martin's friends was Charles W. Randall, manager of a Wakelee drugstore, owner of a mine in the Mother Lode country, and consequently interested in electric power. Randall had discussed the Nevada County power project with de Sabla and, thinking he might help Martin to a pipe contract, arranged a luncheon meeting of the three men at the Continental restaurant on Bush Street, one day late in 1894.

Martin was late for his appointment, explaining when he arrived that his delay had been caused by the birth of his fifth child earlier in the morning.

The three men talked electric power and pipe and electric equipment. De Sabla told of his and Tregidgo's studies of available generators. He expressed the opinion that the Stanley Electrical Manufacturing Company was making the generators best adapted to their purposes in Nevada County. Martin appeared to be more attracted by this phase of the discussion than in obtaining an order for pipe. He had a talent for mathematics and a long-cherished interest in machinery. He and de Sabla did not meet again for two or three months, and de Sabla assumed Martin had forgotten all about their luncheon discussion until one day he encountered Martin on Montgomery Street. "I'm ready now for your order," said Martin. "What order?" replied de Sabla. And then the story came out.

Intrigued by the luncheon talk about the opportunity offered by electric power development, Martin had gone to Pittsfield, Mass., where he obtained an interview with William Stanley, the inventor, head of the Stanley Electrical Manufacturing Company which later was merged into the General Electric Company. Although Martin had had no training or experience in electrical construction, he was convincing enough to obtain the California agency for the Stanley company's products.

So, as a result of all these dovetailing relationships, John Martin entered into a contract with the Nevada County Power Company under which he agreed to provide and install the electrical equipment in the new plant and also to build and equip a transmission line from the powerhouse to Nevada City and Grass Valley.

That contract was the instrument which brought de Sabla and Martin together into a remarkable team, the two men responsible more than any others for creation of Pacific Gas and Electric Company. Each has been called the "father" of the P. G. and E. system. It is difficult, if not impossible, to separate their activities into lines that would give either one precedence over the other. Having quite different characteristics, they complemented each other in a loosely bound but forceful combination that undeniably got results. In a little more than 10 hectic years they built hydroelectric power plants, organized one corporation after another, consolidated gas and electric systems, snowballed their small beginnings into the extensive foundation upon which the P. G. and E. structure was raised. It is doubtful that either one could have realized fully during those years exactly where they were heading.

After he had closed the contract with the Nevada County Power Company, John Martin awakened to the fact that, as he said afterward, "I had entered into a contract for the building of this plant and had no technical knowledge whatever in regard to it. I immediately communicated with the Stanley company, requesting that they send out at once to me an electrical engineer, competent to educate me and also to have charge of the erection of the plant."

The Stanley company sent Edgar E. Stark who for four months gave his pupil an intensive course in electrical theory and practice. It is a mark of Martin's mental capabilities that, without engineering education or background, he acquired in a very few years a sound working knowledge not only of electric installations but of gas utility operations.

Work on the Nevada power plant started with a rush July 5, 1895. Tregidgo, something of a human dynamo in his own right, supervised construction of the dam, the flume, and the powerhouse. De Sabla attended to the business details. He handled the payrolls and canvassed the territory for customers—the mines of Nevada City and Grass Valley, town governments, owners of buildings, wherever there was need for power and light. Martin and Stark drove ahead on the pole line and installation of equipment.

W. R. Eckart, veteran construction and mechanical engineer, A. M. Hunt and W. F. C. Hasson, electrical engineers, served

Illumination of the California State Capitol, an electric parade and carnival, celebrated the first transmission of electricity from Folsom Powerhouse.

An early Pacific Gas and Electric Company service wagon and its crew kept wires and
street lamps in repair in Sacramento.

Alfonso A. Tregidgo, mining expert (left), and Eugene J. de Sabla, Jr., in 1895, while constructing a flume for the Nevada plant of the Nevada County Power Company.

John Martin, with Eugene J. de Sabla, Jr., built power plants, consolidated utility systems, formed the foundation for Pacific Gas and Electric Company.

Eugene J. de Sabla, Jr., as he appeared in 1950. Both de Sabla and Martin have been called "father" of the P. G. and E. system.

as consultants during the building of the plant. L. M. Hancock was the engineer in charge.

The hydro pioneers had none of today's heavy construction equipment—no bulldozers, no huge dump trucks, no motored transport. They moved tons of machinery over steep mountain roads with long teams of horses and mules. They lowered equipment down precipices to the powerhouse at streamside with cables and windlass. They built roads and reservoirs with horse-drawn plows and scrapers.

Despite the obstacles, the Nevada power plant was finished in seven months. Power flowed into Nevada City in February, 1896; to Grass Valley, a month later. Initial installed capacity was 300 kilowatts, soon to be raised to 1,200 kilowatts.

Demand for electric power was immediate, and it increased from the beginning. To consolidate the business, the Nevada County Electric Power Company purchased the little Deer Creek plant that had been built earlier by John Glasson of Nevada City and operated it for three years. The company increased the capacity of its own powerhouse installation by adding generators and building a second flume and storage reservoir, Lake Vera, named for one of de Sabla's two daughters.

The Nevada plant was operated successfully until 1910, when it was abandoned as obsolete. In most of its years it was known as "Rome" plant, a friendly abbreviation of the name of Romulus Riggs Colgate, wealthy New Yorker who had become interested in the de Sabla-Martin enterprises. How he happened to enter the hydroelectric picture is another of those stories of accidental meetings and unexpected consequences which are found so frequently in California.

Colgate was a grandson of the founder of the Colgate Soap and Perfume Company. His father had established the Atlantic White Lead Company of Brooklyn, N.Y., and the son had joined in his father's business. But the lure of the West caught his interest, and he had acquired gold-mining properties in Grass Valley and Nevada City, one of which was the historic Spanish mine.

After the Nevada plant had been placed in operation, Eugene de Sabla was convinced that more power could be sold. He wanted to add another generator and told his plan to E. W. Hopkins who had a considerable investment in the power company.

"You must be crazy," said Hopkins. "You now have all the power the district can use." To which de Sabla replied, "On the contrary; inside of five years I'll be delivering 20,000 horsepower, maybe 50,000, to the cities on San Francisco Bay."

Fearing his backer was going to prove too conservative, de Sabla asked him if he would sell his interest in the company and Hopkins said, "Yes, at the price it cost me."

The next morning in San Francisco de Sabla had determined to buy Hopkins' holdings. He would go to New York and ask for funds from his granduncle Peter Marie de Sabla, who had told him to call upon him whenever he needed assistance.

As the power promoter was on his way to the railroad ticket agency, he met Arthur Begbie. Begbie, manager of Colgate's mining properties, was accompanied by his employer. De Sabla explained that he was bound for New York to interview Uncle Peter Marie. "So you are a nephew of Uncle Peter Marie," Colgate said. "I know him and have dined at his home. But why go to him for money? Maybe I can take his place."

So Colgate was taken to Nevada City to inspect the power plant and to learn details of the company's plans. He loaned $40,000 to de Sabla for purchase of the Hopkins' stock and in return received a one-fifth interest in the Nevada County Electric Power Company. From that time he was a strong backer of hydroelectric development.

Tregidgo was the first superintendent. He was followed by L. M. Hancock and George Scarfe. The Cornish miner had made good his plans of the earlier years. He had brought electric power to the mines, but he had the pioneer's yearning for new fields, new adventures. When news of the Klondike gold strike started the rush to Alaska, he yielded to an offer from Augustus J. Bowie and became superintendent of mine operations in the north for James R. Keane, New York financier. Tregidgo never returned to hydroelectric projects. When he came back to California, he went to the St. John's quicksilver mine in Solano County where he remained as superintendent until his death in 1913. He had lived to see those who had scoffed at electrically operated mines become some of the largest users of power from the plant he built on the South Yuba.

One of the pioneer's two sons, Eugene de Sabla Tregidgo, named for his father's patron, today is a member of the P. G. and E. engineering staff in San Francisco.

CHAPTER 13

Copper Trails of Progress

AFTER the Nevada Powerhouse had been placed in operation, de Sabla devoted himself to organizing the distribution business and to exploration of water sources. He made frequent trips to Nevada City from his home in San Francisco. In the mountains he drove a prized team of fast standard-bred mares—Fleeting and Annie—hitched to a California mountain buggy. The big, bearded man in a linen duster, coated with the red dust of the hills, became a familiar figure in the mountain towns.

John Martin gradually left his equipment business in charge of employees. His real interest was in utility company promotion. He found his next project in Brown's Valley, 12 miles from Marysville. Here Martin had an interest with Charles Webb Howard, president of the Spring Valley Water Company in San Francisco, in a group of mines which were operated with water from the Brown's Valley irrigation district ditch. Martin's keen mind saw an opportunity there for economical production of electric power. He made a contract with the irrigation district under which he was to have use of the water for electric power generation in exchange for a nominal annual payment and upkeep of the ditch system. The Brown's Valley ditch was supplied from the north fork of the Yuba River at a diversion dam some 20 miles above the powerhouse site.

With de Sabla's assistance, Martin turned to R. R. Colgate for financial backing of the Brown's Valley project. It was a simple problem for the hydro engineers—no costly dams, no water sources to develop. The irrigation ditch ran along the mountainside at such a height that a fall of 295 feet could be obtained merely by dropping the flow of water from the ditch to a powerhouse built on the valley floor. The spot chosen was in a section called Wild Hog Glory, a favorite feeding ground for the native porkers.

The Yuba Power Company was incorporated October 27, 1897. Five months later, on March 21, 1898, the Yuba plant was ready to deliver electric power. Its capacity was 1,080 kilowatts, transmitted at 16,700 volts to the Brown's Valley mines and to Marysville, 18 miles distant. The Buckeye Flour Mill in Marysville was the first large power customer.

Colgate became an enthusiastic hydro man. He told Martin he derived more pleasure from playing a constructive part in the development of the country than could be gained from any financial returns he might receive. He went with de Sabla and Martin on their inspection trips, walking on narrow planks along flumes that clung to precipices, slogging wearily over rough, steep trails but never complaining of the unaccustomed hardships.

Life at the Yuba Powerhouse was not without its compensations. A. J. Stephens, who in later years became manager of the utility company's Vallejo District, was one of three young operators of the plant's machinery. During the fishing season, Stephens wrote, the ditch tenders at the diversion dam on the North Yuba, 20 miles higher in the mountains, would share their catches of salmon with the powerhouse boys by using a novel means of fresh fish delivery. They would nail two or three salmon on boards, place them body down in the ice-cold ditch stream, and ten hours later the night's dinner would come floating down to the trash rack in the ditch above the powerhouse, where waiting hands would lift the fish out and hurry them to the camp cook.

Yuba Powerhouse was operated until obsolescence overtook it in 1911. Its transmission system, operated at still higher voltage than that from Folsom Powerhouse, marked another forward step in hydroelectric development.

* * *

Record-breaking drought in the winter of 1897–1898 was directly responsible for the next project of the tireless de Sabla and Martin team. The flow of the American River, during that extra-dry season, was so diminished that Folsom Powerhouse could produce only a fraction of its 3,750 kilowatts capacity. The following summer the Sacramento street railway system, which depended upon Folsom for its power supply, was hard pressed to keep its cars running. The emergency suggested to the two enterprisers a new and larger project, a powerhouse on the Yuba River where there was available an ample flow of water from the Brown's Valley Irrigation District flume. The Brown's Valley ditch's head dam was in the north fork of the river, but at the point selected for the powerhouse the flume traversed the canyon wall of the main stream. From the new plant, power would be transmitted 61 miles to Sacramento to supply the increasing demand for electricity. The new power plant was to be known as Colgate Powerhouse in honor of R. R. Colgate.

Martin opened negotiations with the Sacramento Electric, Gas and Railway Company and emerged from the conferences on March 25, 1899, with a contract to deliver a maximum of 2,200 kilowatts of electric energy for use in Sacramento. One-third of this was to be transmitted not later than September 1 of the same year. With characteristic daring he had committed himself and his associates to a far larger undertaking than they had yet attempted.

The Yuba Electric Power Company, a new $1,000,000 corporation, was organized January 30, 1899, to take over the Yuba Power Company and its Brown's Valley Powerhouse and to build the new plant. Work started with a rush on all fronts. The powerhouse site was at the river crossing of the Missouri Bar trail, historic route of the early gold seekers to the high country and about 8 miles below the head dam of the old Brown's Valley flume.

Hauling materials and equipment to the site over a rough, steep road was slow and troublesome, but the mountain men accomplished the job. Captain James H. Luttrell, a retired shipmaster in charge of the Yuba Company's Marysville office, was placed in charge of transportation. When John Martin gave him the assignment, he said, "All right. I'll move the cargo in, but you'll have to let me do it in my own way." And he did—by using a sailorman's knowledge of block and tackle in the handling of heavy weights.

The building of the Colgate flume was an achievement in itself. Height of the dam on the north fork of the Yuba was raised and a new, larger flume was constructed directly above the old waterway, 7.6 miles from the dam to the powerhouse site. A stand of timber on the Slate range 10 miles away was purchased and a sawmill erected. A tramway and bridge were built to transport the finished lumber down the steep mountain and across the river. High above the river on the rock wall of the canyon the flume was built, sometimes on high trestles across deep gorges, sometimes clinging to the precipice at dizzy heights. Construction of the waterway, 7 feet wide and 6 feet deep, was so solid that a railway might have been operated over it. From the lower end, the mass of water dropped in penstock pipes a vertical distance of 700 feet to the impulse wheels in the powerhouse on the river's bank.

A supplementary water source was provided in Lake Frances, created by a dam across Dobbins Creek near the town of Dobbins. A wood-stave pipe line ran from the lake to the penstock.

Three generators with a total capacity of 2,700 kilowatts were installed. As power demand grew, four more units were added to bring the total capacity to 15,575 kilowatts. From the plant a pole transmission line carried Colgate's power output, first at 22,000 volts, later at 40,000 volts, 61 miles out of the mountains to Sacramento. A second line transmitted power 30 miles to gold dredgers operating near Oroville.

In spite of rockslide troubles on the penstock slope above the powerhouse, transportation difficulties over the steep roads, and delays in flume construction, the job was completed September 4, 1899, and power began flowing into the street railway motors of Sacramento the following day. The project had been finished in just five months and eleven days. Martin and de Sabla had kept their delivery contract only four days after the stipulated date.

Colgate plant attracted attention everywhere in the electrical world. Engineers visited the powerhouse and reported its progress.

L. M. Hancock, who had served as engineer for the Nevada County Power Company during and after the building of Rome Powerhouse, was brought to the Colgate project when rockslides and other troubles delayed its completion. He was placed in charge of the general engineering and finished the job. Later he became chief engineer of the Bay Counties system and of the California Gas and Electric Corporation, establishing a reputation for cool-headed supervision, especially in emergencies.

Many a young man served his operating apprenticeship at Colgate Powerhouse. J. M. Kelman, who won a high place in electrical history by his development of the oil circuit breaker, was one of them. Mr. Kelman, who now heads his own electrical manufacturing company in Los Angeles, has a fund of anecdotes about the old plant. One of them concerns a prankish experiment which might have been one of the forerunners of today's diathermy treatments. An old Negro living near the powerhouse complained to the operators about his sufferings from toothache. They devised their own method of cure. One of them placed one wire from a magneto in the patient's hand and held the other on the affected tooth while the second operator turned the magneto slowly. The effect was miraculous. The excruciating pain vanished. But clinical experiments grew tiresome, and one day the boys decided to give the old Negro "the works," as they expressed it. Two magnetos were used, the second running at high speed. When the patient received the resultant shock, he yelled and ran. The toothache was permanently cured.

Harry F. Scott, known throughout the West as a champion tunnel builder, was another who started his career at Colgate. When only thirteen years of age he took his first job there in 1905, delivering supplies to maintenance crews along the flume. One day he slipped and fell into the fast-flowing stream in the flume and broke a leg. The fracture failed to heal and the injured leg was amputated. When he returned to duty, Scott was given a job as water tender on the Colgate penstocks but he did not stay there long. Reared in the mining tradition, he developed a natural talent for tunnel driving. Not always in the employ of P. G. and E., he worked on tunnels all over the West. One of them was the Twin Peaks street railway tunnel in San Francisco. As superintendent for P. G. and E. he drove the 11-mile Stanislaus bore through the granite mountains of Tuolumne County, and he fought to conquer the shifting "heavy" ground in the tunnel for Pit 5 Powerhouse on the Pit River. He returned to Colgate in 1941 to drive a tunnel that supplanted the original flume. Seemingly immune to cold and the rigors of underground work and ignoring the limitations placed upon him by his disability, Harry Scott created for himself a reputation as a master tunnel builder.

Colgate plant occupies a milepost position in California electrical history. The length and high voltage of its transmission to Sacramento were the preliminaries to a greater advance in hydroelectric development, the interconnection of the remote hydroelectric powerhouses of the Sierra for delivery of power to the cities of San Francisco Bay and the communities of the Central Valley.

The original plant was damaged by fire in 1946, and in 1949 it was replaced by a new, modern plant with a capacity of 25,000 kilowatts.

CHAPTER 14

Power Spans Carquinez Strait

NO SOONER had Colgate Powerhouse been completed than new opportunities opened to de Sabla and Martin. They were then operating three powerhouses, Rome, Yuba, and Colgate. They were serving electricity to Marysville, Grass Valley, and Nevada City, to mines and industries in Yuba and Nevada Counties, and to gold dredgers near Oroville in Butte County. They held a contract to supply up to 2,200 kilowatts to the Sacramento street railway system. With additional generating units being installed there would be a surplus of power available.

Suddenly a market for that extra power appeared in the city of Oakland. The Oakland Transit Company was seeking refinancing in negotiations with the Eastern bond firms of E. H. Rollins & Sons and N. W. Harris & Company. The bankers believed the street railway company should have cheaper electric power. They sent their engineers to Yuba and Nevada Counties to investigate the ability of the hydro plants there to supply Oakland's requirements. The report was favorable and thereupon a new and record-breaking transmission project began to take form—a line 142 miles long from Colgate plant to Oakland, with an aerial cable crossing over Carquinez Strait, the waterway that connects the upper and lower portions of San Francisco Bay.

At the suggestion of the bankers a new corporation, the Bay Counties Power Company, was organized June 4, 1900, to consolidate under one ownership the properties of the Nevada County Electric Power Company and the Yuba Electric Power Company. The new company had an authorized capitalization of $5,000,000, and by agreement with the Rollins and Harris banking houses $3,000,000 in bonds were issued to cover the costs of line construction and corporate consolidation.

De Sabla was elected president and general manager; W. M. Pierson, vice-president and attorney; C. A. Grow, secretary. New names appeared on the list of directors—John C. Coleman, mine owner; Richard M. Hotaling, member of a pioneer San Francisco mercantile firm; and George A. Batchelder, representative of the bond houses. R. R. Colgate continued his interest and was elected a member of the board of directors.

The building of that transmission line was a courageous journey into the unknown, for little was recorded then about transmission at high voltage over so great a distance. John Martin had learned something about the technical problems only a few months previously. As agent for the Stanley Electrical Manufacturing Company, he had won a contract to install five 2,000-kilowatt Stanley generators in Prince Poniatowski's Standard Electric Company Electra plant on the Mokelumne River. Standard planned a transmission line from Electra to San Francisco, with a branch to Oakland by way of Mission San Jose.

General Electric Company would guarantee a voltage of only 30,000 on these lines, and Westinghouse only 25,000 volts. Martin went to Pittsfield to consult William Stanley, John F. Kelly, and C. C. Chesney, the famous SKC team of the Stanley company whose electrical products were known by the three initials. They assured him a line could be built that would carry 60,000 volts with a large saving in operating cost. When he returned to San Francisco, Martin offered to sell Standard the equipment for a 60,000-volt line. His own Colgate-Oakland transmission was designed for the same voltage.

De Sabla and Martin attacked the problems of the new project with accelerated energy. While the engineers were designing the cable crossing, unprecedented in length of span for high-voltage wires, right-of-way agents went into the field. There was some trouble there because of the farmers' fear that supercharged wires might fall during storms and kill their cattle and children. Along one 10-mile stretch of the Feather River near its junction with the Sacramento, the company's right-of-way agent reported he was stymied. The river folk were antagonistic. One rancher, with shotgun under his arm, had ordered him off his land.

So de Sabla, president of the Bay Counties Power Company, filled his diplomatic pouch with cigars for the men, brooches for the women, and toys for the children, boarded his mountain buggy, and drove to the scene of action. With gifts and fluent Spanish he convinced one Mexican that as *presidente* his promise of safety and proper compensation to the property owner would be carried out. With praise for her onion soup and an appointment as district agent for the power company, he mollified the woman leader of the opposition. Similar approach won over the proprietor of the crossroads store, and de Sabla returned to his office, mission accomplished. Utility executives were also fieldmen in those days.

Construction of the transmission line from Colgate Powerhouse by way of Woodland, Dillon's Point at the Carquinez crossing, and thence to Oakland was a new test of the organizational and engineering skill of the pioneers. Two parallel lines of cedar poles, 25 feet apart, carried the copper and aluminum wires, the second line being erected as a stand-by precaution against accidents and interruptions in service. The builders had none of today's mechanical helpers. They used dynamite on the pole holes and teams of horses for hauling. All other work was done by hand tools and brawn.

J. D. Galloway, construction engineer, was in general charge of the line project, assisted by R. H. Sterling, superintendent of the company's Bay Division, and T. E. Theberath, superintendent of the Yuba Division. All three joined in the electrical planning; the tower insulators were designed by Sterling; F. A. Koeditz, engineer for the Pacific Construction Company, was responsible for the structural features of the Carquinez crossing.

There was no precedent for the cable crossing. The longest span in any transmission line on the American continent prior to 1901 was the crossing of the Columbia River in 1897 by lines of the West Kootenay Power & Light Co. of British Columbia, 1,576 feet from tower to tower. At Carquinez a single span of

4,427 feet was required. The four cables reached from the steel North Tower at Dillon's Point, 225 feet high, to the 64-foot South Tower on a high hill near the town of Crockett. The lowest of the four cables was 280 feet above the water at high tide, to allow full clearance for the tall topmasts of the sailing ships of that era. The cables were staggered, one below the other, with a clearance of 20 feet between each pair to prevent their swinging together in the wind.

John Martin told later how E. H. Rollins, whose bond firm was financing the transmission project, lost a night's sleep over this phase of the construction. Martin was leaving San Francisco on a trip to New York when he received an urgent telegram from Rollins: "PLEASE SEE ME AT DENVER FOR CONSULTATION ON IMPORTANT MATTER."

When they met in Denver, Rollins told why he had sent for Martin. "John," he said, "I'm worried about the Carquinez cable crossing. There are high winds through the Strait. How are you going to keep those wires from swinging together and blowing out the whole line?"

"Just this way," replied John, extending his hand with his fingers spread vertically.

"Oh," said the banker, with a crestfallen but much-relieved grin, "I thought they would be horizontal." Mr. Rollins was an extra-hospitable host for the remaining hours of Martin's stay in Denver.

Colgate power was first delivered in Oakland April 27, 1901. The initial potential was 40,000 volts, but this was raised in 1903 to the 60,000 volts for which the line was designed. In Oakland, power was delivered to the Oakland Transit Company for operation of its 126 miles of street railway in Oakland, Berkeley, and Alameda. Through a tie line to the substation of the Standard Electric Company, which had not yet completed its Electra plant on the Mokelumne River, power was supplied to that company for delivery under contract to the Oakland Gas, Light and Heat Company. Standard also took Bay Counties power for delivery to San Jose, a transmission distance of 184 miles from the generators at Colgate Powerhouse.

Electric energy generated by the falling waters of the Sierra at last had leaped across mountain heights and canyons and across the wide valley of the Sacramento, to serve the bustling communities on the east side of San Francisco Bay. The accomplishment marked the beginning of a new era of industrial development in Northern California.

The record keepers generally agree that the 142-mile Colgate-Oakland line surpassed in distance all past records for transmission at 40,000 to 60,000 volts. Under the heading, "The Longest Power Transmission in the World," a writer in the magazine *Review of Reviews* said, "As late as September, 1896, Dr. Louis Duncan, a foremost authority, in his inaugural address as president of the American Institute of Electrical Engineers, remarked 'If we consider the record of the present transmission plants, we can safely say that it would not be going outside the safe limits of development to transmit at least 50 miles at a potential of 20,000 volts.' "

This limit had been exceeded in 1899 by the Colgate-Sacramento transmission of 61 miles at 40,000 volts. Only three years later the Oakland line topped all others. The bogy of electrical planners had been routed.

* * *

More electric power was needed by the expanding system of the Bay Counties Power Company. With transmission to Oakland successfully accomplished, the indefatigable de Sabla and Martin could see no limit to the potential market for electricity in Northern California. They were determined to supply it.

Late in 1902 it became apparent that more hydro generators would have to be installed. With L. M. Hancock, the company's engineer, de Sabla explored the mountains seeking a site for a new powerhouse. They found it at French Creek, in Butte County, a stream which empties into the Feather River 6 miles above the present Big Bend Powerhouse. With water rights already secured, they decided to dam French Creek to create a storage reservoir and divert the water through a tunnel to a point above the Feather River where a fall of 1,200 feet to the powerhouse could be obtained. A plant of about 10,000-kilowatt capacity was planned.

The Butte County Power Company was incorporated, the stock to be owned by the Bay Counties company, and sale of an issue of $1,000,000 in bonds was arranged with a San Francisco bond house.

Having secured all but one parcel of land for the proposed storage reservoir, the new company prepared to go ahead with construction. Access roads were built to the site, a camp was established, and considerable preliminary work was done. On the day the bond sale was confirmed, de Sabla went to the mountains to meet the owners of the still unpurchased portion of the reservoir site. They were personal acquaintances and he anticipated no difficulty. He was shocked when the landowners, observing how far the project had been advanced, calmly demanded $200,000 in cash or half of the stock of the Butte County Power Company.

Knowing the price to be exorbitant, de Sabla without hesitation turned to T. E. Theberath, who was in charge of construction, and ordered him to close the camp, discharge his men, and abandon the project. "It was as artistic an attempted holdup as I had ever seen," said de Sabla.

De Sabla turned to Butte Creek for another powerhouse site. Already established there was the Centerville plant of the Butte County Electric Power and Lighting Company, incorporated in 1899 by O. W. Meysenberg, Judge J. A. Waymire, S. C. Dennison, H. B. Snow, and C. C. Jones. The powerhouse was completed in 1900, and just before that time Park Henshaw had joined the company and become its president. Two transmission lines from the plant, which had an initial capacity of 800 kilowatts, served Chico, 14 miles distant, and Oroville, 32 miles away. An extension from Gridley reached to the distribution system of the town of Colusa.

Retaining his plan to build a new generating source, de Sabla purchased the Centerville property and on January 24, 1902, organized the Valley Counties Power Company to handle the project. The Bay Counties Power Company was to own all the stock of the new company and was to guarantee a bond issue of $2,500,000. In the new company were John C. Coleman, Theodore Low, R. R. Colgate, R. M. Hotaling, W. M. Pierson, and de Sabla and Martin.

To ensure an ample water supply, de Sabla also purchased the water system—dam, ditches, and pipe line—of the early-day Cherokee Mining Company which was owned by banker Andrew Mellon and his brother of Pittsburgh, Pa.

The new powerhouse, named later in honor of de Sabla, was situated on the bank of Butte Creek above Centerville Powerhouse. An intricate system of water conduits, parts of the old mining ditch system, was reconditioned to supply the new generating plant. The Cherokee Mining Company's Butte Creek Canal and the historic Hendricks and Toadtown ditches from the west branch of the Feather River delivered a constant flow to the De Sabla forebay reservoir. From that point the water was dropped 1,531 feet to the plant's impulse wheels. After turning the generators, water from De Sabla Powerhouse flows on for use in the Centerville plant. De Sabla plant's ultimate capacity was 13,000 kilowatts. It was placed in commission October 10, 1903.

The new powerhouse represented the work of a number of engineers who later took leading parts in development of the P. G. and E. system. J. D. Galloway was consulting engineer on the job. Frank G. Baum, James H. Wise, George H. Bragg, T. E. Theberath, and D. H. Duncanson all had a hand in the engineering and construction of the powerhouse, its water-supply facilities, and electrical installation.

The building of De Sabla Powerhouse was notable for the technical problems it presented and the group of young engineers who solved them. The high head—the 1,531-foot fall of water—was in itself a step above previous records that called for the best of hydraulic engineering skill to ensure safe operation.

Frank G. Baum had joined the staff of California Gas and Electric Corporation in 1903 as engineer in charge of operations and construction. He had received his postgraduate degree as electrical engineer from Stanford University only four

Nevada hydroelectric powerhouse, first of the de Sabla-Martin ventures, was also called "Rome" after Romulus Riggs Colgate, early financial backer.

Colgate Powerhouse, on the Yuba River, marked another advance in long-distance

Transmission lines were strung more than three-quarters of a mile across Carquinez Strait to carry power from Colgate Powerhouse to Oakland in 1901.

Prince André Poniatowski built Electra Powerhouse which supplied first hydro power to San Francisco and the peninsular area.

W. H. Crocker, San Francisco banker, was associated with Prince Poniatowski in building Electra Powerhouse. Crocker was a director of Pacific Gas and Electric Company from 1906 to 1937.

years earlier. At Stanford he earned his education by working long extracurricular hours in the campus barbershop.

Baum's first assignment after graduation was as assistant to Dr. F. A. C. Perrine in the design and installation of Standard Electric Company's Electra Powerhouse on the Mokelumne River. From there he returned to the university in 1900 to serve as instructor in electrical engineering under Dr. Perrine. During that period he acted as consultant for the Bay Counties Power Company. When he joined Eugene de Sabla's new company, he applied his brilliant talents to solution of the numerous problems confronting the builders—how to unite in synchronous operation the scattered generating plants of the partly developed system, problems of long-distance transmission and insulation, high voltage, and substation equipment.

After three years of corporation employment, Baum resigned in 1907 to open his own office as consulting engineer. In 1912, following the death of James H. Wise, he returned to the company as chief engineer of the hydroelectric department. He completed the work on Spaulding Dam and Drum Powerhouse and built Halsey and Wise Powerhouses as additional power sources of the South Yuba–Bear River project. Later he drew up the general plan for development of the great hydroelectric resources of the Pit River in Shasta County where P. G. and E. now operates five plants with a total capacity of 296,000 kilowatts.

Among his outstanding contributions to the electrical industry were development of the correct theory of the performance of long, high-voltage lines; improvement of the pioneer 60,000-volt transmission system and switching equipment; and design of the pioneer 220,000-volt transmission line from the Pit River to the Bay region. Frank G. Baum died March 14, 1932, from the effects of an accidental fall.

James H. Wise, a graduate of the University of California College of Mining, stepped from the Berkeley campus to fieldwork for the California Gas & Electric Corporation. Starting as an instrument man with a surveying crew, he rose rapidly to the post of civil and hydraulic engineer. For a little more than a year he was associated with Baum as a consulting engineer.

Returning to the company July 1, 1911, as assistant general manager, Wise initiated the South Yuba–Bear River hydroelectric project and started construction of Spaulding Dam and Drum Powerhouse. His career, promising much in accomplishment, was cut short by a fatal accident, September 16, 1912. He was only thirty-two at the time of his death. The esteem in which Wise was held is marked by the James Hugh Wise Memorial Library in the P. G. and E. headquarters building in San Francisco and by Wise Powerhouse in Placer County.

De Sabla Powerhouse was the scene of the first work of Josiah P. Jollyman, whose name stands high on P. G. and E.'s long list of great engineers who have been members of its staff. The young man, who started his career in 1903 at the De Sabla plant, had just been graduated from Stanford University as electrical engineer. Except for two years' service with the Great Western Power Company, 1909–1911, he was a member of the P. G. and E. staff until his retirement January 1, 1945.

For 34 years, as engineer of electrical construction and, since 1920, as chief of the division of hydroelectric and transmission engineering, he directed the planning of equipment in the company's hydro plants. He contributed much to the progressive interconnection of the P. G. and E. system of generating plants and transmission lines into a single integrated network. Engineers from distant places brought their problems to him for consultation. He planned the installation of equipment in a hydroelectric plant built by a mining company in Korea. In 1926, upon invitation, he addressed the students of Princeton University on "The Electric Transmission of Power." Modest and unassuming, Jollyman gave immeasurably to hydro development during his long career.

Still another of the de Sabla group was George H. Bragg, Stanford graduate in electrical engineering, who joined California Gas and Electric Company in 1903 after a postgraduate year at the works of the Stanley Electric Manufacturing Company at Pittsfield, Mass. From 1922 until his retirement in 1945 George H. Bragg was engineer of maintenance for P. G. and E.

CHAPTER 15

Spreading Network Wires

DE SABLA and Martin realized that their next step must be service to customers in the towns—retail distribution of hydroelectric power. By doing so, they would assure a wider market to the Bay Counties Power Company, owner of the generating sources, and would reap added revenue from the operating utilities to be acquired.

The custom of the time was to finance new projects separately, even though the stockholders of an existing company and those of the new enterprise were identical. Consequently, when the Bay Counties Power Company group decided to go into the retail distribution of electricity and gas, they organized a new company. This was the California Central Gas and Electric Company, incorporated March 25, 1901, with authorized capital of $1,500,000. An issue of $1,000,000 in bonds was authorized for purchase of town systems and plant extensions. Officers and directors of the new company were: John Martin, president; John A. Britton, vice-president; Fred H. Pierson, secretary; H. M. Roeding and H. R. Noack, directors.

Pierson was a son of W. M. Pierson, general attorney for the de Sabla-Martin companies. Roeding and Noack, employees of Martin in his equipment agency business, were serving as temporary directors and gave way to others when stock investors joined the company.

The new electric company might well have been named "John Martin, Inc.," for at the second meeting of the board the enterpriser was voted all but five of the authorized 15,000 shares of the company's stock in exchange for assignment to the corporation of certain contracts he held. These included an agreement between himself and the Bay Counties Power Company giving him the right to Bay Counties power supply in Sonoma and Marin Counties and a contract to purchase from Bay Counties its gas and electric systems in Nevada City and Grass Valley.

After a few months Eugene de Sabla joined the company's board of directors, the membership of which had been increased to seven. Walter B. Cope and Joseph C. Love were the new directors. The plan of acquiring town utility properties was then inaugurated by purchase of Martin's optioned stock control of nine small companies and by direct dealing with three others. As a result, the California Central Gas and Electric Company within less than a year acquired the following town utilities:

Consolidated Electric Light, Gas and Power Co. of Woodland, July 12, 1901; Woodland Gas and Electric Co., September 20, 1901.
Marysville Gas and Electric Company, July 31, 1901.
Chico Gas and Electric Co., August 1, 1901.
Petaluma Gas and Electric Co., September 20, 1901; Western Refrigerating Co., Petaluma, October 2, 1901.
San Rafael Gas and Electric Light Co., October 2, 1901.
Nevada County Gas and Electric Co., October 2, 1901.
Merchants Lighting Co., Santa Rosa, October 2, 1901; Santa Rosa Lighting Co., October 19, 1901.
Napa Gas and Electric Co., October 7, 1901.
Colusa Gas and Electric Co., January 23, 1902.

The development was historically important. The magnet of centralized utility operation was beginning to draw the small particles together into a pattern. The result, accomplished at first somewhat haphazardly, was to be the P. G. and E. integrated system.

In the beginning, the utility companies taken over by California Central retained their identities and were operated under lease from the parent company. The plants and distribution lines in each town were reconditioned and modernized. A new gas plant was built to supply Nevada City and Grass Valley. In Marysville and Chico, Leon P. Lowe was called upon to install the improved Lowe gas process in the old plants. An electric transmission line was built from Napa to Petaluma, with branches from Petaluma to Santa Rosa and San Rafael, with distribution lines in Marin County to San Quentin, Ross, Mill Valley, Tiburon, Belvedere, and Sausalito. Branches from the Colgate-Oakland transmission line supplied the budding network with hydroelectric power.

Along with integration of the physical facilities went centralization of administration. District agents were appointed to take charge of the business in each town under direction from the San Francisco headquarters of the company. As the organization developed, John Martin planted the seeds of those public- and employee-relations policies which in full flower distinguished P. G. and E. in later years.

California Central Gas and Electric Company had been launched without any distribution of stock. John Martin held all the stock except the five qualifying directors' shares. In 1902 the shares gained increased distribution and other interests joined the board of directors. The new members were Frederick W. Zeile, president of Mercantile Trust of San Francisco, which was trustee for the company's $1,000,000 bond issue and which had assisted in financing the purchases of utilities; William Babcock, capitalist; and R. R. Colgate, faithful backer of all the de Sabla-Martin projects. Although the company's active life was brief, it was a vital spoke in the great corporate wheel of which eventually P. G. and E. was to be the hub.

* * *

John A. Britton, director and vice-president of California Central Gas and Electric Company, had already won a reputation in the utility business. Born in Boston, Mass., October 9, 1855, he was thirteen years old when his family migrated to San Francisco. He entered high school but before the year was out decided to seek a job instead of going on with his education. Work in a grocery store and as clerk in the San Francisco Musical Institute occupied him until 1871, when he began to study law in the office of Judge Charles A. Low and, after a few months, with the law firm of Curry and Evans. For three years he worked in the law office by day and went to night school after hours. Then, still too young to qualify as a lawyer, he found a job in Oakland with the Oakland Gas Light Company.

Britton's first work was nominally as a collector for the gas company, but added to that duty were ditch digging, setting meters, meter reading, and roustabout labor in the gasworks. By his twenty-fourth birthday he was made the company's bookkeeper. When his monthly salary was raised to $100, he married the stepdaughter of his boss, Van Leer Eastland, superintendent.

Britton continued studying and working. When electricity was introduced, he went back to night school for more education. Before he was thirty he was secretary-treasurer of the Oakland Gas Light Company, and in 1900, when he was forty-five, he was elected president of the company, which by that time had become the Oakland Gas Light and Heat Company, serving Oakland, Berkeley, and Alameda.

This was the man John Martin chose to be a director of his California Central Gas and Electric Company. When Britton joined Martin's company, he started a new phase of his career which was to place him at the general manager's desk of P. G. and E. where he remained until he had completed nearly 50 years of service with the Company and its predecessors.

CHAPTER 16

De Sabla and Martin Reach Out

EVEN WHILE John Martin was absorbed in the organization of his California Central Gas and Electric Company and Eugene de Sabla was occupied with Bay Counties affairs and the building of another power plant, both men were envisioning further conquests. The concept of a consolidated utility system, with its advantages of economical administration and operation, began to take form in their minds. They wanted an organization which would place them at the head of electrical and gas development in the northern part of the state.

There were other more immediate reasons for bringing together under single corporate control the scattered properties of the Bay Counties Power Company and California Central Gas and Electric Company. De Sabla and Martin and their associates were considering additions to their system, some of them of substantial size. Financing their acquisitions would call for the backing of a solid, consolidated company with ample assets in one strongbox.

And so California Gas and Electric Corporation was created December 6, 1901. The new company was capitalized at $30,000,000, but this was found to be unnecessarily high and the authorized stock issue later was reduced to $15,000,000. After a long delay required to complete arrangements, a bond issue of $10,000,000 was negotiated to provide funds for purchase of utility properties. Times had changed. Less than 10 years earlier it had been a struggle to sell only $200,000 in bonds for construction of Rome Powerhouse.

The first officers and directors were R. R. Colgate, president; Eugene J. de Sabla, Jr., vice-president; John Martin, vice-president; W. M. Pierson, attorney and secretary. Leon P. Lowe,

Arthur E. Childs of Boston, and R. M. Hotaling completed the board of seven members. In addition to members of the board, each of whom held 500 shares of stock, John C. Coleman and C. A. Grow were listed as original stockholders, each with 500 shares.

Long before these corporate developments John Martin had started negotiations for additional utility properties. The Oakland system especially attracted his attention. Under John A. Britton's management, the Oakland Gas Light and Heat Company was serving gas and electricity to Oakland and Berkeley and gas to Alameda. (The municipality of Alameda owned and operated the electric distribution system within the city, buying its power at wholesale rates from the Oakland Company.)

The Oakland system was conservatively handled and for 33 years the company had paid to its stockholders a monthly dividend of 25 cents per share. Its stock was quoted at $50 per share. Martin and John A. Britton had become good friends.

One day the two men went to Marysville to inspect a new Lowe gas installation. Britton was impressed by the plant's low cost of operation and remarked:

"I wish we had a plant like this large enough for us in Oakland."

The chance observation started Martin thinking and figuring. After the California Gas and Electric Corporation had been organized, he went before the directors of the Oakland Company and laid before them a purchase proposal.

"Give us an option for 18 months," he said. "We will pay you $70 per share on all outstanding stock. We will build on your property a gas plant of sufficient capacity to serve your entire system and will sell the gas produced there at half your present cost."

Six months later the purchase was consummated, and the Oakland stockholders had taken a substantial profit. The new California Gas and Electric Corporation, on its part, had gained its first large distribution market on San Francisco Bay for its hydroelectric power. John A. Britton resigned his presidency of the Oakland company and in February, 1903, was made general manager and a member of the board of directors of the newly established system. He was succeeded in Oakland by F. A. Leach, Jr.

There was another strategic point to be included in the expanding system—the state capital, where, since 1895, Livermore's and Gallatin's Sacramento Electric, Gas and Railway Company had provided electric power from historic Folsom, plus additional kilowatts purchased from the Bay Counties Power Company. Martin wanted to add that string to his bow because he felt that with electric distribution in his company's control, the Sacramento system could be made more profitable than by merely selling to it the electric power supply at wholesale rates. He invited Albert Gallatin, Charles R. Lloyd, and the executor for the L. P. Drexler estate, who then controlled the Sacramento company, to meet in his office without telling each one that the others were to be there.

"Gentlemen," he said, "your stock is worth $30 a share on its present dividend basis. I want an option to purchase. I will pay you on a basis of $40 a share—$1 per share down, $3 in 60 days, $6 in six months, $10 in a year, and $20 in two years. In the meantime you receive dividends, and if I fail in any of the payments, all that I have paid shall be forfeited and the stock returned to you."

The offer was accepted, and instead of the two years agreed upon, California Gas and Electric Corporation completed the purchase of the Sacramento system within six months, March 16, 1903.

The new company went still farther afield. In Fresno, far distant from any of its properties, was the Fresno Gas and Electric Company, which served the city with gas and some electricity. Despite the distance from San Francisco headquarters, the gas business of this company was added to the de Sabla and Martin list of operating utilities. All three system purchases—Oakland, Sacramento, and Fresno—were concluded March 16, 1903, when sale of the California Gas and Electric Company's $10,000,000 bond issue had been completed. In the following year there were other acquisitions—

Prince Poniatowski's Standard Electric Company and the properties of the United Gas and Electric Company which served the peninsula communities from San Francisco south to and including San Jose.

* * *

During the process of welding into one system the scattered electric and gas systems they had acquired, de Sabla and Martin found they must pay increasing attention to the problems of gas manufacture. Their purchases included many old gas plants. It was necessary to modernize them and place them on a paying basis. In this connection they had frequent conferences with Leon P. Lowe, builder of oil-gas plants under his own patents. The relationship led to Lowe's election as one of the original directors of the California Gas and Electric Corporation.

A few months later it appeared to the board that large savings in cost of plant modernization might be realized if the company owned territorial rights to the Lowe patents. Consequently a deal was made with Lowe in 1902 by which exclusive rights to use the Lowe oil-gas process, covered by the patents of 1889, were purchased by the company. The license included 16 northern counties. In return Lowe was granted 95,500 shares of the company's stock, which a Federal court many years afterward found to be worth "not less than $300,000." The company installed Lowe gas generators in a great number of its plants.

The denouement came two decades later. In 1920 Lowe brought suit against Pacific Gas and Electric Company, successor to California Gas and Electric Corporation. He alleged infringement of patents issued to him in 1905 and 1906 and asked for injunction and $1,000,000 in damages. Lowe charged that E. C. Jones, the company's gas engineer, had unlawfully used improvements covered by his recent patents in constructing oil-gas plants.

The defense replied that Jones had installed the apparatus and process in Fresno, Sacramento, and Woodland before the Lowe patents of 1905 and 1906 were granted and that, in fact, Lowe had obtained his ideas from Jones.

Judge M. C. Sloss, acting as special master, heard the evidence and found in favor of the defendant company. He recited the facts of the contract under which Lowe had sold his patents for $300,000 and declared the suit unjustified. His decision was confirmed by Judge Partridge of the U.S. District Court, September 23, 1924.

CHAPTER 17

Prince Poniatowski's Venture

A FRENCH Prince and a San Francisco bank president built Electra Powerhouse, the first to send its hydroelectric output into San Francisco. Their company was Standard Electric of California.

Prince André Poniatowski initiated the enterprise and promoted its advance throughout the construction period. W. H. Crocker, his brother-in-law and son of the Central Pacific railroad builder, stood by with substantial financial backing and wise counsel.

Of all the principal actors in the story of P. G. and E., Prince André Poniatowski is one of the most colorful. As this is written, Prince André, eighty-eight years old, dwells in retirement in the south of France. Four years ago, a thick volume of his memoirs was published in Paris under the title, "D'un Siecle à L'Autre" ("From One Century to Another"), and from this source have been taken Prince André's own comments and many of the facts of his California experiences in hydro.*

Prince Poniatowski was born in Paris, January 24, 1864, during the ascendancy of the Empire. His great-great-grandfather was the eldest brother of Stanislas, the last King of Poland. His uncle, Count Walewski, a son of Napoleon I and Countess Walewska, was minister of foreign affairs for the Empire.

Young Prince André thus was reared in the atmosphere of the Imperial Court. Reaching manhood, he served as a sub-

* Prince André Poniatowski, "D'un Siecle à L'Autre," Presses de la Cité, Paris, France, 1948.

lieutenant in the French cavalry and early developed a passion for horse racing, becoming expert as a gentleman rider.

Yachting, big game hunting in Russia and South Africa, serious training in banking, and a financial mission to Russia occupied him in his twenties. It was the South African trip, undertaken to investigate the gold mines of the Rand for a group of bankers, that gave him the background experience for his later California projects. In the Transvaal he inspected mines, learned something of engineering methods, and even bought a mine and organized a company for its promotion.

In 1892 Prince André came to the United States in behalf of the same bankers to learn financial conditions and again in 1893 during the Chicago World's Fair when he met the Vanderbilts, the Belmonts, D. O. Mills, the Astors, the Armours, the Seligmans, and Stillmans—the leaders in New York, Chicago, and Washington society and finance. Charles A. Coffin, president of General Electric Company, in 1892, showed him the wonders of the Niagara Falls hydroelectric project.

At a dinner at Delmonico's in New York, the Prince met a charming and cultured young woman, Miss Maud Alice Burke, to whom he was greatly attracted. Other meetings and correspondence followed. After he returned to France, suddenly there came a premature and mistaken announcement of his engagement to Miss Burke. (In his memoirs he gallantly refers to her only as "Maud Alice," but the San Francisco and New York newspapers of the period supplied the full name.)

The Prince sailed again for the United States and arrived in San Francisco, where Miss Burke was visiting, with the distasteful task of breaking an engagement he had not contracted. While in San Francisco, he was entertained at the home of Mr. and Mrs. W. H. Crocker and there met Miss Elizabeth Sperry, sister of Mrs. Crocker. In the succeeding months Prince André and Miss Sperry became engaged and were married in Paris, October 6, 1894. The event is here historically important because one consequence of the Crocker relationship was the building of Electra Powerhouse on the Mokelumne River only a few years later.

The Prince and his bride came back to San Francisco where he turned to mining. With W. H. Crocker, who in 1893 had become president of the Crocker-Woolworth bank, and Alfred Schiff, a London broker, he organized a syndicate, each putting up $25,000. With these funds the syndicate obtained favorable options on some 20 Mother Lode mines in Calaveras and Amador Counties which seemed to offer promise of further development. Prince André then went to London and, with the aid of Schiff, induced Percy Tarbutt and Edmond Davis, operators of Transvaal mines, to come to California to inspect the optioned properties. They brought with them Richard A. Parker, an American engineer who had been employed by Consolidated Goldfields in South Africa.

The visit was a complete success. The Englishmen agreed to invest in the Prince's project and placed $300,000 to his credit in the Crocker bank. The California Exploration Company was incorporated April 13, 1896, with Prince André as president, W. H. Crocker, treasurer, and Richard A. Parker, general manager. This company was succeeded two years later by California Exploration, Ltd., an English corporation. During preliminary surveys of the mining properties, when printed boundary signs bearing the company's initials, CEC, were posted, the wags of the mining camps translated them to mean "Catching English Capital."

It must have been at about this time that Crocker, genial president of the bank that bore his name, was given a new title. The incident occurred at one of the social events for which the hospitable Crocker mansion was famous. Prince Poniatowski and his bride were among the guests. The time for toasts had been reached, when J. B. Casserly, one of the party, raised his glass and quipped, "To our host, Will Crocker, Prince of Bankers and Banker of Princes."

While Engineer Parker was busily engaged in bringing back to life and production the score of mines controlled by the Exploration company, the Prince began studying two urgent problems—economical transportation to the mines and low-cost electric power for their operation.

The transportation problem was solved fortuitously. Into his office one day walked a stranger who introduced himself as Thomas S. Bullock, railroad builder. He had constructed a short rail line in Arizona from Seligman to Prescott. His railroad had been crowded out by the transcontinental lines, and he now proposed to move rails and equipment to California and build a line into the Mother Lode region. The result was the incorporation of the Sierra Railway, February 2, 1897, with Poniatowski as president.

The single-track Sierra Railway was built from Oakdale to Tuolumne, 56 miles, with a 20-mile branch from Jamestown to Angels Camp. The old line still is in operation for freight from Oakdale to Tuolumne. Bullock became a firm friend of Poniatowski and aided him materially in his hydroelectric enterprise.

The question of providing electric power was answered by W. Frank Pierce, president of the Blue Lakes Water Company which had been organized in 1887 for the purpose of building a pipe line from Amador County to Oakland to supply 17,500,000 gallons of water daily to that city. Many years passed before the line was built to Oakland by others. The Blue Lakes company had a long line of predecessors reaching back to 1855 when the miners of Slabtown, Butte City, and vicinity spent $75,000 to build the Butte ditch, 19½ miles of flume and canal to serve the placers south of the town of Jackson with water diverted from the north fork of the Mokelumne River. In 1870 the Sutter Canal and Mining Company started construction of the Amador Canal along the same route as the Butte ditch but at higher elevation. Then in 1873–1874 the Amador Canal and Mining Company completed the new canal to a point above Sutter Creek.

In 1895 the Blue Lakes Water Company acquired control of the Stockton Water Company, and in the following year W. Frank Pierce took charge as president. His negotiations with Prince Poniatowski resulted in construction of the Blue Lakes Powerhouse on an old millsite on the Mokelumne River 5 miles from Jackson, where water could be dropped 1,040 feet from the Amador Canal and a rebuilt section of the original

Butte ditch. When the three 450-kilowatt generators of the new plant began operating October 25, 1897, the camp was christened Blue Lakes City. The plant had been built with $122,500 advanced by the Prince's company, the amount to be repaid in power.

First superintendent of the Blue Lakes plant was Paul M. Downing, a young electrical engineer only two years out of Stanford University. From that beginning he rose steadily until he became vice-president, general manager, and, at the time of his death in 1944, executive vice-president of P. G. and E.

Construction of the Blue Lakes plant turned Prince André's thoughts to bigger things, a larger hydro plant. No office-chair promoter, he determined to examine for himself the water resources of the Blue Lakes region. For two weeks, ignoring the hardships of frigid altitudes and rough trails, the Prince traveled from one mountain lake to another, gathering engineering data from which could be calculated water-storage capacity, size of dams to increase that capacity, and estimates of cost.

Back in San Francisco, Poniatowski realized the project he had in mind was too large for his California Exploration Company. "We had indeed found on the Mokelumne River the ideal site for obtaining the maximum pressure of waterfall upon the turbines," he said, "but it was not for the generation of the four or five hundred horsepower needed by our [mining] company but for ten, fifteen, perhaps twenty thousand horsepower [15,000 kilowatts] to which the project was suited."

He dreamed of a plant that could serve San Francisco, 143 miles away. "But the next day the engineers told me that the longest electric power line did not exceed 130 miles; that the 40,000 volts necessary for operation at a greater distance had never yet been attempted on any line."

The Prince wrote to General Electric, Westinghouse, and the Stanley Electrical Manufacturing Company. They offered to send their engineers to investigate and submit bids. W. H. Crocker conferred in New York with Charles A. Coffin, president of General Electric, and agreed to a plan of financing the project without asking the help of their English associates. Thus came into being the Standard Electric Company of Cali-

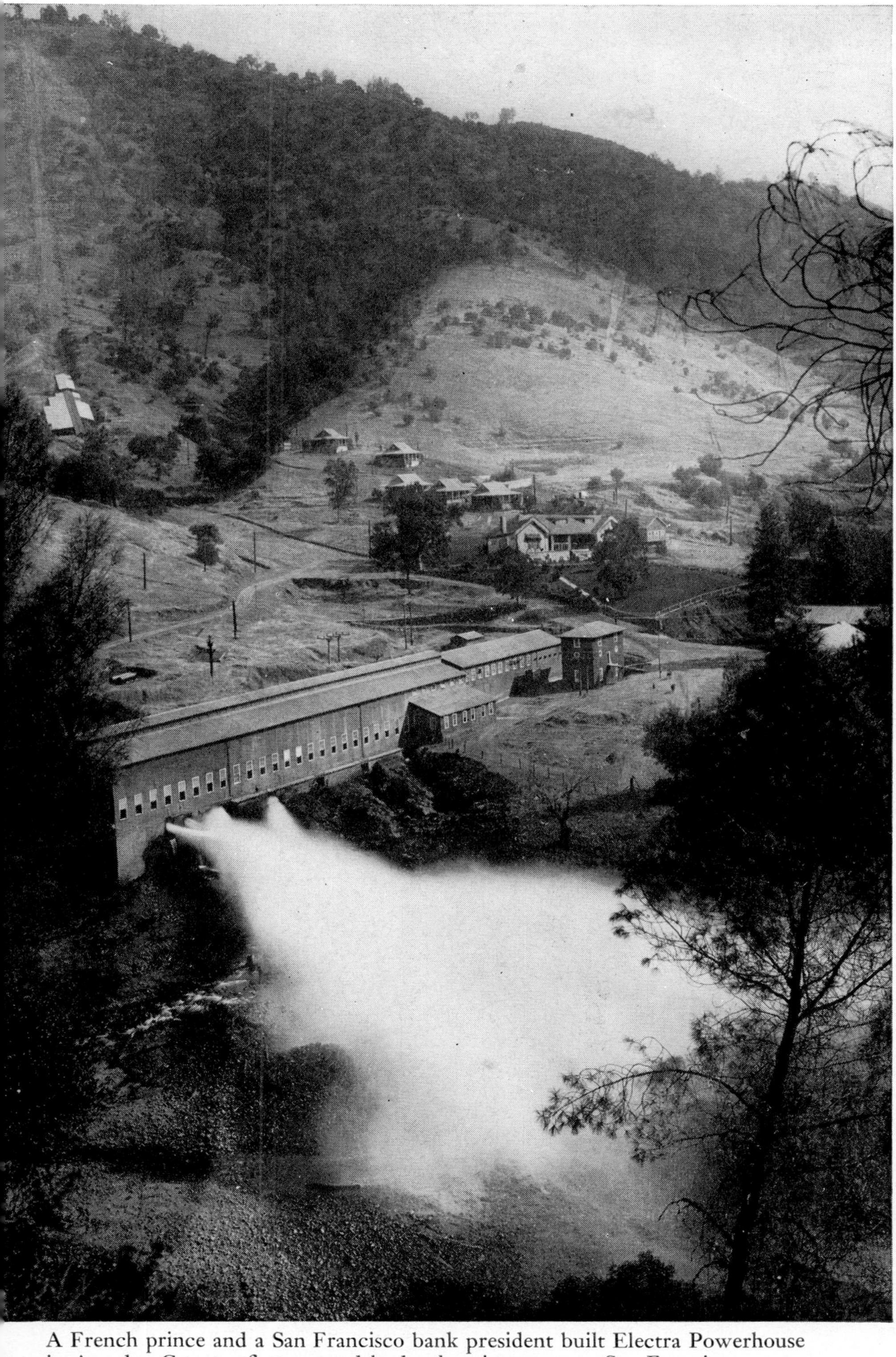

A French prince and a San Francisco bank president built Electra Powerhouse in Amador County, first to send hydroelectric power to San Francisco.

New Electra Powerhouse was commissioned in 1948 by Pacific Gas and Electric Com-

fornia, incorporated under the laws of West Virginia on November 27, 1897, to build Electra Powerhouse. The company was reincorporated in California on February 7, 1899.

Prince André threw himself into the new enterprise with concentrated enthusiasm. He studied electrical science and practice, hydraulics and mechanics, and informed himself further about American methods of finance. Fearful that the engineers might be confirmed in their doubts that power could be transmitted successfully to San Francisco, he constructed a pole line from the Blue Lakes plant to Stockton to provide a backlog of business for the new company.

The Blue Lakes Powerhouse was operated successfully until November 1, 1899, when fire destroyed its wooden interior. It was rebuilt and continued in operation until 1902, supplying power for construction of the Electra plant.

The Prince, determined that Electra Powerhouse should be the last word in design and construction, retained as chief engineer Dr. Frederick A. C. Perrine, first professor of electrical engineering at Stanford University and later president of the Stanley Electrical Manufacturing Company. Dr. Perrine was responsible for the design of the electrical parts of the project and for the transmission system. Associated with him were Frank G. Baum, brilliant Stanford engineer, and A. C. Bunker, young electrical engineer who had had experience with the Stanley Electrical Company, manufacturers of Electra's generating equipment. Engineers C. P. Gilbert and C. H. Ellison were members of the extensive staff.

In charge of design and construction of mechanical and hydraulic equipment was veteran W. R. Eckart who had a broad background of experience in mining and hydraulic work. He was an engineer officer of the Navy in the Civil War. He had designed the first locomotive built in California by Peter Donahue's Union Iron Works. He designed and built for the Bliss family the steamer *Meteor* which was operated for years on Lake Tahoe. At Virginia City he had been consulting engineer for Mackay, Flood, O'Brien and Fair in the Comstock mines, installing high-pressure pipe lines to lift water from the lower workings to the surface by huge Cornish pumps.

His son, Nelson A. Eckart, who afterward became chief engineer of the San Francisco Water System, gained some of his early engineering experience on the Electra project.

When plans were completed, work proceeded at Electra on all fronts. Camps were established at Blue Lakes, Meadow Lake, and Bear River, a tributary of the Mokelumne, for construction of storage reservoir dams. Materials were hauled to these remote places by wagon, 60 miles from Ione, the nearest accessible California shipping point, or from Carson City, Nev. Heavy equipment required the use of teams of 12 to 20 horses and mules; sometimes donkey engines on wheels did the hauling. At one time 1,500 men were employed in 14 mountain camps. Work at the highest elevations could be done only during the summer months. At the beginning of the second season, labor crews refused to sign on without a contract specifying they would not be sent to camps above 6,500 feet elevation. The Blue Lakes are above the 8,000-foot level. Poniatowski met that emergency by finding a shipload of 400 Greeks at New Orleans and having them transported through Nevada to the sky-high camps.

There were other difficulties. After John Martin had obtained an order for Stanley generators and had assured Prince André and his engineers that a 60,000-volt transmission line could be built from Electra plant into San Francisco, the way appeared to be blocked by lack of adequate insulators. Not one of the three electrical manufacturing companies would accept the responsibility of installing insulators, which they declared would not be safe above 30,000 volts.

Prince André rushed to New York where he was met by C. C. Chesney, chief engineer of the Stanley company, and a young assistant who had been working on a design for large capacity insulators. They discussed the problem with the F. M. Locke Insulator Company, which finally agreed to undertake the job subject to an indemnity in case of failure and a firm order of $30,000 in case of success.

Two months later, in upstate New York, the Prince witnessed severe but successful tests of the new insulators which consisted of a shaft of glass mounted on a threaded eucalyptus pin and a grooved top of porcelain. The three parts were assembled in California where the wooden pins were made. Although defects appeared after installation, the Locke-made insulators served their purpose and carried from 40,000 to 60,000 volts over the Standard lines.

The original plan had been to carry the transmission lines across the shallow southern arm of the Bay on steel towers, but Federal navigation authorities refused permission. Consequently the line was run from Electra to Mission San Jose, where one branch was built to Oakland and a second around the lower end of the Bay and north to San Francisco. The distance to Oakland was 119.8 miles; to San Francisco, 143.2 miles. A tap line connected San Jose to the system. By using a 37-strand aluminum cable instead of copper conductor, the Prince declared he saved $200,000 in cost of the transmission line.

For four years the work of construction went on. The Blue Lakes water-storage system was completed after long delays caused by the shortness of the season in which work could be carried forward. The last of the reservoirs, Meadow Lake and Lower Blue Lake, were not completed until 1903. The new dams tripled the total storage capacity to 23,554 acre-feet. A new canal, to be known as the Upper Standard, was built above the old Amador ditch to transport the water along the canyon wall of the Mokelumne River to Lake Tabeaud, an artificial reservoir created high above the powerhouse site.

W. Frank Pierce was in general charge of the construction forces. In the latter part of the building period he was ably assisted by Superintendent Randall Ellis, who in later years served the city and county of San Francisco as valuation engineer.

Another of the builders of the Electra system was Silas H. Palmer, now a member of the P. G. and E. board of directors. Not long out of the University of California at the time, Palmer was engineer in charge of construction of Lake Tabeaud dam and Tiger Creek dam and tunnel, acting for the contractors E. B. and A. L. Stone.

One of the pioneers of the Mokelumne River electric development is W. E. Eskew, who spent 41 years in the service of P. G. and E. and its predecessor companies. For 35 of those years he was on the river or at Jackson as superintendent of the water system and later as district agent.

Water was turned into the canal February 8, 1902, and on

May 6, 1902, Electra Powerhouse took over the load from the Blue Lakes plant, which then was closed down. The five generators, humming with a total capacity of 10,000 kilowatts, began serving the mines of the Mother Lode area and the cities of Oakland and San Jose. Power was delivered to the 34 Kansas Street substation in San Francisco on November 3, 1902. A second line from Mission San Jose to San Francisco was completed in 1905 and the voltage was raised to 60,000. Additional generating units were installed at Electra to bring the plant's capacity to 20,000 kilowatts.

Toward the end of the construction period Prince Poniatowski, suffering from illness caused by an old wrist injury, had relaxed his furious pace of supervision. W. H. Crocker took over the completion of the job and direction of the company's activities, even finding time to leave his presidential chair in the Crocker-Woolworth bank for visits to Electra Powerhouse.

Electra plant was in operation, but disposal of its electric power at profitable rates was not yet assured. As soon as the transmission line to Oakland had been completed, a contract had been made with the Oakland Gas Light and Heat Company for a part of Electra's output. A similar commitment had been made to supply electricity to the San Jose Electric Improvement Company. Many months before the Electra plant was placed in commission, John Martin and Eugene de Sabla had begun delivery of power to Oakland over their new long line from Colgate plant. It was to them the Prince was compelled to turn for the kilowatts he needed to fill his Oakland and San Jose contracts until his own powerhouse and line should be completed.

The San Francisco situation had not developed favorably. Knowing that he must have an outlet for sale of power in the metropolis, the Prince, at the beginning of his project, had attempted to purchase the system of the Pacific Power Company. This small organization distributed electricity to a limited area bounded by Pine, Howard, Fremont, and Third Streets. Live steam also was sold for operation of elevators. Before Poniatowski's Standard Electric Company could complete the deal, however, the San Francisco Gas and Electric Company checkmated by purchasing Pacific Power's distribution system.

Poniatowski then carried on negotiations with the San Francisco Gas and Electric Company, the United Railroads, and some of the larger industries for sale of power to them. In the midst of the discussions came rumors of discoveries of petroleum in the San Joaquin Valley and farther south, which, if true, would place oil fuel in sharp competition with hydroelectric power. To this new factor Prince André attributed the financial conditions which prevented the placing of Standard Electric stock upon a paying basis.

In his memoirs he declared: "These whispers gaining more and more in consistency, we were led to sign with the biggest consumers, contracts which would just take care of our bonded debt, leaving no margin as eventual dividends for our shares."

In anticipation of the day when the Standard Electric Company's lines should traverse San Mateo and Santa Clara Counties, W. H. Crocker and Prince Poniatowski had taken early steps to gain control of the small companies serving the peninsular region. The vehicle was the Consolidated Light and Power Company, incorporated January 2, 1900, by Crocker and a number of his friends to purchase and merge under one management the systems of the San Mateo Electric Company, the San Mateo Gas Light Company, the Peninsula Lighting Company, and the Redwood City Electric Company.

The four companies provided electricity and gas to Burlingame, San Mateo, Belmont, and neighboring communities. Redwood City and Palo Alto at that time operated their own distribution systems. Palo Alto and Stanford University maintained their own generating stations. The new Consolidated company added generators to its existing stations and, with the promise of eventual electric supply from the Prince's Electra–San Francisco transmission, added the two towns and the university to its roll of customers.

Consolidated Light and Power Company operated until April 19, 1902, when the United Gas and Electric Company was incorporated by the Crocker interests to bring into the merged system the San Jose Light and Power Company and the Electric Improvement Company of San Jose. United then provided electricity, and gas in some localities, to the entire peninsula from San Bruno in the north to San Jose.

The peninsular area was notable for the early application of electric power to industrial and other uses. Numerous vegetable and berry farms used motors for pumping irrigation water. On the estate of Walter S. Hobart, capitalist, polo player, and gentleman farmer, motors drove the deep-well pump, a feed cutter, a circular saw, a horse clipper, a cream separator, and a refrigerating plant. There was even a one-horsepower motor to operate a boot polisher and buffer. Prince Poniatowski's Sky Farm, high in the hills west of San Mateo, was another large user of power for farm purposes. At the turn of the century such general employment of electricity as a farm worker was a novelty rather than the common practice it is today.

United Gas and Electric Company became an important customer of Prince Poniatowski's company when the Standard's line and the Electra plant were completed. When the Standard's system was purchased by California Gas and Electric Corporation, the United properties also were taken over by de Sabla and his associates in a separate transaction March 1, 1904.

Electra plant was in continuous operation for nearly 50 years, until it was superseded by a new and greater Electra in 1948. The water facilities of the Mokelumne River watershed have been enlarged so that five powerhouses are now operated by the falling waters drawn from the Blue Lakes—Salt Springs Powerhouse, Tiger Creek, the new Electra, West Point, and a plant downstream at Pardee Reservoir operated by the East Bay Municipal Utility district for Oakland and its neighboring communities.

In a recent letter, the Prince wrote: "When the line was completed to San Francisco I resigned the presidency of the company . . . already the merger of the Standard with the de Sabla group [California Gas and Electric Corporation] was in the mind of my brother-in-law [W. H. Crocker] who could not very well assume such activities . . . [because his] banking interests called for his attention."

With, as he expressed it, "the somewhat forced liquidation of my interests in Standard Electric Company," Prince André returned to France with his wife and his sons early in 1903.

CHAPTER 18

Portentous Mergers

THE YEAR 1903 was an eventful one in the progress of the young California Gas and Electric Corporation, which then was established in new offices in the Rialto Building, San Francisco. R. R. Colgate, who repeatedly had invested money in the de Sabla-Martin projects, resigned as president of the company, sold his stock interest, and returned to his Eastern home. He was succeeded as president by de Sabla.

Colgate's resignation brought into the company a new and powerful figure—Frank G. Drum who had purchased the Colgate stock and, April 20, 1903, was made a member of the board of directors. Drum, then in his fortieth year, was the son of an Oakland businessman, a graduate of St. Ignatius and Santa Clara colleges. In his youth he had been a member of surveying parties in Nevada and in the Northwest for the Hill railroads. He had spent four years in the Oakland Bank of Savings of which his father was a director. In 1887 he entered the office of J. B. Haggin and Lloyd Tevis and soon became manager of their extensive properties. In 1899 he had been one of the organizers of the Mercantile Trust Company of San Francisco.

Under Lloyd Tevis the young manager gained a broad knowledge of business and finance and of California lands. Tevis had been a frequent investor in San Francisco gas and electric utilities and had imparted to Drum a store of information about their operations.

Before Drum joined de Sabla and Martin, he had learned much about utility finance and economics through close association with Henry T. Scott, then president of Pacific Telephone and Telegraph Company. The Tevis estate was a large stockholder in the telephone company which at that time was engaged in consolidating into its system a number of scattered independent telephone companies.

How Frank G. Drum happened to enter the gas and electric utility business is not officially recorded. In later years Eugene de Sabla gave a version that throws an interesting side light upon the customs of a half century ago. De Sabla had returned early in 1903 from a vacation trip to Europe to find that the California Gas and Electric Corporation had not yet completed sale of its $10,000,000 bond issue. Financing was imperative for closing the purchase of the utility systems on which Martin had secured options. The list of possible bond buyers was nearly exhausted, but de Sabla remembered Will Tevis, whom he knew only slightly, and decided to call upon him. At the Haggin and Tevis offices in the Mills Building he encountered Drum instead of Will Tevis, who was out of the city. To him he told his story.

After hearing the details of the corporation's plans, its finances, and its ambitions, Drum said, "How much do you need?"

De Sabla hesitated, then grasped his courage in both hands and replied, "Two hundred thousand dollars."

Without a word, Drum took the subscription list from him, wrote his name and after it, "$200,000."

The complete story probably would reveal that Drum had considered such an investment and was well informed before he signed for the bonds. Three or four weeks later, Drum asked de Sabla if the Colgate stock could be purchased. The result was that the major part of Colgate's shareholdings were transferred to Drum, the remainder being purchased by de Sabla. Drum became an active participant in the company's operations as a member of the board's executive committee.

New strength had been brought into the company with the election of four additional directors—E. W. Hopkins, John C. Coleman, Frank B. Anderson, and Frederick W. Zeile. Hopkins, Coleman, and Zeile long had been associated with the de Sabla-Martin utility enterprises. Frank B. Anderson, vice-president of the Bank of California, brought the powerful support of his bank to the new company. He continued as a member of the board after he became president of the bank in 1909, and in 1914 he was made a member of the executive committee of Pacific Gas and Electric, the successor company. When he died in 1935 he had served more than 32 years as a director of Pacific Gas and Electric and its predecessor company.

A further change was made by the retirement of W. M. Pierson because of ill health. As attorney for their companies, Pierson had charted the legal course for de Sabla and Martin since the beginning. He was succeeded by Garret W. McEnerney as general counsel and W. B. Bosley as attorney. Bosley went on to become general counsel for P. G. and E. He retired in 1948 after 45 years of service with the Company and its predecessor.

* * *

After the utility systems of Oakland, Sacramento, and other towns in the northern counties had been brought under its control early in 1903, the California Gas and Electric Corporation still had no access to San Francisco, its greatest potential market. Although Prince Poniatowski had completed Electra generating plant and a transmission line up the peninsula to San Francisco, Standard had not found an outlet for all its Electra power output.

When the California Gas and Electric Corporation purchased control of the Oakland gas and electric system, Standard lost its largest customer, which had been buying Electra power to supplement its own supply. So Standard sold all its physical properties in Oakland—two substations and pole lines—to E. J. de Sabla, Jr., R. R. Colgate, and R. M. Hotaling for $300,000. The date of this sale was March 3, 1903. It then seemed evident that only a merger of both enterprises could strengthen their respective weak points, and it was in this spirit that Eugene de Sabla decided to call on W. H. Crocker. He found the banker in a receptive mood.

In March, 1904, control of the properties of the Standard system and the United Gas and Electric Company passed into the hands of de Sabla, Martin, Drum, and their associates. With the Standard lines and power resources in their possession they had gained entrance to the metropolis. They were then in a strategic position for further advance.

* * *

The growing California Gas and Electric Corporation prospered. Beginning in April, 1904, monthly dividends of 25 cents a share were regularly paid. However, there was the problem of an outlet for Standard's electric power still to be solved.

John Martin had an idea. He had been studying the San Francisco situation. The United Railroads, the Eastern-owned street railway system of San Francisco under Patrick Calhoun's adroit management, needed more electric power. It would purchase the output of Standard's Electra plant if—and there was the stumbling block—if it could be assured of a firm supply throughout the year. Streetcar service could not be interrupted by power failure. California Gas and Electric Corporation had no adequate steam-operated generators to support the variable hydro output of the Electra plant.

Martin proposed that a stand-by plant be built in Visitacion Valley on the southern outskirts of the city and that, instead of steam engines, large gas engines be installed to drive the electric generators. The proposal was a revolutionary one; gas engines of the requisite power had not previously been installed in electric powerhouses. Martin was convinced that gas engines could be used much more economically than steam in a stand-by plant because they could be started from standstill to carry full load in less than three minutes, whereas steam engines required constant fueling and attention to be ready for emergency service. Gas engineer E. C. Jones, after a tour of the East, became a firm believer in Martin's plan. John A. Britton also supported him.

The engineering world watched the experiment with interest. It was called "a bold departure from accepted practice." In the East a gas much lighter than the rich oil-water gas made in California had been used in smaller engines of similar type installed for other purposes.

After long discussion, the directors accepted Martin's plan and on October 31, 1904, approved a contract to supply power to United Railroads. The gas engines were to be built by the Snow Steam Pump Works of Buffalo, N.Y., with an unusually sweeping guaranty of performance. Three engines, each of 5,333 horsepower, were built and installed. A fourth engine was delivered for installation in Oakland, but it was never placed in service. The three electric generators had a total capacity of 12,000 kilowatts. To supply gas, an oil-gas plant of the latest design, named Martin Station, was built in Visitacion Valley near the Bay shore. The old red brick building still stands, serving as a warehouse.

When the first of the massive gas engines was placed in operation April 16, 1906, the result was a bitter disappointment. The engines overheated. Their drive was irregular, and attempts to regulate the generators failed. While the plant was operating and was connected to the transmission network, the voltage pulsation caused lights to flicker all over the system.

After desperate efforts to correct the technical faults of the plant, it was closed down August 12, 1910, a nearly total loss. The gas plant was dismantled in 1916 and all the equipment was moved to Fresno where a new plant was erected, thus recovering a part of the heavy loss. The Snow Steam Pump Works stood by its guaranty and went into bankruptcy. The San Mateo Power Company, which had been organized to operate the plant, met a quick death. John Martin was crushed by this defeat and, his friends believed, never fully recovered from the blow to his prestige.

Not long afterward, United Railroads, forced to look elsewhere for a power source, formed the Sierra and San Francisco Power Company from the wreckage of the bankrupt Stanislaus Electric Power Company and imported its kilowatts of energy from Tuolumne County, operating its own steam plant in San Francisco to ensure a constant power supply.

* * *

The year 1904 saw the end of the first decade of hydroelectric commercial operation in Northern California. In that period Eugene de Sabla and John Martin, starting from scratch, had built a utility system that was great in their time and not inconsiderable even now. They too were nearing the peak and the end of their spectacular rise in gas and electric utility promotion.

With the acquisition of the South Yuba Company's properties in 1905, the system boasted 10 hydroelectric powerhouses and many small steam-operated stations. It served gas and electricity to customers in 22 counties. The first lines of an interconnected transmission network had been strung. A centralized organization had been created for the administration and operation of the scattered units.

All Northern California had reaped great economic benefits from the power, fuel, and light supplied by the utility. Industrial electric motors had multiplied, and farmers were beginning to learn the value of electric pumping and irrigation.

The capstone of the structure de Sabla and Martin had built was to be placed within a year by organization of Pacific Gas and Electric Company. The event was to mark the end of one historic period and the beginning of another—a new half century of building a greater structure upon the foundation the Donahues, George H. Roe, C. O. G. Miller, the Livermores, Eugene de Sabla, John Martin, Prince Poniatowski, and scores of others had laid.

PART TWO

Two great utility systems—San Joaquin Light and Power Corporation—John S. Eastwood, the Wishons, John Hays Hammond, W. G. Kerckhoff, A. C. Balch—Mt. Whitney Power Company—Irrigation and electric pumping—Rural electrification—Great Western Power Company—E. T. and Guy C. Earl, Julius M. Howells—Lake Almanor—Dr. Pierce and Big Bend Powerhouse—Edwin Hawley and the syndicate.

CHAPTER 19

Power Builds a Farming Empire

ALMOST at the same time that hydroelectric plants were being built in Northern California, mountain streams in the Southern San Joaquin Valley were being harnessed for the generation of electricity to serve communities and lands some 20,000 square miles in area.

The story of the San Joaquin Light and Power Corporation properly starts with the Mt. Whitney Power Company and the men who built its first plant—A. G. Wishon, William H. (Billy) Hammond, and his mining engineer brother, John Hays Hammond. The Mt. Whitney company never became a part of the San Joaquin Light and Power Corporation, but A. G. Wishon did. How he happened to enter the hydroelectric field, therefore, is important as a prelude to the events that followed.

Albert Graves Wishon was a Missourian, born in 1858 at Coppedges Mill near the town of Rolfe. Ambitious to become a civil engineer, he entered the State School of Mines at Rolla, Mo., but lack of funds cut short his college career. After trying the life of a railroad station agent and various mercantile pursuits, he migrated first to Oregon and then to Tulare, Calif., where, with his family, he arrived in 1889.

All he could find at first was work in a lumber yard at $65 per month, with $10 additional for posting the books at night. As assistant to the cashier of the local bank he did a little better, and in 1893 he was able to establish his own business in real estate and insurance.

In the few years of his residence in Tulare, Wishon had observed the fertility of the soil in the semiarid valley and noted that with irrigation, crop production was enormously increased. At the same time he had followed the rapid expansion of the young electrical industry in California and had learned of the water power awaiting utilization in the canyons of the Sierra. So he determined to try his hand at building an electric system, primarily to provide water for irrigation and power to operate farm wells.

Like so many of the pioneer promoters of electric projects, Wishon was a novice in the science. His engineering knowledge was limited to what he had learned before leaving college. In 1894 he launched promotion of the Kaweah Power and Water Company. A small hydro plant was to be built at Lime Kiln Point on the Kaweah River near Lemon Cove in Tulare County. From the powerhouse the water was to be carried in a ditch to the orange groves of Exeter. Power was to be used to pump additional water from the gravel beds nearby. The estimated cost of the power plant was $150,000 and, with wages at $1 a day, the ditch was to cost about $1,000 per mile.

Obtaining capital was not easy. The financial men of Tulare County were not interested. But in Los Angeles and Pasadena Wishon found a group of five men who were willing to risk investment in his plan. When work started early in 1895, a crew of some 200 men was employed. Wishon was general superintendent, timekeeper, bookkeeper, and camp boss.

After a few months he realized he had cut his cloth on too small a pattern. He visited the Mill Creek plant near Redlands, which then was in successful operation, and the plant of the San Joaquin Electric Company, then under construction to transmit power 37 miles to Fresno. Wishon decided he must find a powerhouse site higher in the mountains where a high head of water would produce more electricity. He proposed to his financial backers that work be stopped on the Lemon Cove project and that his new plan be adopted, pointing out the economic advantages of increased electric output at lower unit cost. The financiers, fearful of loss, would not accept his arguments and withdrew their support. In 1896 Wishon went back to selling real estate and insurance.

One of Wishon's friends in Visalia was W. H. Hammond, county clerk and brother of John Hays Hammond, California mining engineer who had won fame and fortune in the South

Albert G. Wishon, starting as manager of the little San Joaquin Power Company, built it into a great and efficient utility system.

A. C. Balch, engineer, with W. G. Kerckhoff, financier, organized the San Joaquin Power Company in 1902 to revive bankrupt utility.

Kerckhoff Powerhouse, completed in 1920, was named in honor of W. G. Kerckhoff, one of the founders of San Joaquin Light and Power Corporation.

Africa gold fields and at that time had his headquarters in London. Billy Hammond saw eye to eye with Wishon, and the two men entered into a partnership agreement under which they were to share equally in any profit from their joint enterprises. Hammond proposed to ask his brother for help in financing their power project. When Wishon received a $4,600 profit from a real-estate sale, Hammond was outfitted and departed for London, armed with an elaborate prospectus laboriously typed by Wishon in his real-estate office. The partners had budgeted $1,500 for the trip, but after Billy reached London he cabled home for another $500. He had quickly learned that the correct attire of London businessmen consisted of tailed morning coat, spats, stick, and top hat. John Hays Hammond tells the story of what followed in his autobiography:

"The idea of irrigation and reclamation, later so publicized by Theodore Roosevelt, had taken possession of my brother William's imagination as early as 1891. He believed that, if water could be delivered to the farms of the valley at reasonable rates, it would bring about an agricultural revolution. In association with A. G. Wishon, his partner in the local water company, and Ben M. Maddox, the owner-editor of the Visalia Times, he worked to bring his theory to realization.

"Having failed in America to obtain the funds necessary to launch the project, Bill, as a last resort, came to see me in London in 1898.

" 'Jack,' urged Bill, 'we already have options on the water sites and the rights of way. As you know, we have a soil and climate that will grow anything. Whenever we drill a well we strike water, and all we need is the power to pump it. Gasoline and steam engines work, but they're too expensive and can serve only a few acres each. With cheap electric power available, thousands of acres will go into cultivation.'

" 'But can you send electricity as far as that?' I asked. 'It's never been done before for irrigating purposes, has it?'

" 'No, but we have an engineer who guarantees it can be done,' he replied. 'Robert McF. Doble. He'll build the powerhouse at Mt. Whitney and bring the current the necessary thirty-five miles. This will put all of Tulare County within reach of our feeder lines.'

"On the night Bill arrived in London, Leopold Hirsch dined at my house. During the dinner he and my brother talked about American affairs and California. The next day I told Bill I would supply half the funds required and would assist him in raising the balance among my friends in London. Naturally, I had Hirsch in mind.

"I made an appointment for the two to meet again, and the banker agreed to underwrite the other half of the funds required. So simply was the Mt. Whitney Power Company launched." *

Billy Hammond sailed for home with a $200,000 credit from his brother and Leopold Hirsch. Work was begun immediately at the new powerhouse site on the Kaweah River where a head of 1,310 feet was obtained for the water that would drive the generators. The plant, known as Kaweah Powerhouse No. 1, had an installed capacity of 1,350 kilowatts. It was completed June 30, 1899. Transmission lines were run to Visalia, Exeter, Lindsay, Tulare, and Porterville.

The Mt. Whitney Power Company was incorporated December 26, 1899, to take over the Kaweah River properties developed by Wishon and Hammond. The corporate name later was changed to Mt. Whitney Power and Electric Company. Wishon and W. H. Hammond divided a 20 per cent stock interest in the company as their payment for the time and labor they had devoted to its promotion. A steam-operated plant in Visalia was acquired, and in succeeding years other powerhouses were built to give the system ultimate generating resources of 15,000 kilowatts in five plants, with about 1,300 miles of transmission and distribution lines. John Hays Hammond bought the Hirsch interest in the company and retained his control of its properties until 1917, when he sold his holdings to Southern California Edison Company of Los Angeles.

* From "The Autobiography of John Hays Hammond," Vol. 2, pp. 736–737. Copyright 1935 by John Hays Hammond, and reprinted by permission of Rinehart & Company, Inc., Publishers, New York.

And so it came about that in the midst of the wide San Joaquin Valley region now served by Pacific Gas and Electric Company there is a service island in Tulare County and portions of neighboring counties which draws its electric power from the lines of the distant Southern California Edison Company instead of from the system whose transmission network surrounds it.

A. G. Wishon left the Mt. Whitney company September 7, 1902, angry and resentful. In one of the published accounts of his early days he wrote: "One day, out of a clear sky, a lawyer came who said he had the voting power of 80 per cent of the stock, and he asked me to resign—and so endeth the first chapter . . . of my experiences."

The lawyer was Charles Stetson Wheeler, an eminent San Francisco counselor who represented John Hays Hammond, principal owner of the Mt. Whitney company. From casual remarks made by Wishon to his associates and from other evidence, it is clear that the dispute was caused by Wishon's persistent reaching for the moon. He was not satisfied to build just one electric plant. After the first powerhouse was completed and a second plant was being built, he urged the immediate adoption of a much more extensive expansion program than the Hammonds wished to finance. They preferred a slower pace, the company to pay its way as it grew. Although three more plants eventually were added, the urgency of Wishon's dreams of a great San Joaquin Valley system appears to have been behind the request for his resignation.

Wishon was not through—far from it. He had proved that electric-powered irrigation pumping could work miracles in agricultural development. His Tulare County experience and the knowledge he gained there were to be applied almost immediately to the upbuilding of a small, bankrupt Fresno utility into the fulfillment of his dreams—the San Joaquin Light and Power Corporation.

* * *

John S. Eastwood, a civil engineer who loved the mountains and knew their watersheds, contours, and elevations, built the first plant of the future San Joaquin Light and Power Corporation.

Eastwood began exploring the southern ranges of the Sierra as early as 1884, when he made a preliminary survey for a railroad to Pine Ridge below Shaver Lake. When the possibilities of hydroelectric development became apparent in the early nineties, he was practicing his profession in Fresno. The town, then with a population of 11,000, had only a small electric system operated by the Fresno Gas and Electric Company.

The engineer decided the time had come for construction of a water-powered generating plant to supply electricity to the growing city. He interested some of his friends, and on April 2, 1895, the San Joaquin Electric Company was incorporated, capitalized for $800,000. Eastwood and J. J. Seymour, a large stockholder in the Fresno Water Company, held the majority of stock. Seymour headed the company as president, with Eastwood as vice-president and chief engineer. To provide funds for plant construction, an $800,000 bond issue was authorized. One of the first acts of the company was to acquire, for $185,000, control of the Fresno Water Company.

The powerhouse site chosen was on the north fork of the San Joaquin River (now known as Willow Creek), 37 miles from Fresno. The project involved two engineering feats—first, the planning of a plant to handle a static head of 1,410 feet, a higher water pressure than had been attempted with the equipment then available; second, economical transmission for 37 miles at 11,000 volts, a problem of distance that was troubling engineers everywhere.

The elevation was gained by building a ditch and flume high on the mountainside for 6 miles from the diversion dam to the penstock above the powerhouse. Through 4,000 feet of pipe laid down the steep slope, the water was dropped to the Pelton wheels that were to drive three generators with a total capacity of 1,050 kilowatts.

San Joaquin No. 1, as the plant was named, was placed in operation May 12, 1896, and served continuously until September 20, 1910, when it was replaced by the larger A. G. Wishon Powerhouse at the same location.

The new electric company suffered more than its share of misfortune. Everything went wrong. There were mechanical troubles with the high-pressure pipes, and the devices installed to control the enormous force of the column of water dropped down the mountainside to the powerhouse. The pipe joints, sealed with lead, expanded under the hot sun and contracted at night, causing troublesome leaks.

A German engineer, employed by General Electric Company to install the machinery, provided the disastrous climax. When all was ready for the first test, the water was turned on, but instead of the expected smooth operation of water wheels and generators, a roaring torrent flooded the powerhouse floor. The German engineer had forgotten to screw into place the nozzle tip inside the wheel housing. Excited and disturbed by the mischance, he touched off an automatic valve which closed the water gates at the forebay and abruptly stopped the fall of the massive column of water in the 20-inch penstock pipe. The resulting explosive shock collapsed the pipe 500 feet above the powerhouse.

Troubles continued. Thousands of gophers took up residence in the banks of the mountain ditch and converted its walls into a sieve that required constant plugging. But more serious was the fighting opposition of the Fresno Gas and Electric Company, which resented interference with its long-standing lighting monopoly. Fulton G. Berry, proprietor of Fresno's Grand Central Hotel and head of the gas company, took simple but effective measures to kill off his competitor. He sent men into the mountains and filed claim to riparian water rights on 480 acres of land bordering Brown's Creek where the electric company drew a large part of its supply. A mile-long ditch was dug through Berry's sagebrush-covered land, and in the summer season virtually all the stream flow was diverted and wasted before it could reach the power company's penstock. Without enough water to operate the generators, the plant was compelled to close down frequently.

Two or three dry years and failure of the bond house which had backed the company's financing completed Berry's campaign of attrition. In August, 1899, the San Joaquin Electric Company, lacking the capital to make improvements and thus meet the attacks of its competitor, was forced into bankruptcy.

J. J. Seymour was appointed receiver. Both Eastwood and Seymour lost heavily by the failure.

Seymour managed to build a small reservoir at the headworks of the ditch to guard against future shortages of water. For more than two years he operated the crippled electric company while efforts were made to find a purchaser. He turned for help to his brother-in-law, Julius M. Howells, a civil engineer, who had built the first Crane Valley dam and acted as consulting engineer in construction of the San Joaquin plant.

Howells learned that C. F. Street, a New York stockbroker, held control of a large amount of the San Joaquin Company's bonds and from him obtained an option to purchase the bonds at a substantial discount. Then, accompanied by Seymour and an attorney, he went to Los Angeles and sought out W. G. Kerckhoff, head of a large lumber company, who had become an active and aggressive hydroelectric enterpriser. In the office of H. W. O'Melveny, Kerckhoff's attorney, an agreement was reached under which, for a cash payment of $35,000 down, Kerckhoff and his associate, A. C. Balch, bought the bonds and thus were in a preferential position to bid in the San Joaquin property at the receiver's sale.

W. G. Kerckhoff had become interested in 1891 in a powerhouse project on the San Gabriel River, near Los Angeles. For seven years he fought a succession of battles with opposing interests until he completed the Azusa plant of the San Gabriel Electric Company in 1898. Associated with him were Abraham Haas and Kaspare Cohn, Los Angeles merchants, O'Melveny, and A. C. Balch who managed the company's operations.

A. C. Balch, a Cornell graduate in electrical and mechanical engineering, had joined Kerckhoff in 1896 after some experience with electric system operations in Seattle and with the Union Power Company of Portland, Ore.

After acquiring two additional hydroelectric plants, Kerckhoff and Balch had incorporated, in 1902, the Pacific Light and Power Company to combine the three properties under one corporate management. The Pacific company was backed by powerful interests. Soon after its organization, Henry E. Huntington, nephew of Collis P. Huntington of the Southern Pacific

Railroad, acquired a 51 per cent stock interest. He needed power for the Los Angeles Railway and for the Pacific Electric Railway's suburban lines he was busy building. The Pacific Light and Power Company continued to grow and later was merged into Southern California Edison Company.

When the Los Angeles men agreed to purchase the San Joaquin property, they moved speedily to complete the deal. Balch left the same night for New York to obtain necessary changes in the option agreement with Street, the stockbroker. Only a few days later, August 11, 1902, the San Joaquin Power Company was incorporated, with Kerckhoff as president and Balch as vice-president. Purchase of the Fresno properties, including control of the Fresno Water Company, was completed the following December.

John S. Eastwood did not give up when his San Joaquin Electric Company failed. He went back to his beloved mountains and began new surveys for power development. His dreams were the practical plans of a farsighted engineer—a vast storage reservoir where Huntington Lake and other storage lakes now hold the waters gathered from the Sierra snowfields; tunnels and conduits that would transport the flow to a series of generating stations at lower levels to produce a half-million kilowatts of electric power. Eastwood communicated his ideas to the top men of the Pacific Light and Power Company in Los Angeles and continued his surveys. From the mountains he wrote to W. G. Kerckhoff:

"Big Creek, October 7, 1902

"It gives me great pleasure to inform you that I have completed the survey for a tunnel line to the junction of Pitman and Big Creeks and I can place before you the most remarkable power project yet presented."

That was the genesis of the Big Creek project. Construction was started in 1911 by Pacific Light and Power. When the project was completed in 1929 by Southern California Edison, successor to the Pacific company, a total generating capacity of 428,000 kilowatts of hydro power had been added to the electric resources of the Southern California system.

When A. G. Wishon reached the parting of the ways with the Mt. Whitney Power Company in 1902, he went to Los Angeles to consult Kerckhoff and Balch regarding water rights he had secured on the Tule River. He left the same day with a contract to become manager of their newly acquired San Joaquin Power Company.

The company's financial resources were strengthened by the addition of Kaspare Cohn and Abraham Haas to its board of directors. Each held a one-sixth interest and took an active part in corporate affairs—Cohn as treasurer in 1903 and vice-president in later years. Nearly 50 years later, in 1949, Walter A. Haas, San Francisco manufacturer and civic leader and a son of Abraham Haas, was elected a director of P. G. and E. He had been a director of the San Joaquin company following his father's death in 1925.

Kerckhoff and Balch took early steps to prevent the destructive and wasteful competition that had ruined their predecessor, the San Joaquin Electric Company. Fulton G. Berry's Fresno Gas and Electric Company, which had caused the downfall of Eastwood and Seymour, was still in the Fresno ring. But in 1903 John Martin bought control of the Fresno company for his California Gas and Electric Corporation. There is no record to show whether Martin and de Sabla planned to invade the undeveloped San Joaquin field, but the possibility doubtless appeared as a threat to Kerckhoff and Balch. So a tripartite agreement was reached. The San Joaquin Power Company contracted to purchase from the Fresno Gas and Electric Light Company, for $25,000, its electric system, franchises, and business. The Fresno company agreed not to engage in the electric business, and the San Joaquin Power Company promised not to manufacture and sell gas within the city of Fresno. That disposed of local competition.

There remained the possibility that Martin and de Sabla, then reaching out in all directions for additions to their expanding network of electric and gas systems, might seek other properties in the south. A. C. Balch handled treaty negotiations with John Martin which provided that neither company would enter the other's territory for electrical development.

The dividing line was defined by the southern boundaries of the counties of Santa Cruz, Santa Clara, Stanislaus, Tuolumne, and Mono. For nearly 30 years the agreement remained in force. When control of the San Joaquin Light and Power Corporation was acquired by Pacific Gas and Electric Company in 1930, it no longer was necessary.

Henry E. Huntington participated in the original deal only to the extent of joining Balch and Kerckhoff in buying the street railway system which then consisted of four cars and limited trackage. Wishon took over management of the railway and supervised its operation until it was sold to Southern Pacific interurban interests. The Fresno water system also was managed by Wishon and remained in the electric company's control for many years. Eventually it was sold to the California Water Service Company and later, in 1931, was taken over by the city.

During his management of the water system Wishon made a ruling that had a pronounced effect upon the beauty of the city. Water users paid a flat monthly rate, with no limit on the amount of water used. Everywhere were lush gardens of lawns and shrubbery. When new wells were constantly required and the water supply sometimes was short, it was proposed to substitute meter rates for the monthly charge.

"No," said Wishon, "if meters were installed, people would neglect their lawns and their gardens. In this climate everything would turn brown in summer and Fresno would lose the charm of its cool, green landscaping." His edict stood, and to this day the residents of Fresno pay a flat rate for their water supply.

A. G. Wishon plunged into his new task of standing the San Joaquin electric system firmly on its feet. San Joaquin Powerhouse No. 1 was placed in good operating condition, and a generating unit was added to bring the plant capacity to 1,400 kilowatts. At that time, the company distributed electricity to commercial houses and residences in Fresno and, over a transmission line built in 1900 from Fresno to the town of Hanford, sold power at wholesale rate to the distributing system there operated by H. G. Lacy.

One of the troublesome tasks was to substitute meter rates for the flat monthly rates that had been charged for customer service. There were only a few meters in Fresno and none in Hanford. Customers' bills were computed at flat rates based on the number of lamps used and the length of time they were lighted. The fixed residential rates varied from 30 cents per month for each 16-candlepower lamp to 10 cents per lamp for the smaller sizes installed in bedrooms, halls, and bathrooms.

There was trouble when Wishon came to deal with Lacy of Hanford, who was paying a flat rate of $400 monthly for his power. When the new meter registered $1,100 for the first month's operation, there was almost a riot. "However," said Wishon, "finally he got used to it and soon it became a matter of course and our relations were ever after very pleasant."

Many years afterward, Lacy had his revenge. He was operating under a 45-year contract with the San Joaquin power company for the electricity needed to supply the Hanford distribution system. Wishon had remarked to him one day, "Any time you decide to sell out, let me know. We'll be glad to take over your business at the right price." Years passed. Then, about 1917, Lacy walked into Wishon's office. "Do you still want to buy my lines?" he asked.

"Yes," replied Wishon. "How much?"

"Twenty-five thousand dollars," said the Hanford man.

Wishon exploded, as he did on occasion, with profane force. "You highway robber," he yelled, "get out of here and don't come back until you can talk sense." Without a word, Lacy departed.

The next morning A. G.'s day was ruined. As he glanced over the news in the Fresno *Republican,* his eye caught a headline: "HANFORD ELECTRIC SYSTEM AND MT. WHITNEY POWER AND ELECTRIC COMPANY SOLD TO SOUTHERN CALIFORNIA EDISON." The verbal fireworks that followed are still talked about by the old-timers.

Demand for electric power and lighting kept pace with the growth of Fresno and improvement of electric service. Wishon urged the building of more hydroelectric generating plants. Soon after he took charge of the San Joaquin company he offered his water rights on the Tule River to Kerckhoff and Balch, but it was decided to defer building there and the Tule Powerhouse was not placed in operation until 1914.

Wishon continued filing for water rights on the San Joaquin, the Tule, and the Kings Rivers. Once he wrote to his employers suggesting he should be compensated for his water explorations and filings by an interest in the company. At the moment there was no favorable response.

Within two years the future of the power company that had been established for the purpose of supplying electricity to Fresno became plain to its promoters. There were growing towns in every direction, and wide areas of vacant land waiting for settlement and cultivation. Transmission lines should be extended to reach the towns, many of which had their own costly fuel-operated electric plants. The same lines would serve irrigation pumps in rural areas.

It was Wishon's job to fill in the gaps with rural line extensions. He continued the campaign to increase electric pumping for irrigation which he had started when he was managing the Mt. Whitney Power Company. "The towns grow in proportion to the development of the back country," he said, "and it shall always be the policy of the San Joaquin to look carefully after the back country so that the industrial business of the towns will keep pace."

Such a policy called for more capital to build more generating capacity and more transmission lines. Kerckhoff and Balch agreed with their manager's view. The San Joaquin Light and Power Company was incorporated May 13, 1905, with authorized capital of $3,000,000, to take the place of the original company.

The first step was to provide additional generating capacity, and for this purpose San Joaquin No. 3 was built upstream from the first plant on Willow Creek, the north fork of the San Joaquin River. It started operating April 6, 1906, with a capacity of 2,100 kilowatts. To make its output available to customers a second transmission line was built to Fresno.

The next four years were busy years of expansion. They were not easy years. Sometimes money was short, and department heads and supervisors would have to wait weeks for their pay checks. Sometimes, secure in their faith in ultimate success, they advanced cash from their own funds to fatten a treasury made lean by "additions and betterments."

Wishon expected his men to place the company ahead of all other interests. His rules were strict—no loafing on the job, rigorous attention to duty, no personal favors—but he knew every man and they called him "A. G." He evinced a friendly personal interest in their welfare and found time to chat with them wherever he went. He encouraged employee activities, attended their social affairs, provided picnic places and vacation facilities at Bass Lake.

Still smarting from the sting of his enforced resignation from the Mt. Whitney company, the San Joaquin manager planned transmission lines to the south that would fence in the Tulare County territory served by John Hays Hammond's system, thus effectively blocking enlargement of Mt. Whitney's service area.

By 1910 power was being transmitted to Merced County where the Merced Falls Gas and Electric Company was absorbed. One line served Merced, Madera, and Athlone. From the old Fresno-Hanford transmission line, extensions reached out to Corcoran and to Coalinga. Branches supplied Selma, Dinuba, Sanger, Reedley, the Kings River area, and a separate connection with Fresno brought Kerman into the network. Rural electrification was beginning to spread.

Acquisition of the Merced Falls property brought an historic installation into the system. At this point, some 20 miles northeast of the city of Merced, the river drops over a low dam on its course from the Yosemite Valley to the plains of the San Joaquin. Here in 1854 William Nelson, an enterprising forty-niner, installed a water wheel to operate his grist mill. Soon a woolen mill was added. Fire eventually destroyed both mills. In 1894 the Mt. Gaines Mining Company placed a turbine and small generator at the falls to produce power for its stamp mill, 14 miles distant. Two years later the Merced Gas and Electric Company set up two small Brush generators and turbines next to the mining company's plant to light the streets of Merced. The year after the San Joaquin company took possession in 1910, a flood wrecked all the structures below the dam, and the powerhouse was not replaced until 1916 when a new 450-kilowatt plant was built.

Increased in capacity and modernized in 1930, the Merced Falls plant still is in operation as a part of the present P. G. and E. system.

While extensions were being made north and west of Fresno, the utility company was looking south to the wastes of land waiting for irrigation and to the oil fields where the use of electric power to drive well pumps had been thought impracticable. Again, lack of capital blocked further expansion until July 19, 1910, when the San Joaquin Light and Power Corporation was organized with a capitalization of $25,000,000 to continue the work of its predecessor companies. Even the forward-looking men in charge of the enterprise did not foresee that in little more than a decade the San Joaquin Valley's growth and its demand for electric power would require raising the corporation's capitalization sixfold, to $150,000,000. This was done March 10, 1921. Much of the economic growth was created by the utility's successful efforts to make electric power available wherever there was work for it to do in industry and agriculture.

Formation of the new corporation brought a personal triumph to A. G. Wishon. The directors recognized his claim to compensation for the water rights and the reservoir and powerhouse sites he had secured for power development. Kerckhoff, Balch, Haas, and Cohn presented Wishon preferred and common stock which amounted to $400,000 at par value.

The first move of the new company was toward Bakersfield where the Power Transit and Light Company had been operating with indifferent success. Controlled by the Haggin–Tevis Kern County Land Company, its properties included the Kern Canyon plant whose three generators were driven by the natural stream flow. Purchase of the Bakersfield company was concluded August 10, 1910.

Three years later, one of the earliest experiments in interchange of power between unrelated companies was made successfully. The Kern Canyon plant had no water storage, and an excessively dry season dropped the river flow so low that the plant was compelled to shut down. Bakersfield suffered a power shortage.

The San Joaquin company promptly ran a connecting transmission line from the powerhouse to the Southern California Edison Company's Kern River plant No. 1, which was 1½ miles upstream. The Edison company placed a 5,000 kilowatt generator exclusively on the Bakersfield load, and service was resumed. Today, thanks to interconnection of adjacent systems, the interchange of electric power is a common practice. The pioneer Kern Canyon plant was rebuilt in 1921 and, with a generating capacity of 10,000 kilowatts, still is in operation.

Although a transmission line had been built to Bakersfield on the east side of the valley to connect the northern and southern parts of the San Joaquin system, it was apparent a steam-operated plant must be provided there to ensure firm service to the street railway and to the increasing number of irrigation pump motors being installed. So urgent was the need that a 750-kilowatt generator was borrowed and placed in operation November 18, 1910, in the new Bakersfield plant, pending completion of the first permanent unit. Natural gas was piped in from the oil fields as fuel.

"Within two years," said Wishon, "we had spent two million dollars in Kern County and had tied in a large amount of business at Maricopa, Taft, McKittrick, and Kern River oil fields and about 300 pumping plants for irrigation."

The rapid spread of the oil fields in the southern part of the San Joaquin Valley brought a new utility personality into prominence. He was A. Emory Wishon, son of A. G. Like his father, Emory made electric-powered pumping his chief business. But he concentrated on the installation of electric motors in the oil fields, while his father promoted motor pumping of water for irrigation.

The younger Wishon had grown to manhood in the atmosphere of electrical development. As a youth he had been an operator in the first Mt. Whitney powerhouse and had held other utility jobs until he was ready to attend college at the

Missouri School of Mines at Rolla, Mo., where his father had been a student. When he returned to California in 1908, a graduate engineer in mining, he fully intended to follow his chosen profession, but instead he joined the staff of the utility company.

Emory Wishon's first assignment was at Coalinga, a booming oil town. He saw that nearly every well was equipped with its own steam plant to operate its pumps and drive its drills. Study convinced him that if a variable-speed electric motor could be devised, electric power could do the work in the oil fields at a great saving. After much experimenting by the manufacturers, a motor was produced that would serve the needs of the oil men. But selling the idea to the oil industry was another matter. The drillers, flushed with their riches in black gold, were not much concerned with operating economies. Also, they were not convinced electric motors could do the job cheaper than their steam engines fueled by the abundant gas and oil already available.

Emory Wishon worked for months without selling a motor. One day, after too persistent solicitation, he was ordered off the Shawmut lease by J. Benson Wrenn, who shouted he wasn't in the market for motors and never would be. Three years later Wishon was called to Los Angeles by W. G. Kerckhoff, president of the San Joaquin company. In his office was J. Benson Wrenn, who said to him, "I have made up my mind to install 30 motors . . . also, that when I sign a contract it will be with you, Emory." Then he told Kerckhoff of the angry Shawmut episode.

Wishon sold his first oil well motors in July, 1910, to the Goodluck Oil Company near Coalinga. After a few more motors had been put to work, their economy became generally known and electric oil pumping spread through all the oil fields. In 1912 the Kern River Oil Fields, Ltd., installed 233 motors on its leases. By 1913 some 669 wells were being pumped by electric power.

The oil companies, especially when the oil market slumped and operating economies were most necessary, went in for complete electrification. Motors displaced steam wherever power was needed—for well drilling, for shop operations, for water pumping, for compressors, and for lighting. The oil fields became a rich source of revenue for San Joaquin Light and Power Corporation.

After his Coalinga experience A. Emory Wishon was appointed manager of the Bakersfield division of the system. From there he was promoted to the post of assistant to his father, and there he gained a knowledge of his company's business that was to carry him to still greater responsibilities.

One more step remained to round out the San Joaquin system. Transmission lines could not be extended northward because of the agreement with de Sabla and Martin. But they could and did cross the mountains to embrace the coastal territory from Monterey County south to and including the northern two-thirds of Santa Barbara County.

A. G. Wishon had extended the San Joaquin company's lines to Coalinga in 1908 to supply several small electric companies operating in the vicinity. The next step was incorporation of the Coalinga Water and Electric Company, November 29, 1909, which then purchased the existing electric distribution systems, thus giving the San Joaquin company a power-distributing outlet in Coalinga and adjacent oil fields. W. G. Kerckhoff and A. C. Balch and their associates backed the new organization with capital of $2,000,000.

Plans then were made to build a line to the coast where the towns were being served by inadequate steam-operated electric stations and some by manufactured-gas plants. After many months of negotiation the Coalinga company acquired, March 19, 1912, the Midland Counties Gas and Electric Company. It also took over the Paso Robles Light and Water Company and the Russell Robison Water and Electric Company which served Pismo and several other towns from its plant in Arroyo Grande.

Better to indicate the scope of its activities, the name of the Coalinga Water and Electric Company was changed in 1913 to Midland Counties Public Service Corporation. From then on, expansion of service to the coastal territory was continuous.

Kerckhoff and Balch added a rich agricultural region to San Joaquin company's territory when they completed the Midland corporation system. Since 1920, when all gas properties in the coastal region were sold to the Southern Counties Gas Company,

Kern steam plant, near Bakersfield, supplies power for irrigation of vast acreages in the southern San Joaquin Valley. It was built in 1948.

Pit No. 1 Powerhouse, with its arched façade and turreted towers, is like a medieval

Guy C. Earl, with his brother Edwin, founded the corporation which later, as Great Western Power Company, was merged into the P. G. and E. system.

Mortimer Fleishhacker, San Francisco financier and utility operator, was president of Great Western Power Company, 1912 to 1924.

Heavy machinery was moved across Feather River by aerial tramway to build Big

the Midland system has been entirely electric, receiving its power supply from the San Joaquin corporation's generating system.

Mounting demand for electricity to feed the transmission network required larger and larger generating facilities. In 1910 a new San Joaquin Powerhouse No. 1 was erected alongside the original plant. In later years it was renamed A. G. Wishon Powerhouse in honor of the pioneer builder. Three other plants were built in succession. In 1920, Kerckhoff Powerhouse on the San Joaquin River 30 miles northeast of Fresno was placed in operation, with a capacity of 38,000 kilowatts. Six generating stations ultimately were in operation on the San Joaquin River.

In the south, a steam-operated plant was erected in 1921 at Midway near Buttonwillow in Kern County, to add 25,000 kilowatts to the system. Still another power source was brought into service in 1927 when Balch Powerhouse on the Kings River was commissioned, with a capacity of 34,500 kilowatts.

As the 1920 decade opened, vital changes in the San Joaquin Light and Power Corporation were impending. The founders, Kerckhoff and Balch, and their general manager, A. G. Wishon, had seen the struggling, bankrupt Fresno company they had taken over in 1902 come to full stature as a far-reaching public utility. Their well-organized electric system was operating a chain of 11 powerhouses and a still-spreading network of transmission lines that reached into every corner of the southern San Joaquin Valley. They could view with satisfaction the creation of a rich agricultural empire, the growth of hamlets into prosperous towns and cities. Electric power had proved its worth as an instrument of progress.

W. G. Kerckhoff, whose vision accurately had pictured electric development in the San Joaquin Valley, had nearly finished his work. For 22 years he served as president of the company, only once, in 1912, temporarily relinquishing his post to A. C. Balch. For nearly a quarter of a century his wise counsel and business acumen had guided the vast expansion of the company's facilities and business. In 1924 he retired from the company and was succeeded, for a short time, by A. C. Balch.

Five years later, February 22, 1929, W. G. Kerckhoff died at the age of seventy-three. During his life and in his will, the utility builder was an open-handed philanthropist. He gave millions to the California Institute of Technology, the University of California, a medical research institute at Bad Nauheim, and to scores of charities. His biographer, H. W. O'Melveny, wrote of him: "He had no thought of self when welfare of others was at stake."

A. G. Wishon, who started as manager of the Little San Joaquin power company and who built a great and efficient utility system, became a vice-president, a member of the board and managing director in 1921. A. Emory Wishon, who had served as assistant to his father, was made general manager. In 1925 A. G. Wishon was elected to the presidency, and his son succeeded him as director, vice-president, and general manager. When his father was advanced to vice-chairmanship of the board in 1930, A. Emory was elected president.

A. G. Wishon died June 17, 1936. He was seventy-seven years of age. In 1904 he had written to A. C. Balch in Los Angeles: "I want to see the day when my dream of development up here is fully realized and when we are selling thousands of kilowatts of power where we are now selling hundreds."

He *did* see that day. The thousands increased to tens and hundreds of thousands but, dreamer though he was, it is doubtful he could have envisioned the peak load of power supplied to the San Joaquin territory reaching 880,300 kilowatts, which it did August 1, 1951.

CHAPTER 20

The Desert Shall Rejoice

WATER, the lifeblood of California! In the history of the state, water is the wellspring of economic progress, and its lack an ever-present threat to the future.

In the primitive days of the late eighteenth century, the Mission padres and their Indian charges dug canals to irrigate their cornfields, vineyards, and vegetable gardens.

In the gold-rush era, water was the *sine qua non* of the placers and the hydraulic mines that followed. Then came the hydroelectric projects. Water again was the essential instrument of development.

California's topography and climate are responsible for the important place water occupies in the state's economy. The fast-running streams of the Sierra empty into the two great arterial rivers—the San Joaquin and the Sacramento. In flood season the runoff wastes rapidly into the ocean, even with the flood control projects thus far built. Climate also puts a premium on water—no rain, usually, between June and October in the great Central Valley region, and the thirsty land must have irrigation.

With the building of hydroelectric generating plants in the foothills of the Sierra, transmission lines were strung across the fertile valleys to reach the centers of population on the coast. Thus, low-cost electricity supplanted gasoline and steam engines and archaic windmills which the early irrigationists used to lift water from wells, rivers, and canals.

Electric pumping for irrigation was not wholly unknown in the early nineties. It had been tried successfully in Southern California by the Redlands Electric Company, which installed seven motors along a 7-mile 10,000-volt transmission line to drive centrifugal pumps in farm wells.

The first recorded motorized pumping in Northern California was in 1898 when, in two separate places, farmers adopted electric power. In the first instance a $200 dinner, paid for by the loser of a wager, provided a background for the experiment. John Martin had completed his Yuba Powerhouse in Brown's Valley and had built a transmission line to Marysville. He erected a tall mast in the town park and equipped it with high-powered arc lamps, following the theory of the day that outdoor lighting should be from the sky.

While the mast and lamps were being placed, Martin took part in a discussion of electric lighting with John P. Onstott, who lived on a 25-acre farm in Sutter County, about 2 miles from Marysville.

"John," said Onstott, "those mast lights of yours are no good. They'll be lost in the darkness of the night. I don't believe I'll be able to see them from my place, and that's only two miles away."

"Want to bet?" asked Martin.

"Sure," said Onstott. "I'll wager you a dinner for the crowd I'm right."

When the lights were turned on, the Marysville beacon could be seen plainly at the Onstott farm, although it is to be doubted that Marysville's streets were much brighter. The rancher paid with a gala dinner that was said to have cost him $200.

Martin pursued his advantage and soon afterward convinced Onstott that electric power could help him on his ranch, which was devoted to vineyard and nursery stock. A line from Marysville to the Onstott ranch was erected and a 5-horsepower motor installed. In addition to operating a raisin stemmer, a cider press, and a pump to lift water for domestic use, the motor drove two walking beams, each of which operated two plunger well pumps for irrigation. This is believed to be the earliest rural line extension and the first use of electricity for irrigation in Northern California. Operation commenced April 28, 1898.

Again in 1898 electric power was applied to irrigation, but the records do not disclose the exact date. Near Mayhews, along the 11,000-volt line that transmitted power from Folsom to Sacramento, Russ D. Stevens and A. B. Humphrey were neighboring orchardists. The power line crossing their properties suggested to Stevens that they might profitably substitute electricity in their pumping plants. He talked it over with Humphrey and then placed the proposal before H. P. Livermore of the Sacramento Electric Gas and Railway Company.

A letter was written to the General Electric Company, which promptly sent an engineer to the scene to investigate. Tapping an 11,000-volt line for power to operate a motor at lower voltage posed new transformer problems. The manufacturer finally agreed to supply three 50-kilowatt air-cooled transformers which would step the power down from 11,000 to 2,200 volts. Two motors, 100 horsepower and 50 horsepower, were installed to operate the pumps. The cumbersome motors, the larger one weighing three tons, were placed in a wooden tower with the transformer and crude switch gear.

For two years the electric pumping plant was operated successfully. Then one night the transformers became overheated and fire destroyed the wooden building. Stevens and Humphrey, enthusiastic over the economical operation and the efficiency of the electric installation, replaced the plant with improved equipment, housed in a brick building.

The farmers of the Sacramento Valley were slow to adopt electric power for irrigation pumping. Martin and his associates were absorbed in plant building and had not then begun promotion of distribution lines to customers. The northern valley also was laggard in its transition from grain and hay production to fruits and other more valuable crops that required irrigation.

Conditions were different in the San Joaquin Valley where parched lands needed only water to produce bountiful crops. A. G. Wishon completed the first plant of the Mt. Whitney Company in Tulare County June 30, 1899. His surveys had shown that under the floor of the southern portion of the valley was a vast subterranean reservoir, sometimes only 25 feet below the surface. He was convinced electric motors would handle the pumping job at a lower cost than any other motive power.

In the district surrounding the town of Lindsay he found some 25 orchardists and farmers operating their pumping plants with gasoline or steam engines that required constant attention.

Wishon talked electric power to them without favorable response. With a salesman's belief in mass psychology, he staged a demonstration of motor pumping at the Lindsay schoolhouse. The discussion lasted until one o'clock in the morning, but not one grower would commit himself to electric power. They balked at the cost of the new equipment and at Wishon's demand for a yearly rate based on the horsepower of the motor installed. The orchardists wished to pay for their power only when they used it.

The next day the manager of the Mt. Whitney Power Company decided to risk everything on a daring move. He went to San Francisco, talked a banker into giving the company a $25,000 loan, and invested the entire amount in motors and transformers. Then he went back to Lindsay and offered the growers a new deal. He would sell them the equipment under a contract which required no down payment, the principal to be paid in five annual installments at 6 per cent interest, and the power bill to be computed at a yearly rate of $50 per horsepower.

Sales resistance melted away. In two days Wishon sold all his motors. The first purchaser was Hugh W. Postlethwaite, member of a pioneer family in Lindsay, who signed a contract for power, June 26, 1899. The well pit where the motor was installed still is intact on a lot in a suburban subdivision of Lindsay. The use of electric power for pumping in the Tulare district spread rapidly, and when Wishon left the Mt. Whitney company in 1902 the efficiency of the motor had been fully demonstrated.

As manager of the San Joaquin Power Company and its successor, Wishon continued his promotion of electric pumping. The network of transmission lines spread over the southern San Joaquin Valley and dry farming gave way to irrigation and increased agricultural production. The San Joaquin company initiated a preferential treatment of agriculture by fixing electric rates and line extension policies that would induce the use of power for irrigation and other farm purposes and thus speed development of the rural areas.

(E. G. Stahl, manager of the P. G. and E. agricultural department and a veteran of 30 years of experience in California rural electrification, estimates that 85 per cent of the wealth and business in central valley towns and cities stems from agricultural production and income.)

The theory and practice were given official sanction after electric utility rates were placed under regulation by the State Railroad Commission, later to be renamed the Public Utilities Commission. In a rate case decision of 1922, Commissioner Chester Rowell enunciated the policy that public interest would best be served by development of the back country along with the cities and that, therefore, the basic industry of agriculture should be aided by the granting of a power rate less than the full cost of service.

The San Joaquin company's agricultural load continued to grow. Two years after the Bakersfield properties were acquired, 300 irrigation pumps in Kern County alone were being operated by electric motors. The program was broadened to include all the uses of electricity that come under the heading of rural electrification. This meant that all the benefits of electric service became available to the farmer as soon as feeder wires reached his land. He had light in his home and in his ranch buildings. Not only were his irrigation pumps operated by electric power; the old oaken bucket and the hand pump over the kitchen sink were quickly replaced by pressure systems that provided water for all domestic uses.

As rapidly as electric appliances and equipment were perfected by manufacturers, the California farmer adopted electric refrigeration, cooking, heating, and air conditioning in his home. For amusement he may enjoy radio and television, and may have his own motion-picture projector. He may live as luxuriously comfortable a life as any city dweller.

For farming purposes he may do much of his work with electric milkers, cream separators, poultry incubators and brooders, motor-driven feed choppers, dehydrators, hoists, sprayers, saws, and a long list of other mechanical aids. Electricity has become the No. 1 farm hand in California.

Pacific Gas and Electric Company, organized in 1905 by consolidation of the California Gas and Electric Corporation with the San Francisco Gas and Electric Company, was quick to recognize the mutual advantages of cooperation with agriculture.

Liberal terms to farm customers and promotion of agricultural development early became a fixed policy of the new utility company.

The University of California, in 1908, with the cooperation of the Southern Pacific Railroad Company, fitted out a seven-car agricultural-demonstration train with educational exhibits of new farm techniques and animal husbandry. The train toured the state repeatedly, bringing to every farming district a practical course of instruction in down-to-date agronomy. In 1912 Pacific Gas and Electric Company added to the train an exhibit of electrical aids to the farmer—demonstration of irrigation pumping and domestic water-pressure systems, models of motorized farm equipment, and a home economics section that included electric washing machines and vacuum cleaners. In that year the train made seven trips through the state and was visited by 90,000 persons.

The university's train was so successful in stimulating interest that Pacific Gas and Electric Company decided to continue the educational campaign on its own account. Working with the Northern Electric Railway Company, it fitted and equipped a passenger car as a traveling exhibit of rural electrification. Among the varied exhibits were an ice-making machine, a motor-driven sewing machine, and a cream separator. The car started its tour April 16, 1912, stopping at every station on the Sacramento Valley lines of the Northern Electric. Later it was placed on exhibit at the state fair in Sacramento where 40,000 farm-minded persons passed through its doors.

Motor-driven pumps for irrigation multiplied, but electrical pumping installations were not always operated with maximum efficiency or minimum cost. In 1911 R. H. Cates of Southern California Edison launched a pump testing service to improve the efficiency of motorized irrigation. P. G. and E. followed suit with an elaborate pumping survey in 1914. The farm area in the vicinity of Dixon, Solano County, where irrigation is general, was chosen for the investigation.

R. E. Fisher, who then was assistant to Stanley V. Walton, manager of the commercial department, was in charge of the survey. A crew of men equipped with measuring instruments tested 85 pumping plants in the Dixon area. They measured and recorded the amount of power used and the quantity of water lifted by the pumps. They reported the capacity and operating efficiency of each plant and the bills paid for electric service. Fisher, who later became vice-president in charge of sales, was ever afterward a leader in rural electrification.

The Dixon tests led to the establishment of the Free Pump Testing Service now maintained by P. G. and E. Two-man crews of expert pump technicians test pumps and motors periodically without charge to the farmers. Upon completion of a test a full report is made to the farmer on the efficiency of his plant. Sometimes the motor or the pump is not of the correct size to lift the needed amount of water from the well. Sometimes repairs or replacements are called for. Repeatedly the pump tests result in lower power bills to the farmer and a better job of irrigation. The number of tests has risen to approximately 7,000 per year. On the P. G. and E. system, which now extends from Kern and Santa Barbara Counties nearly to the northern boundaries of the state, 55,000 electric motor-driven pumps lift 65 per cent of all water used in irrigation of farm lands.

In the early twenties, when electrical appliances for farm use began to multiply, a Farm Power Advisory Service was established by Vice-President Fisher and the late sales manager, Hugh M. Crawford. Farm power advisers stand ready throughout the system to help the farmer. In 1951 25 farm power advisers made approximately 40,000 helpful calls on customers.

Through the years the Company has worked in close cooperation with the University of California's College of Agriculture, with the State Agricultural Department, and with farm organizations. Recognizing the importance of keeping youth on the farm, it aids 4-H clubs and the Future Farmers of America with annual prizes and motion pictures. In 1924 a national movement for rural electrification was responsible for creation of C.R.E.A. —California Committee on the Relation of Electricity to Agriculture. On the committee are represented electrical utilities, manufacturers of equipment, farm organizations, the College of Agriculture, and state regulatory bodies. The power companies of the state make annual grants to C.R.E.A. to support its experimental studies and investigations. Its program includes economic studies helpful to the farmer, such as a standard purchase agreement for deep-well pumps. Experimental projects have included use of electricity for soil heating, soil sterilization, and precooling of vegetables for shipment. Today, there are 200 uses of electricity available to farmers, but 80 per cent of all farm power used is for irrigation pumping.

Historically, the electric utility's operations have been linked in many places with those of the irrigation districts. In the late nineties, when John Martin built his little Yuba Powerhouse in Brown's Valley, he obtained a flow of water for his turbines by tapping the flume and ditch of the Brown's Valley Irrigation District which at that point ran at a 300-foot higher elevation than the powerhouse. It was a cheap source of water supply—no capital outlay for dams and conduit.

In return Martin signed a 45-year contract with the district to maintain the flume and, upon expiration of the contract, to turn it back to its owners in working condition. Only a year later, when Colgate Powerhouse was built upstream from the Yuba plant, a new and larger flume was erected above the old conduit. The Colgate flume was operated from 1899 until 1941, when it was replaced by a tunnel.

The original contract still was in force, however, and after negotiations were concluded, P. G. and E. paid for its cancellation with a check for $180,000 to save the cost of restoring the old flume. The district then was faced with a dilemma—irrigation law did not permit the investment of district funds in United States government bonds which were the securities the district directors wanted to buy. So State Senator W. P. Rich, then representing Yuba County at Sacramento, secured passage of an amendment to the law making Federal securities permissible for irrigation district investment. Brown's Valley Irrigation District, with a substantial bundle of United States bonds in its strongbox, still is in operation. The waters of the Yuba, having done their productive work in Colgate and other powerhouses, still flow through Brown's Valley ditches to produce rich crops on the 4,000 acres now under irrigation in the district.

Ten irrigation districts are now supplied with water, wholly or in part, from the P. G. and E. hydro system. Falling waters, releasing their vast energy to drive turbines and electric generators, flow on with undiminished bounties for the people of the valleys and towns.

The electric utility, on the other hand, also benefits from the works of the irrigation districts. Twelve of its hydroelectric plants are operated wholly or in part by the waters controlled by the irrigationists.

The close relation of electricity to agriculture has been fully established. In a little more than half a century electric power, starting at zero, has been brought to 98.5 per cent of all the farms in the territory now served by P. G. and E. In 1951 the Company's lines delivered electricity to 80,000 farms. Since August, 1945, when wartime restrictions were relaxed to permit the resumption of utility building, P. G. and E. has added more than 16,000 miles of rural lines to its system.

In all Northern California there are only two rural-electrification districts sponsored and subsidized by the Federal government; both are outside the P. G. and E. service area. One of these is in Modoc County. The other in Plumas and Lassen Counties is supplied with power by P. G. and E.

California farming today is big business. Irrigation, electric power, and advanced scientific and mechanical methods have brought abundance and extraordinary diversification of crops—257 separate farm products.

Deep well drilling has tapped hitherto unsuspected water tables as far as 2,500 feet under the desert floor. Huge pumps operated by electric motors irrigate land that runs to thousands of acres in a single ranch. Rotating cash crops—cotton, potatoes, barley, wheat, produced in king-size quantity, have made many a millionaire. Cadillacs, helicopters, private planes, and swimming pools on the farm no longer attract attention.

Land which without water would produce a crop worth an average of only $20 now rewards the grower with average yields as high as $280 per acre. Gross income from agriculture in California was $2,787,000,000 in 1951. The average individual farm income for the year was $20,000 compared to the national average of $7,000. In total farm income, Fresno, Tulare, and Kern Counties ranked first, third, and fifth of all the counties in the United States. And the statisticians will prove to the curious that the average cost of electric power used was only 3½ per cent of the total cost of crop production.

Twice in recent years the achievements of Pacific Gas and Electric Company in rural electrification have been recognized by the bestowal of national honors. The Thomas W. Martin Rural Electrification Award, which is administered by the Edison Electric Institute, went to the Company in 1939 "in recognition of its invaluable contribution to the rural life of the territory served by it through providing electric service for stimulating the improvement of the economic and cultural advantages of farm life."

In 1950 the Company won the Frank E. Watts Award which is conferred annually under the direction of the *Farm Journal*, a national publication, for the best program "to promote and sell the use of electrically operated farm equipment as a means of improving agricultural productive efficiency."

P. G. and E. may rightfully claim rural electrification as one of its greatest contributions to the economic advancement of the territory it serves. With only a slight tinge of exaggeration it may say: "Where the power poles stop, cultivation stops; where cultivation stops, civilization stops."

CHAPTER 21

Great Western Power

VOLCANIC upheavals of the earth in prehistoric times, Professor Alexander Agassiz of Harvard University, and Civil Engineer Julius M. Howells all played important parts in the events that led to the building of the extensive electric system of Great Western Power Company of California.

The vast lava flow of the ancient age wrought cataclysmic changes in the earth's surface through the northwestern portion of the American continent. In Northern California, fiery Lassen Peak rose from the mass to crown the mountain range that had been formed by the upheaval. Erosion and silting during succeeding centuries filled the chasms and left wide plateaus and basins cupped between the higher peaks and ridges.

One of these basins was Big Meadows in Plumas County through which runs the north fork of the Feather River. In the first 74 miles of its plunging course from the shoulder of Mt. Lassen, the Feather drops 4,350 feet.

Early in the 1880s, Professor Agassiz, pursuing his geological studies from his faculty chair in Cambridge, sent an exploration party into the Mt. Lassen region. The purpose was to prove or disprove a theory that the gold-rich ancient river channels that had been found in that section of the Sierra continued their course under the floor of the many basins and meadows formed by erosion centuries after the lava flow. Julius M. Howells, a cousin of author William Dean Howells, was a member of that party. Howells came upon Big Meadows which was then devoted to cattle raising on a considerable number of ranches. As he looked over the wide expanse of rolling land, Howells' engineering mind noted the ideal conditions of the location for a great storage reservoir.

What Howells saw was an expanse of some 50 square miles hemmed in by mountains with a drainage area of 500 square miles. From this basin the river dropped through a narrow gorge to lower levels. All that was needed was a dam across the canyon's head to convert Big Meadows into a great storage reservoir.

The years passed. Howells, with headquarters in Los Angeles, explored the mountains for hydroelectric sites. In the Sierra, east of Fresno, he located water rights and was a principal figure in the events which resulted in establishment of San Joaquin Light and Power Corporation.

In the 1890–1900 decade, the fever of hydroelectric development was sweeping California. Men everywhere were looking for sites where water could be dropped from higher elevations to drive wheels and turbines at streamside. Howells recalled his visit to Big Meadows in Plumas County and returned there early in 1901 to refresh his memory and to collect accurate topographical and stream flow data. His half brother, Captain S. H. Day, who knew the country, assisted him. Howells believed that in the Feather River, backed by ample water storage in Big Meadows, he had found one of the finest potential sources of hydroelectric power in all the state. One of its important advantages lay in the underground storage of water and in perennial springs created by the porous volcanic ash deposits that covered the land.

Returning to Los Angeles, the engineer consulted James D. Schuyler, an eminent hydraulic engineer, who arranged an interview for him with Edwin T. Earl, successful citrus fruit shipper, newspaper publisher, and capitalist. A shrewd and skillful businessman, Earl recognized the value of Howells' project. He sent for his brother, Guy C. Earl, a practicing attorney in Oakland. The Earls decided they had in their hands a rare opportunity for large-scale hydroelectric development. The first step was to secure options on the Big Meadows lands.

Arthur H. Breed, real-estate operator, then Oakland's city auditor, and state senator in later years, was called upon to make the trip to Plumas County. His was a highly diplomatic assignment. The hydroelectric plan of the Earls must be a closely guarded secret. Breed was questioned by the curious but managed to conceal the true purpose of his visit, explaining only that he expected to sell the land he optioned. He memorized the option agreement so that each deal would appear to be spontaneous. When he telegraphed to Guy Earl reporting options secured, his messages were in code.

Defying winter's snow, Breed traveled the length and breadth of Big Meadows late in 1901 and in the first months of 1902, obtaining options, paying for them from $10,000 in deposit certificates he carried. His aide was Augustus R. Bidwell of Greenville, member of the pioneer family which for many years had owned land in the Meadows. Bidwell was first to sign an option on his property, and although he accompanied Breed for many days, never once did he suspect that a huge storage reservoir was to replace the dairy and cattle ranches they were buying. When all the options had been recorded at Quincy, the Plumas County seat, the Earl brothers held in their hands the right to purchase 11,481 acres of Big Meadows land and 3,139 acres in adjoining Butt Valley. Later purchases increased the area controlled to 30,063 acres.

There was one more step to be taken before the Earls could proceed openly with their hydroelectric project. Notices of claims to water rights must be posted and recorded. Julius M. Howells went into the mountains in April, 1902. Accompanied by Bidwell, he journeyed in an old spring wagon from Greenville to Bunnell's, a mountain resort about 6 miles from the lower end of Big Meadows, and spent the night there. Early the next morning Bidwell called a friend in Prattville, a little settlement in Big Meadows, and learned from him that two strange men had left there, evidently bound for the river gorge below the Meadows. Howells immediately became suspicious. He recalled seeing on the train that brought him from San Francisco a man wearing the high-laced boots that in those days were standard costume for surveyors and engineers. He suspected competition for the water rights he was seeking.

Howells and Bidwell drove first to a spot in the Meadows that had been selected for construction of the projected dam.

Here they posted formal notice of appropriation of 100,000 inches of the waters of the north fork of the Feather River for "milling, mining, manufacturing, irrigation and domestic purposes and for the purpose of water power and the *generation of electric power.*"

Howells and Bidwell then traveled downstream in search of the two strangers. True to the scenario, they found them a little more than 2 miles below, nailing a notice of water appropriation on a tall tree that stood close to the stream.

The spot was in the rock-walled chasm through which the Feather River plunges as it leaves Big Meadows, about 1,000 feet below the site eventually chosen for construction of the present Lake Almanor Dam. The strangers' notice of water appropriation claimed the use of 50,000 inches of water "for the purpose of creating water power to be converted into electric power." Howells' suspicions were fully justified.

"You're too late," said Howells. "We have already posted our notice upstream from here." The law at that time recognized the rule of the gold-rush miners—"Prior in time, prior in right."

One of the strangers refused to accede and finished nailing the notice on the tree. Then the pair drove off. Knowing they were bound for the Plumas county seat at Quincy, 31 miles away, to record their claim, Bidwell followed. Howells went on to nearby Butt Valley to post another water claim there. The long drive of the rival water claimants ended at Quincy after nightfall, with Bidwell in the lead. He lost no time finding the county recorder and filed his papers at 8:25 P.M., April 8, 1902. The strangers followed at 9:15 P.M. According to the county records, Julius M. Howells had gained prior rights for Guy C. Earl's hydro project by a margin of 40 minutes.*

* * *

* The author has yielded here to the urge of accuracy. A more dramatic tale of the incident has become traditional over the years, one involving a wild chase in the night in sleighs over snow-drifted roads and the midnight awakening of the county recorder to score victory for Bidwell. The facts as stated here, though less exciting, relate what actually happened.

Beautiful man-made Lake Almanor has been enlarged over the years until it is now one of the largest hydroelectric storage reservoirs in the United States.

Julius M. Howells designed and helped build the massive dam that created Lake Almanor, site of which he had discovered [illegible] years earlier.

Subsequent events explained the mystery of the two strangers. Under strict orders of secrecy they were acting for the heirs and associates of G. P. Cornell of Greenville, Plumas County, who had worked out a plan of his own for development of the Feather River's hydroelectric resources.

G. P. Cornell, a pioneer, had come to Plumas County in his youth and for many years had been occupied with mining. In 1868 he had been one of the promoters of the Feather River and Beckwourth Pass railroad. The venture failed to materialize, but Cornell gained from it a thorough knowledge of the topography and hydrography of the Feather River Canyon. He was well informed on the generation of electricity by water power and had developed a bold and comprehensive project for utilizing the stored waters of the Feather's north fork for hydro purposes. The plan was nearly identical with the one contemplated by Julius Howells and the Earl brothers. It included a dam at the outlet of Big Meadows, conversion of an old mining tunnel at Big Bend to the uses of hydro, and the building of generating plants at sites in between.

Negotiations for financial support were in progress in Los Angeles when Cornell died suddenly in February, 1902. His son, Lloyd P. Cornell, a young graduate engineer, carried on. He interested H. F. Lange and Charles L. Morrill, San Francisco promoters, and through them obtained the backing of A. S. Macdonald, who then was promoting the new industrial city of Richmond on San Francisco Bay.

Lange was one of the participants in the race with Howells and Bidwell for priority in water appropriation. Being a city man, unfamiliar with the canyon, he was accompanied by N. B. Kellogg, a civil engineer, who served as guide. They carried a detailed map and a photograph of the tree on which their notice was to be posted.

Undeterred by their experience in filing their water appropriation claim, the Macdonald-Cornell interests continued with their project. The next day, April 9, 1902, Charles L. Morrill posted a notice of water appropriation at the intake of the old Big Bend tunnel, and later other claims were posted at intermediate points on the river. The project was incorporated by Macdonald and his associates, October 1, 1902, under the name Golden State Power Company. Until 1906, Golden State Power stood as an obstacle to full realization of the plan of Howells and the Earls.

Before the securing of lands and water rights was completed, the Earl brothers incorporated the Western Power Company, a California corporation, March 24, 1902. Engineer James D. Schuyler joined the Earls in organizing the new company and became a considerable stockholder. He made many trips to the Feather River and often served as consulting engineer.

Western Power Company was the first of the group of corporations which was to build a great power system to be known in the end as Great Western Power Company of California.

Sometime after the Western Power Company was formed and the land options had all been secured, E. T. Earl and his brother must have had a moment of doubt whether they should proceed with the enterprise. They asked Arthur H. Breed to approach John Martin and Eugene de Sabla with a suggestion that they purchase their lands and water rights and undertake the development as a part of the California Gas and Electric Corporation system.

Breed told of the incident in a letter to W. H. Spaulding, attorney member of the Earl group. "I knew John Martin quite intimately," he said, "but I had never met Eugene de Sabla. I was delegated to sound them out and if they wished to proceed further to give them the details. . . . John Martin was immediately interested and said he would advocate opening negotiations."

De Sabla disagreed. At an interview the following day he "threw cold water on the idea from the beginning." While admitting the plan had merit, he thought it would be impossible to finance a new project so large as the Feather River development. Breed was so incensed at what he called de Sabla's "cold-blooded attitude" that he withdrew his offer at once and declared the negotiations would not be renewed. When he heard the story, E. T. Earl promised there would be no further attempt to sell out.

With the site for a magnificent storage lake in its hands, the new company could not proceed until location for one or more powerhouses had been secured and a plan of development formulated. A survey of the Feather River led the engineers to Big Bend, 16 miles above Oroville and 65 miles downstream from Big Meadows. Here was a spot to delight the builder of hydroelectric powerhouses, with an essential part of the project already partly completed.

Big Bend was so named because of an oxbow in the stream's channel some 12 miles in length, with a neck of land only 3 miles wide separating the beginning and end of the bend. Big Bend had a long history of riches gained and fortunes lost. In the early days the stream bed had yielded plentiful gold to the placer miners. Below Big Bend at Cape Claim, $600,000 had been recovered in 40 days in 1865. The Union Cape placer paid $275,000 in one season, and Toland Bar gave up more than a million dollars in 1856 and 1857. Miners believed that if the stream flow could be diverted from the Big Bend channel, another great fortune could be recovered from its gravel.

Dr. Ray V. Pierce, Buffalo manufacturer of the widely advertised medicinal pills that bore his name, became interested in a scheme submitted to him in 1880 to drive a diversion tunnel through the neck of the Big Bend oxbow. With Major Frank P. McLaughlin and Colonel J. C. Logan, he organized the Big Bend Tunnel and Mining Company and the Eocene Placer Mining Company, the first to drive the tunnel and the second to operate the mining venture.

The tunnel was bored, found to be too small, and was then enlarged to 16 feet by 12 feet, 12,000 feet long. It was completed in 1887 at a cost of $750,000. The Sprague Electric Company installed a water-powered electric generating plant to operate pumps and hoists for mining.

Like many another post-gold-rush mining venture, Dr. Pierce's project failed. The elaborately equipped plant was placed in operation, but the expected gold was not found in paying quantity.

Soon after the formation of the Western Power Company, Dr. Pierce ordered Major McLaughlin, his Pacific Coast agent, to incorporate the Eureka Power Company. This was done July 3, 1902, and word spread that the new company would use the Big Bend tunnel to supply water for a large hydroelectric plant. The result, perhaps, was precisely what Dr. Pierce anticipated; E. T. Earl and his brother saw that they would have to acquire the Big Bend properties. It would be folly to go on with the water-storage project at Big Meadows while an alien power plant on the lower river stood ready to reap the benefit.

At about this time, promoters Frank L. Brown and Harley P. Wilson of San Francisco were called in to assist the Earls in launching their project. Brown and Wilson arranged for purchase of the Eureka Power Company's holdings at Big Bend, and an option was given to Western Power Company.

Cornell's Golden State Power Company still was to be reckoned with. Unknown to the Earls, the Golden State group had filed claim to the waters of the Feather at the intake of the Big Bend tunnel and had acquired from the Central Pacific Railroad some 3,000 acres of land along the river above the Bend.

The time had come to find the millions that would be needed to build a powerhouse at Big Bend, a dam at Big Meadows, and a transmission line to carry electric power to the San Francisco Bay cities. The year 1903 passed without any progress; that was the time of the "rich man's panic" on Wall Street and capital was still nursing its burned fingers. In 1904 Brown was commissioned to arrange for the sale of $5,000,000 in Western Power Company bonds, but he reported that Eastern investors were reluctant to buy California bonds. He and Wilson did succeed, however, in interesting Edwin Hawley of New York, who through his connection with the Western Pacific Railroad knew something of the wealth of water power hidden in the Feather River Canyon. Hawley was joined by a group of New York and Boston financiers who formed a syndicate, first, to investigate and then to invest if the outlook was promising.

They were a distinguished group: Colonel Frank H. Ray, vice-president and organizer of the American Tobacco Company; A. C. Bedford, who rose from a position as clerk in a wholesale dry goods firm to president of Standard Oil of New Jersey in 1916; James H. Wallace, president of Central Trust Company of New York; Phillip Stockton, a young industrial engineer of Boston who, after his graduation from Harvard and Massachusetts Institute of Technology, became president of the Old Colony Trust Company when he was thirty-six and director of a dozen or more banks and utility companies.

These men were formally known as syndicate managers in the transactions that resulted in formation of Great Western Power Company. They were joined by other investors, including multimillionaire Clarence Mackay, son of John W. Mackay who made his fortune from the Comstock Mines in Virginia City, Nev. Clarence Mackay was then in the first years of a career which brought him fame as head of the Postal Telegraph Company and associated cable companies. Another prominent syndicate man was H. J. Pratt, one of the Eastern Standard Oil group and member of a family long identified with John D. Rockefeller and oil development.

Few electrical projects have been given the exhaustive examination that was devoted to the Earls' Feather River enterprise. The Eastern engineering firm of Viele, Cooper and Blackwell was engaged to make a field survey of the entire undertaking. Their report covered every element of a well-rounded hydroelectric development. John R. Freeman and Emil Kuichling, eminent hydraulic engineers, made a study of water storage and supply. Engineers Sargent and Lundy reported on possible competition from steam-operated electric plants. Dr. Thomas Addison of General Electric Company submitted a survey of available power markets. The work required about 18 months to complete.

Calling attention to the favorable volcanic character of the terrain and the 4,000-foot drop in elevation between Big Meadows and Big Bend, the engineers concluded: "No other water power in California can be so economically developed." They recommended that a $4,000,000 generating plant be built at Big Bend and outlined plans for other powerhouses to be built at sites between the Bend and the storage reservoir which was to be constructed later.

Even before the engineers' final report was submitted, the syndicate managers, confident of their position, had signed an agreement with Brown to organize a company which would purchase control of the Earls' Western Power Company and its valuable rights and properties. While all this was going on, the promoters of the Golden State Power Company, seeing that the Earl project would be financed, gave up their contest in 1906 and sold their holdings to Western Power Company. Lloyd P. Cornell, son of the pioneer originator of the project, eventually joined the engineering staff of the Great Western Power Company and, subsequently, the P. G. and E. He retired January 1, 1947.

The fire and earthquake of April 18, 1906, nearly wrecked the entire Feather River project. On the evening of April 17, Guy C. Earl and W. H. Spaulding, who had assisted in charting the legal path of the enterprise, met in Earl's office for a conference. At last, after four years of effort, the way seemed to be clear.

The next morning they awakened to view the ruins of San Francisco and the possible collapse of all their plans. When the Eastern financiers read the news of the disaster, they decided there was no use to go on if the metropolis of Northern California had been destroyed. They telegraphed Earl to call off all negotiations. They were not prepared to risk more of their money on so perilous a venture. They were through.

But Guy Earl would not admit defeat. With Spaulding's help he composed a fervent reply, written in long hand because there were no stenographers available. The Feather River project had not lost a dollar because of the San Francisco earthquake. In fact, it was in a better position because the city's electric facilities had been wrecked. San Francisco would be rebuilt. The prospects for success of the hydroelectric development were better, not worse, than before the disaster.

His appeal, written with the sincerity of desperation, had immediate effect. The Eastern financiers were reassured and wired back they would not withdraw.

There followed a welter of agreements, contracts, incorporations, and stock and bond issues, typical of the financial methods of the 1900–1910 decade. Out of the seeming confusion emerged the Western Power Company of New Jersey, a holding company incorporated August 23, 1906, in which the syndicate held the controlling stock interest. H. P. Wilson, who had shared with Brown in promotion of the plan, became a director and secretary of the New Jersey company. Under California laws, the Great Western Power Company was incorporated September 18, 1906. All but directors' shares were held by the New Jersey holding company.

In the California company was vested ownership of the rights, contracts, and properties acquired by E. T. and Guy C. Earl and their associates. Great Western was capitalized for $25,000,000 and a bond issue in that amount was authorized. The New York syndicate subscribed for $6,967,000 of the company's bonds.

The Earls and their associates received $1,500,000 in stock of the New Jersey Western Power Company and $1,000,000 in Great Western Power bonds. Brown and Wilson, who had carried the burden of promotion, received in commission for their work a total of $473,000 in stocks and bonds of the New Jersey and California companies.

After the organization of the Great Western company, Edwin Hawley was elected president and Guy C. Earl, vice-president. Bedford and Ray were named to the executive committee of the board of directors. Within a few months the number of directors was increased from nine to eleven and E. S. Pillsbury, San Francisco attorney, J. Downey Harvey, San Francisco capitalist, Henry E. Huntington, railway builder of Los Angeles, and William G. Henshaw of Oakland were elected directors. E. T. Earl, Frank L. Brown, and H. P. Wilson also were made directors and Wilson was appointed secretary of the company.

With funds in its treasury the company immediately began construction of Big Bend, its first power plant. The site was on the steep south bank of the Feather opposite the present Western Pacific railroad station, Las Plumas. (The Spanish name of the Feather River was El Rio de las Plumas.)

Camps were established to accommodate a thousand workmen. The Western Pacific Railroad, then under construction, had not yet reached the powerhouse site and all the early hauling was over the steep mountain roads by lumbering freight wagons. Toward the end of the construction period, however, the rails had been laid to Las Plumas station and the problems of the builders were simplified. The heavy machinery, steel, and other materials then were brought in by rail to the station across the river from the powerhouse. Two aerial cable tramways were erected to span the 1,200-foot chasm between the river banks, and over them enormous tonnages were moved across the river. One of these cable crossings still is in operation, offering a dizzying and thrilling ride to uninitiated visitors.

For about two years the big work continued. Dr. Pierce's old tunnel was enlarged and extended to provide a fall of 465 feet. A timber diversion dam was constructed. It was replaced in 1910 by a larger concrete dam designed by Engineer John R. Freeman.

The generating station is a massive, imposing structure of steel and concrete rising from foundations set deep in the bedrock of the precipitous riverbank. In continuous operation for nearly half a century, it still produces electric power for beneficial use in the distant cities of Northern California.

The first 10,000-kilowatt generating unit of Big Bend Powerhouse was placed in operation December 23, 1908. Five additional units were placed in succeeding years to bring the total capacity to 70,000 kilowatts, its present rating. The *Electrical World* of the period said: "The project is on a grander scale than any of the transmission plants on the Pacific Coast." At the time, the plant was the largest hydro operation west of the Mississippi.

W. G. B. Euler, now executive vice-president of P. G. and E., started his career in utility company operation at Big Bend Powerhouse. Graduated from the University of California in 1905, Euler joined the General Electric Company's staff and gained a thorough experience in electrical construction and installation in Northern and Southern California. He came to Great Western Power Company in 1910 as division superintendent in charge of powerhouse operation and transmission, and then as general superintendent. When he joined the P. G.

and E. staff, successive promotions brought him to the post of vice-president and general manager of P. G. and E. in 1947 and to his present position three years later.

At one time during construction of Big Bend, the builders gave thanks for their Eastern financial sponsorship. At the height of the money panic of 1907, when cash went into hiding and clearinghouse certificates were issued in San Francisco to be used in place of currency, the work went on without interruption. Many other California building projects were closed down temporarily for lack of cash, but Great Western payrolls were met by gold. Coin was necessary because in Oroville, where the Big Bend men spent their days off and their money, clearinghouse certificates were not accepted. To provide the weekly payroll cash, Wilson, then in New York, arranged with the United States Subtreasury there to telegraph a credit payable in gold at the San Francisco Subtreasury. This was not done without much labor on Wilson's part. The Subtreasury refused to order coin delivered in San Francisco unless coin in equal amount was deposited in New York. Currency was not acceptable. To satisfy this requirement, Wilson would make nightly rounds of theaters, hotels, and other places where he was known and collect gold coins sufficient for deposit in the New York Subtreasury to meet the California payroll. And regularly during the crisis Charles E. Mynard, the first Great Western auditor and assistant treasurer, would draw the coin in San Francisco and, with a guard, transport it to the Big Bend works.

The power output of the plant was transmitted on a steel tower line to Brighton Substation at Sacramento and thence to Oakland. Power was transmitted at first at 60,000 volts, and November 1, 1909, the pressure was raised to 100,000 volts, another advance in the long struggle of electrical engineers toward the high tension goal of 220,000 volts.

Hydroelectric power from Big Bend was flowing into Oakland. The next step in Great Western's ambitious plans was to provide steam-operated stand-by generating facilities to ensure continuous delivery. For this purpose, the California Electric Generating Company was incorporated November 23,

1908. A site was secured on the Oakland estuary and a plant erected there with a generating capacity of 10,500 kilowatts.

Financing of the steam plant project was accomplished by a complicated series of corporate transactions, all backed by the New Jersey holding company. Pacific Securities Company, a new organization, built the powerhouse and sold it to the California Electric Generating Company, which in turn leased it to the Great Western Power Company. The Oakland steam plant was placed in operation November 27, 1909.

When the Great Western Power Company entered Oakland it was compelled to sell its Big Bend electric output to the recently organized Pacific Gas and Electric Company. The Earls' utility had no distribution system, no franchises, and no access to the San Francisco power market, but it was going to have these facilities. Great Western had only begun to fight.

Seven years had passed since Julius M. Howells had told E. T. Earl of his vision of a great hydroelectric system on the Feather River. His plan for a storage reservoir at Big Meadows had not yet materialized, but the power project at last was under way. Great Western Power was to become a hard-hitting rival to P. G. and E., which was then struggling to get on its corporate feet. For a score of years the courses of the two utilities ran on parallel but hotly competing lines.

PART THREE

[1905-1952]

Birth of a greater system—P. G. and E. is incorporated—N. W. Halsey—Frank G. Drum—Disaster of 1906—Financial crisis—Restoration—de Sabla and Martin fade away—A. F. Hockenbeamer—Customer ownership—W. E. Creed—Reorganization—Expansion—Interconnection—Great Western Power Company competition—James B. Black—Major consolidations.

CHAPTER 22

P. G. and E.

THE YEAR 1904 was a fateful one in the history of Northern California's gas and electric utilities. It was the year of the critical decision which resulted in creation of Pacific Gas and Electric Company.

In the train of that decision came unification of existing systems, centralized utility management and operation, and ultimate integration of facilities to serve the people of an area 89,000 square miles in extent. It was to be an era in which advanced concepts of utility financing and operation, of customer and stockholder relations, and of rate regulation were gradually to take form and gain general acceptance.

In P. G. and E. was to be found the crystallization of the dreams and hopes of the pioneers, from Peter Donahue in 1852 to George H. Roe in 1879 and de Sabla and Martin in 1895. They had dared to enter unexplored fields of gas and electric utility service primarily, of course, because they believed there was opportunity there for profitable business. But they also had a vision of bigger cities, bigger industries, and bigger agricultural production in Northern California.

In 1904 California Gas and Electric Corporation stood at the crossroads. De Sabla and Martin had built a loosely knit utility organization which was serving gas and electricity, either or both, to Oakland, Sacramento, Fresno, Stockton, and a number of towns north of San Francisco Bay. They were operating hydroelectric plants in Sacramento, Yuba, Nevada, and Butte Counties. They had recently acquired the Standard Electric Company which was delivering power from Electra plant on the Mokelumne to Stockton, Oakland, San Jose, and San Francisco.

The framework of centralized management and operating control had been raised. But there were weak points in the structure. The California Gas and Electric Corporation had no retail outlet for power in San Francisco, the greatest market in the north, and its system lacked steam-operated power sources large enough to assure a firm, uninterrupted supply of electricity in the event hydro sources failed. There was needed also a broader base for the additional financing that would be required for the expansion of producing and distribution facilities. Merger with the San Francisco Gas and Electric Company would provide the metropolitan market and the base for financing—one that would qualify the company's stocks and bonds for listing on the New York Stock Exchange and the opening of the Eastern securities market to the Western enterprise.

San Francisco Gas and Electric Company, product of the welding of Peter Donahue's gas company and George H. Roe's electric company, also had its weak spots. It controlled the gas field, but its electric system, composed entirely of steam-operated generating plants costly to operate, could not compete with hydroelectric power produced at lower cost. When California Gas and Electric Corporation contracted with United Railroads to supply power from its Standard lines to operate the San Francisco streetcar system, the old San Francisco Gas and Electric Company began to realize the vulnerability of its position.

In the offing appeared also the aggressive Great Western Power Company, threatening both of the older utilities with its powerful New York financial backing and its known plan to invade the San Francisco field.

De Sabla, Martin, and Drum had discussed this situation many times. De Sabla, then only thirty-nine years old, wanted to retire from the presidency of California Gas and Electric Corporation. In 10 years he had gone far. He had amassed a fortune, and he wanted to relinquish responsibility.

Martin, shrewd and far-sighted, realized that markets for power must be developed and that a single efficient organization could distribute electricity at lower cost than the little community systems which served so many of the northern towns. He and de Sabla had turned to Frank G. Drum as the man who could help them.

De Sabla and Drum opened conversations with W. B. Bourn, president of the San Francisco Gas and Electric Company, and obtained informal approval of a proposal that the San Francisco company be purchased by California Gas and Electric Corporation. In February, 1905, Drum, Martin, de Sabla, and Garret W. McEnerney, their legal counselor, went to New York to consult the investment brokerage house of N. W. Halsey & Company. They were accompanied by Cyrus Peirce, Halsey's San Francisco manager.

N. W. Halsey, whose firm then had the backing of James Stillman, president of the National City Bank, was well informed on the California utilities situation. He had only recently underwritten a part of the $3,000,000 bond issue of the Valley Counties Power Company, a Martin-de Sabla subsidiary which had built De Sabla Powerhouse.

The prolonged New York negotiations ended with Halsey's agreement to take charge of the proposed consolidation, subject to an auditing and engineering examination of the properties involved. A staff of Halsey auditors and engineers worked through the summer of 1905 before the plan was formulated. Representing Halsey was his attorney F. W. M. Cutcheon, who drew the legal specifications and managed to introduce many of the structural complexities that were common in corporate promotions of the day. The San Franciscans at times were inclined to rebel at his red tape.

After stock options had been secured and preliminary agreement reached, Pacific Gas and Electric Company was incorporated October 10, 1905, with capital of $20,000,000 in common stock and $10,000,000 in 6 per cent cumulative preferred. Issues of $10,000,000 in 5 per cent collateral trust bonds and $4,500,000 in 6 per cent debentures were authorized.

In accordance with the plan, the 10 millions of preferred stock were used to purchase the outstanding stock of California Gas and Electric Corporation by an equal exchange, share for share. The 10 millions of bonds of the new company, and cash derived from sale of the debentures, went for purchase of the

$15,848,433.33 outstanding stock of San Francisco Gas and Electric Company. The old San Francisco company retained its corporate identity, and its purchased stock was deposited with the Union Trust Company as security for the new bond issue. The basis of payment for the San Francisco Gas and Electric stock was $65 per share in P. G. and E. bonds and $25 per share in cash.

And then, when the ink was barely dry on the papers of P. G. and E.'s incorporation, came Mr. Cutcheon's master device—the Pacific Gas and Electric Investment Company, incorporated under the laws of Nevada, November 18, 1905. The company was a Halsey creation, headed by Cyrus Peirce as president, its first officers and directors all Halsey men—George K. Weeks, George W. Lewis, Alexander N. Kemp, and attorney Carl Taylor. The Halsey men all resigned within a month and were replaced by directors and officers chosen from the office of Garret McEnerney, attorney for P. G. and E.

The Investment company's announced purpose was "to acquire by purchase, subscription or otherwise, . . . any shares of capital stock, bonds, mortgages, etc., created by other corporations." Its authorized capital was $20,000,000 divided into 200,000 shares, of which two shares each were subscribed by the five directors.

There followed a complex series of agreements. N. W. Halsey & Company assigned to the Investment company its options on the stock of the California Gas and Electric Corporation and San Francisco Gas and Electric Company and agreed to advance not more than $4,500,000 (secured by note) to supply funds for cash payments on the San Francisco Gas and Electric stock.

In return for the assignment of rights, the advance of funds, and his expensive year of investigation, Halsey received from P. G. and E. Investment Company all but 10 shares of its capital stock, 199,990 shares.

The Investment company then made a similar agreement with the P. G. and E. Company. Under almost exactly the same terms, the rights and claims (and obligations) it received from Halsey were transferred to the new company in exchange for 199,985 shares of P. G. and E. common stock. The net result of the chain

Headquarters of the San Francisco Gas and Electric Company, at 450 Post Street, was destroyed by the earthquake and fire of 1906.

The earth heaved and rocked, shattering buildings and disrupting water and gas mains.

of transactions was that N. W. Halsey & Company received, by control of the Investment company, all but 15 shares of the common stock of P. G. and E., potentially worth 20 millions of dollars. The value of the stocks, rights, and properties of the two old companies acquired, it was declared, "is and will be far in excess" of the total paid by the new corporation. How accurate was that statement is attested by the market course of P. G. and E. common which, as the system developed, attained a firm position which never has been relinquished.

Although not in the official record, it was understood that Halsey shared his P. G. and E. common stock, held by his wholly owned P. G. and E. Investment Company, with de Sabla, Martin, and Drum, one-fifth to each and the remaining fifth to the Company's treasury, in return for their work in creating property values deemed greater than the new company had paid. It was the custom of the day for the promoters of great corporate projects to receive a speculative bonus.

Pacific Gas and Electric Company on January 2, 1906, assumed control of California Gas and Electric Corporation and San Francisco Gas and Electric Company, each of which retained its corporate identity. From its temporary offices at 326 California Street, P. G. and E. moved to the three upper floors of the Shreve Building at Post Street and Grant Avenue. At the same time the offices of California Gas and Electric Corporation were moved from the Rialto Building to the Shreve Building. The office of the San Francisco Company remained at 450 Post Street.

Thus when P. G. and E. started in business January 2, 1906, it found itself without working capital and without funds for expansion. Its authorized securities all were committed to meet the purchase requirements of the consolidation plan. Halsey had even advanced the $3,500 required to pay the expenses of incorporation. A program of financing still was to be formulated.

One effect of the consolidation was to lodge control of the new corporation entirely in the hands of stockholders of the de Sabla-Martin-Drum group at the head of the California Gas and Electric Corporation and members of the Halsey company who had received P. G. and E. stock for their interests. The stockholders of San Francisco Gas and Electric Corporation received cash and bonds for their shares and thus were left without voice in management of P. G. and E. That they fared well financially when they accepted $90 per share for their stock was indicated by the fact that competition had driven the San Francisco company's shares to low points of $55–$60 during the period between 1903 and 1905. Later testimony proved that the true value of the stock was nearer its par of $100 than the $90 paid when consolidation was effected.

John A. Britton, general manager of California Gas and Electric Corporation, succeeded W. B. Bourn as president of San Francisco Gas and Electric Company, and Samuel L. Napthaly was appointed superintendent of the San Francisco system.

Organization of P. G. and E. was completed by election of N. W. Halsey as chairman of the board; John A. Britton, president; Frank G. Drum, first vice-president; C. W. Conlisk, secretary; and Cyrus Peirce, treasurer. The Halsey influence was strong in the beginning. His attorneys, Cutcheon and Carl Taylor, were members of the executive committee.

From January to April, 1906, engineers and management were busily engaged in examining the physical properties, formulating plans for coordinating and unifying the two gas and electric systems, and completing their organization.

At the end of the first quarter the directors, on March 29, declared a dividend of $1.50 per share on the new 6 per cent preferred stock. It was to be the only such dividend paid until August 1, 1909.

Early in April of that tragic year, John A. Britton, needing a vacation after months of exhausting work, sailed for Japan on extended leave of absence. He was aboard ship midway between Honolulu and Yokohama on April 18, the day of the San Francisco earthquake. John Martin served as acting president during his absence.

The evening of April 17, 1906, was an eventful one in the annals of San Francisco. Caruso was singing at the old Grand Opera House on Mission Street between Third and Fourth. The house was packed with the usual opera crowd—gorgeous evening gowns and furs, white ties and tails in the pit and the stage boxes; a cosmopolitan throng of music lovers in balcony and gallery. The opera was *Carmen* with Olive Fremstad as the tempestuous cigarette girl and the great Italian tenor as José.

In a stage box sat Eugene de Sabla with members of his family. As he waited for the first strains of the overture to quiet the buzzing, rustling, expectant audience, the utility promoter mused. He had spent the afternoon at his suburban home in San Mateo which was being remodeled under the direction of architect Willis Polk. His thoughts strayed to P. G. and E. and his own plans for retirement.

Late that night the de Sablas retired in their city home at 1916 Octavia Street. Elsewhere at their homes Frank G. Drum, John Martin, Garret McEnerney, and others of the P. G. and E. group slept with no inkling of what the morrow would bring. In only a few hours their rest and the course of all their lives were to be broken by the rumbling, jolting, and twisting of a tortured earth, the crash of falling buildings, the screams of a frightened populace—the earthquake of April 18, 1906.

CHAPTER 23

Disaster Strikes

SAN FRANCISCO slept through the predawn hours of April 18, 1906. Only the late stayers and the early risers were abroad. An occasional streetcar brought the first of the workers to their downtown posts. Scavenger wagons rumbled through the canyons of the business district. Down deserted Market Street, wagons piled high with vegetables from outlying truck farms plodded toward the produce market near the water front. The endless low undertone of ironshod wheels and horses' hoofs on cobbled streets was becoming audible. Another day was beginning in the city by the Golden Gate.

Suddenly in the half-light that preceded the sun, the furies descended upon the slumbering people. The time, according to the seismograph record, was 5 hours, 12 minutes, 6 seconds, A.M.

San Franciscans were not unused to earthquakes. There had been temblors before, some destructive. But this was different. The earth heaved and rocked in a first titanic shock that shattered buildings, disrupted water and gas mains, and opened wide gashes in the ground. In the first hour a dozen more jolts continued the destruction. Before the day was done, 31 shocks were recorded. This was disaster.

Perhaps nowhere was there more immediate reaction than among the gas and electric operating men. They knew the danger of broken gas mains and the imminence of fire. They realized that death and flame might be carried by severed high-voltage electric wires and disjointed wiring in homes. Operators on duty, without waiting for orders, closed the valves of the gas storage holders that survived the shocks and pulled switches on electric feeder circuits. But there remained in the streets of the city miles of pipe packed with explosive, inflammable gas.

Within minutes after the first crashing wrench, fire added to the terror of the morning. Sixteen alarms were recorded in quick succession. Overturned kerosene lamps, lighted gas and gasoline stoves, burning gas jets, and ruptured furnaces and chimneys started most of the early fires. An early proclamation by Mayor E. E. Schmitz and orders of General Frederick Funston forbade the lighting of fires of any kind. From then on, family meals were prepared out of doors on rusty stoves or over open grates. Candles supplied light at night and all homes were dark at eight o'clock.

There are contradictory reports as to the principal cause of the fires that swept the city, but the weight of evidence indicates that prompt action of gas and electric operators at least delayed or reduced the scope of the holocaust. When the last fire was extinguished April 22, the fifth day, 4 square miles of the city's business and residential districts east of Van Ness Avenue and north and south of Market Street to the Bay Shore had been destroyed by earthquake and fire. Extensive damage had been suffered in the remainder of the city.

Facilities of the San Francisco Gas and Electric Company were hard hit. All but two gas and two electric plants, located far from the center of the city, were destroyed or disabled. The central offices of the company at 450 Post Street and of P. G. and E. and California Gas and Electric Corporation in the Shreve Building were damaged by the quake and then swept by fire.

The distribution systems—many miles of gas mains and other miles of overhead and underground electric wires—were dismembered. Pipes and conduits were broken and thrown out of line; poles were down and wires were in a tangled mess. Scores of concrete manhole-vaults were smashed by the moving earth or crushed by gas explosions.

The North Beach gas plant was damaged and made useless, although its storage holders withstood the shocks. The Pacific Gas Improvement gasworks and the Equitable plant were lost, but one of the three Pacific Gas Improvement storage holders survived the earthquake. Professor T. S. C. Lowe's San Francisco Coke and Gas Company's works on Beach Street between Powell and Mason which then was producing oil gas was so little damaged that only small repairs were needed to place it in operating condition.

The Jessie Street plant of the old Edison Electric Light Company, which had been partly destroyed by fire in February, was not seriously hurt by the quake, but falling walls from neighboring buildings and tons of brick and concrete from its collapsed smokestack placed it out of commission. Although surrounded by burning buildings, it was almost untouched by fire.

Every electric substation and small generating plant in the downtown area was destroyed with the exception of the new plant of the Mutual Electric Light Company at Spear and Folsom Streets and one substation near Third and Townsend Street. All generating stations were shut down.

Two gas and two electric plants escaped destruction. In the Potrero, south of the fire zone, the electric plant and the gasworks built by the Spreckels Independent companies remained in good operating condition. Farther south in Visitacion Valley, John Martin's new gas plant and gas engine-operated powerhouse were only slightly damaged.

Outside San Francisco, the generating and transmission facilities of the newly organized P. G. and E. escaped with comparatively small harm. Along the path of the quake from Santa Rosa to San Jose and southward there was wreckage of gas and electric facilities but none that could not be repaired quickly. In San Jose, Superintendent R. H. Hargreaves, veteran P. G. and E. man now retired, lived at the gas plant and thus was able to close all valves only a few minutes after the first shock. The plant was disabled but service was restored within a week.

Even before the extent of the disaster was realized, emergency crews were organized at supply and equipment yards. As rapidly as they could care for the safety of their families, the linemen, pole setters, pipe fitters, electricians, meter men and their helpers reported for duty. Many of them were on the job the first day while the earth still was shaking. As the widespread damage to gas and electric lines became apparent, other crews of workers were brought in from towns outside San Francisco. The first repair job was at Van Ness Avenue and Vallejo Street where a 24-inch arterial gas main had been broken.

The work of restoration went on with numberless difficulties. Tools and materials were salvaged where possible. New equipment was scarce. Little or no transportation was available. Men carried heavy burdens of repair materials over wreckage-filled streets. Broken gas pipes were filled with water from the ruptured city system. The work was made doubly laborious by the fact that maps and records of the tangled street main system had been burned or were locked in inaccessible vaults.

On the fifth day, when the last fire had been extinguished, the utility company and city authorities decided on a program to restore gas service to the unburned section of the city. Every main crossing the perimeter of the burned district was plugged. Those extending into the unburned area were connected with a 30-inch feeder main on Franklin Street supplied by the Potrero gasworks.

Nine days after the fire, 400 miles of street mains had been repaired and purged, ready for service. Before gas was turned into the feeder lines, however, gangs of meter men, pipe fitters, and plumbers visited every house and turned off the stopcock at the meter.

Gas was turned into the main at the Potrero May 7, but before service could be restored further safety precautions were taken. The earthquake had left house gas pipes twisted and broken, and chandeliers and wall brackets shaken loose. The danger of fires and accidents, perhaps another conflagration, could not be ignored. Under direction from the official Committee of Light and Power, engineer E. C. Jones carried out a second program of inspection. Every house again was visited by a company gas fitter and a meter clerk. Fixtures and pipes were tested for leaks and open stopcocks. Where damage was revealed, the meter was disconnected, the service pipe plugged, and the householder notified that he must have all defective piping repaired before service could be given. With almost military precision the enormous task of inspection was completed in 14 days.

The first gas lighted in San Francisco was at the Company's temporary headquarters at O'Farrell and Franklin Streets, May 10, 1906. The first consumers connected were the United States Mint and the Post Office, May 11. On May 12, after 24 nights of dangerous and depressing darkness, the streets of the unburned western portion of the city became bright with light from 2,193 gas lamps.

The electric distributing system of the city had also been shattered. L. E. Reynolds and his assistant, A. J. Theis, took charge of restoration plans. While the fires were burning, little could be done except to organize crews and salvage materials. Copper wire worth $60,000 eventually was recovered from the debris that littered the streets. On the morning of April 18, when the fire neared the supply storehouse of the electrical department, the men loaded line tools, tape, solder, and other materials into an automobile and a horse-drawn buggy and moved them to safety.

Connection was reestablished between the Potrero generating plant and a city substation that had been saved from burning. A temporary line restored connections with a substation on Kansas Street where power from the mountain hydro plant was received.

A telephone line was strung between stations to provide communication for operating control. A power circuit was turned over to the Army to serve as a telegraph connection between the Presidio and a military command post at Eleventh Street and Bryant. An unnamed army sergeant had reason to remember that line. Many days later, not knowing that this circuit had been returned to the electric company for power use, he attempted to reconnect his instruments to wires then charged with current at 2,400 volts. The resultant "blowout" left a severely shocked sergeant thanking the fates that he had escaped with his life.

The first earthquake shock occurred on Wednesday; by Saturday night 100 street arc lights were connected in the unburned section, 200 more on Sunday. By Monday night some homes in the Western Addition were lighted with electricity. Block by block the wiring of standing homes was inspected by crews representing the municipal department of electricity, the utility company, and the Army, and current was turned on wherever service was safe. Three emergency substations were installed in galvanized iron structures erected in the streets at Seventeenth and Folsom Streets; Arguello Boulevard and Geary; and on Bush Street between Polk and Larkin. By the first week in May electric service was restored in nearly all parts of the unburned section.

Work went on for months, and in some respects it was years before all the damage had been repaired. When a record of electric distribution line losses was compiled, it was found that they included 385 miles of wire, 1,896 poles, more than 8,000 meters, 15,000 insulators, and other line equipment that cost altogether approximately $430,000. This was only one part of the total loss.

When reconstruction was started in the downtown section, the electrical engineers found baffling obstacles. Through much of the 4 square miles of devastated area, Edison underground conduit cables had carried electric power. The lines were broken. Sometimes both ends of a severed cable could not be found. Sometimes it was necessary to run the lines outside the manhole and along the sidewalk to tie in again at the next block crossing. Excavation was impeded by piles of rubble.

Street surfaces that had settled 2 and 3 feet gave more trouble. Conduit trenches were out of line and had to be relocated to agree with new street grades.

In the first reconstruction through the burned district the electrical workers used emergency methods. In some blocks as many as six gas mains installed by the old competing companies ran side by side with the broken electric conduits. Frequently the new electric cables were carried through an abandoned gas pipe to save the time required to lay new conduits.

On lower Market Street where the filled ground had sunk below grade, the obstacles multiplied. On some blocks crews of the water system, the telephone company, the telegraph companies, the United Railroads, and the gas and electric companies were all attempting to relocate their lines at the same time and at new grade levels.

A few months after the fire, George C. Holberton, electrical engineer who had been stationed in Oakland, was transferred to San Francisco and given the job of completing restoration of the distribution system. A. J. Theis was made his assistant. One wonders that they ever succeeded in bringing order out of chaos. But they did.

* * *

The morning of the earthquake was a period of uncertainty and fear for everyone. None could guess how far the disaster extended or how extensive the losses might be. Before the fires had reached the center of the financial and business districts, officials of Pacific Gas and Electric Company began making their way downtown, some walking and some taking any conveyance they could find. D. H. Foote, Eugene de Sabla, C. W. Conlisk, John P. Coghlan of the law department, and others succeeded in reaching the Shreve Building at Post Street and Grant Avenue, intent on recovering private papers and any Company records that could be removed. They found the building seriously shaken, its plaster walls cracked, and the sheathing of its steel columns shattered in many places but still erect.

Each man climbed laboriously up the littered stairway to the upper floors, searched for his papers, and departed. No one cared to stay long in a tall building that morning. Not until the next day, however, did fire sweep through the offices of the structure.

When the Company had moved into the three upper floors of the 11-story Shreve Building, a brick vault was built for the storage of records. The precaution proved effective, for minute-books and other papers later were found unharmed within the makeshift storage room.

Driven from its offices in the Shreve Building, the P. G. and E. staff was homeless for weeks afterward. Electrical Engineer Frank G. Baum opened an office in Oakland where he directed operation of the powerhouses and transmission lines outside San Francisco. F. V. T. Lee, assistant manager, took an office force to Oakland to care for the immediate administrative needs of the system.

C. W. Conlisk, secretary, established city headquarters in his own home at Oak and Broderick Streets. The second week, the books and papers that had been saved were moved to the San Francisco Gas and Electric Company's branch office on Haight Street near Fillmore. Finding overcrowded conditions there, the wandering utility moved successively to the home of William Hammond Hall on Haight Street near Webster, to a house at O'Farrell and Franklin Streets, and then to the Loughborough home on the opposite corner.

In June the office of P. G. and E. and its subsidiaries was established in the Academy of the Sacred Heart at the southwest corner of Franklin and Ellis Streets. The school building was vacated by the Order and leased to the Company for a term of three years. And so it happened that in the assembly room of a convent school the Pacific Coast Gas Association convened September 18, 1906, for its fourteenth annual convention. Undaunted by the disaster of only five months ago, the industry's representatives met to consider the lessons of California's most disastrous earthquake. Not until August 23, 1909, was P. G. and E. able to move into its new home at 445 Sutter Street in the rebuilt business section of the city. An additional eight-story building at 447 Sutter was completed in 1916 to accommodate the expanding forces of the Company.

During the tense weeks after the earthquake and fire, the men of P. G. and E. threw themselves into the complex work of recovery and reconstruction. John Martin, acting president of the Company, Chief Counsel Garret W. McEnerney, and Director Frank B. Anderson were members of the mayor's Committee of Fifty, the citizens' body in charge of the situation since the first day of the disaster.

The Company's expenditures for rehabilitation of gas and electric services, repairs, replacements, and rebuilding amounted to $2,481,000. Of this amount only $310,000 was recovered from insurance. Losses in revenue were severe. Street lighting revenue dropped. A total of about half a million dollars evaporated in uncollectible accounts. Although customer ledgers were saved and a great number of bills eventually were collected, the gigantic shuffling of a whole city's population, many of whom were left penniless, resulted in heavy loss to the gas and electric company.

There was another peculiar and expensive circumstance. First repair of gas lines stopped the larger leaks, but there remained numberless smaller cracks and holes through which gas seeped into the ground. For many months after service was resumed, about one-third of all the gas sent out from the generators was lost through leakage.

The ashes of San Francisco were scarcely cool before financial necessities began to press the directors of the fledgling P. G.

and E. In a city where every major business had suffered crippling loss, cash became the universal need. Creditors of the utility company were demanding payment. With inadequate working capital, the condition quickly became acute.

Three members of the executive committee of the P. G. and E. board of directors met on April 23 at the home of Frank G. Drum. They were Cyrus Peirce, Eugene de Sabla, and Secretary Conlisk. A report was received from N. W. Halsey that he had telegraphed to New York for $100,000 which would be used for payrolls. The board of directors did not meet until June 27, and from then until the next year was well advanced the Company lived virtually from hand to mouth, borrowing more funds from Halsey, $500,000 from this bank, $300,000 from that lending agency. Frank G. Drum advanced, early in 1907, more than $400,000 in emergency funds. Approximately $1,400,000 was borrowed to carry the Company through that troubled time.

San Francisco had learned its lesson. Measures were immediately adopted to protect the city against a repetition of the fire and earthquake disaster of 1906. To ensure an ample supply of water for fire fighting a high-pressure system was installed. It is separate from the domestic supply system. Reservoirs were built on the crests of the hills on which much of the city is built. One hundred and fifty cisterns were sunk at street crossings on the higher levels. Provision was made for pumping salt water into mains and the reservoirs and cisterns. The Fire Department's equipment was increased and modernized. Every precaution was taken to make certain that if disaster again threatened, the department would have adequate water supply and adequate fire-fighting tools.

The municipal building code was revised to make all structures as nearly earthquake- and fireproof as possible. In their rebuilding and in construction of added facilities, the utilities adopted improved standards and methods designed to protect their systems from damage. The new regulations and restrictions were based upon studies of engineers and architects and observation of the effects of the 1906 earthquake. "It shall not happen again," said San Francisco.

CHAPTER 24

"There Will Be No Receiver"

SAN FRANCISCO was pulling itself out of the ruins in 1907. Reconstruction had started. Thousands of workers were clearing the burned city of wreckage and debris. Plans for new buildings were under way; restoration was being rushed on structures that survived the earthquake and fire.

The problem of financing was universal. Every business had lost heavily; few had cash reserves adequate to meet the emergency. To the leaders of Pacific Gas and Electric Company full realization of its serious condition came gradually. "We were all a little punch drunk after the strain, the nervous tension and the excitement of the disaster. Time was needed for a sober appraisal of what we faced," said one of them.

The discussions all led to one conclusion. The Company's treasury must be supplied with funds sufficient to restore the system to full efficiency and maintain it until the lost revenue could be regained. The floating debt, which during the emergency had mounted close to $10,000,000, also must be paid.

Affairs of the utility reached a crisis in midyear of 1907. Bond interest amounting to nearly a million dollars fell due July 1. Two days later, John A. Britton resigned as president of P. G. and E. and Frank G. Drum was elected to succeed him. He served without salary for the first year, waiting for his compensation until funds were available. Britton was appointed first vice-president and general manager, a position created to meet the need of the hour.

It must be said here that a recital of the historical fact does not tell the whole story of Frank G. Drum's contribution to the progress of P. G. and E. after its severe setback almost immediately following its organization. Drum was a calm, clear-headed, conservative business executive, a rather stern man of few words, little given to spectacular performance but endowed with keen analytical powers and unswerving determination once he believed himself upon the right course. His self-sacrificing spirit and his capabilities for a difficult task may be found as much between the lines as in the words of this account.

From the Tevis estate and from personal sources the new president managed to borrow the million required for bond interest. N. W. Halsey in New York was advised that a bond issue should be prepared immediately. The proposal brought Halsey's attorney, F. W. M. Cutcheon, posthaste to San Francisco with a counterproposal.

"Mr. Halsey and his staff have discussed your plan to get out a bond issue," he said to President Drum. "He believes this is not a good time to float bonds and has come to the conclusion that P. G. and E. must gain the time it requires by means of a receivership."

"What do you mean?" asked Drum.

"Ask for the protection of the courts," replied the attorney. "Take the legal course provided for conditions such as yours, until reorganization can be effected. We have already prepared the necessary papers, and I am ready to file application for a receivership immediately."

Drum called Cutcheon's attention to the fact that the subsidiary companies of California Gas and Electric Corporation had not yet been merged into P. G. and E. and that multiple receiverships, with correspondingly increased costs and complications, would be the result of such a move. Drum told Cutcheon he would think over his proposal and give him a decision the next day.

Drum talked with Garret W. McEnerney, Eugene de Sabla, John Martin, and other P. G. and E. directors. They agreed that there should be no receivership. They agreed also to a new plan which Drum outlined to them—that an assessment be levied at once on the equity stock of P. G. and E., common and preferred, to raise cash for the Company's immediate needs.

The next day Drum broke the news to Cutcheon. The refusal of his receivership plan was a shock to him. There was added shock in the proposal to levy an assessment upon the Company's stock. His client, N. W. Halsey, had received a large allotment of P. G. and E. common stock in payment for his labors in organizing the corporation and would not welcome an assessment. The attorney returned to New York, his mission not accomplished.

Although they were penalizing themselves, the directors of P. G. and E. carried out Drum's plan to the letter. An assessment of $10 a share on both preferred and common was voted July 15, 1907, payable on or before August 14. The levy on preferred shares was fully paid, yielding $997,000 to be used in paying the Company's debts.

By agreement, Frank G. Drum, John Martin, and Eugene J. de Sabla, Jr., who with Halsey and Pacific Gas and Electric Investment Company held the outstanding P. G. and E. common stock, allowed their shares to become delinquent. The stock was bid in by the Company at a public sale and returned to the treasury. The Investment company, possessing no assets and having failed of its original purpose, was allowed to lapse.

The assessment laid a heavy burden upon every shareholder. In that postfire period, every man was struggling to recover his financial balance. De Sabla had been hard hit. He held 28,000 shares of P. G. and E. preferred in addition to the common, and on the preferred he was compelled on 30 days' notice to raise $280,000 to meet the assessment. His associates suffered similarly.

By a fortunate turn of events, the stock assessment was all paid before the unhealthy economic conditions of the year reached a climax in the market crash of October, 1907. Directors of the utility persisted in their belief that only by a bond issue could its financial ills be cured. Drum converted N. W. Halsey to this viewpoint, and the New York investment firm began the necessary preparations.

In the meantime, P. G. and E.'s financial ship was kept afloat by every possible device—daily collection of outstanding bills, deferred payment of bills for operating expenses, use of clearing-house certificates instead of cash, short-term loans, postponement of plant expenditures, and the use of the lifesaving common stock held in the Company's treasury. General Electric Company and other equipment suppliers in the East were induced to accept P. G. and E. stock in lieu of cash in payment of their accounts.

Preparation for the bond issue proceeded. On November 1, 1907, the California Gas and Electric Corporation, wholly owned by P. G. and E., authorized the issuance of $45,000,000 in unifying and refunding mortgage, 5 per cent Gold Bonds. While the greater part of the proceeds from these bonds was dedicated to refunding underlying bonds of the Company and its components, other millions were to be used in paying the unfunded debts of the corporation and for new properties and betterments. Despite the depressed condition of the financial market, $6,000,000 in the new bonds were issued at once, and through an extraordinary display of business cooperation the bonds were successfully underwritten. Banks that held the utility Company's notes agreed to underwrite the bonds in amounts equal to the indebtedness. Other creditors accepted bonds in payment. P. G. and E. common stock in some cases was given as a bonus to buyers of bonds.

Another move remained to complete the absorption of California Gas and Electric Corporation by P. G. and E., which already owned all its outstanding stock. Effective December 31, 1907, title to all the properties of the older corporation was conveyed to P. G. and E.

Successful flotation of the California Gas and Electric bonds marked a turning point in the financial career of the young corporation. The vision of Drum, Martin, and de Sabla—a merged organization strong enough to have its securities listed on the New York Stock Exchange—was about to be realized. The bond issue of 1907 was listed on the New York Exchange June 22, 1910. P. G. and E. had reached maturity. From that time on, its securities were to bear the Wall Street stamp of approval for trading in the national investment market.

The period of most acute financial strain had been passed safely. In the years between 1907 and 1911, revenue increased. John A. Britton, as general manager, assumed the task of unifying the scattered members of the Company's gas and electric properties into a centrally controlled system. Duplications in

Frank G. Drum, president of Pacific Gas and Electric Company, 1907–1920, piloted the young utility through its early years—"a wise counselor and courageous leader."

John A. Britton served briefly as first president of Pacific Gas and Electric Company, then as vice-president and general manager from 1907 to 1923.

Spaulding Powerhouses No. 1 and No. 2 are powered by water behind the 275-foot Spaulding Dam across the Yuba River gorge.

Drum Powerhouse is part of a hydro system which utilizes the waters of Lake Spaulding and Yuba and Bear Rivers to drive the generators of eight power plants.

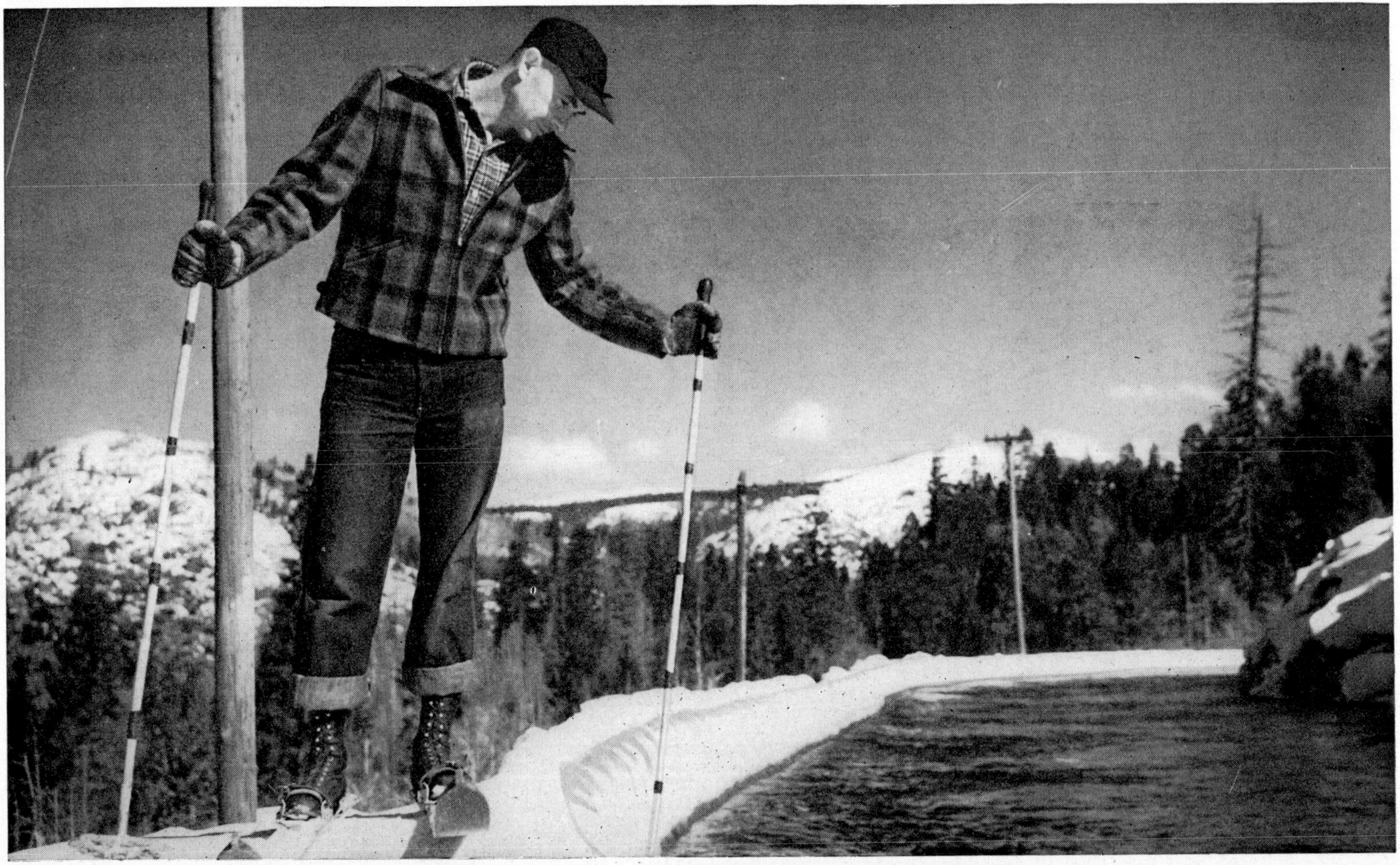

Ditch tenders in the Sierra sometimes have to travel on skis as they fight snow and ice

service were cut out; the electric generating and transmission system was brought under centralized direction; district managers were made responsible for the conduct of the business in their areas. Both gas and electric generating and distributing plants were overhauled and improved. Promotional campaigns were instituted to increase the use of electric power by agriculture and industry.

Earnings of the Company had improved to such an extent by August 1, 1909, that payment of long deferred dividends on the cumulative preferred stock was resumed. No dividend had been received by preferred stockholders since Dividend No. 1 was paid April 1, 1906. Now the accumulated liability was wiped out by distribution of one-half a share of common stock for each share of preferred outstanding.

Common stock, the lowly security which had only potential value when the Company was formed, was beginning its long climb toward par. There is on record a sale of December 31, 1909, direct from the P. G. and E. treasury, of 5,000 shares of common at $55 per share, with option on an equal number of shares at the same price.

Common shares were placed on a dividend basis November 22, 1911, with a payment of one-half share of common for each share held. Dividends were paid intermittently thereafter for several years. It was not, however, until 1924, when the stock was paying dividends at the rate of 8 per cent, that the market value reached par. Since 1919 common stock dividends have been paid unfailingly, and the 8 per cent rate established in 1924 has been continued without change except for a period of about three years (1933–1936) when the rate was temporarily reduced to 6 per cent.

President Drum had devoted his first attention to the financial structure of the Company. Drum was a developer rather than a promoter. He believed that the gas and electric company should be built into a strong economic unit, contributing to growth and progress of the community and receiving proportional return for its service. By 1911 it became clear that more capital would be needed, and on October 23, 1911, at a special stockholders' meeting, these steps were taken:

1. Authorized common stock of the Company was increased from $20,000,000 to $150,000,000 at $100 per share par value.

2. Issuance of $150,000,000 in general and refunding bonds was authorized, proceeds to be used to refund all the underlying issues of the Company, which then amounted to $64,404,-502, the remainder to be reserved for plant and system expansion.

With authorization of the new general and refunding bonds, P. G. and E. was ready to assume the position for which it was designed as a fully rounded operating company. Terms of the 10-million-dollar bond issue which had been used in 1906 to purchase the stock of San Francisco Gas and Electric Company had severely restricted needed additional financing of that company's operations. It was possible now to call in those original bonds and to convey title to all the San Francisco company's properties to P. G. and E. This was accomplished November 27, 1911.

Marketing of the general and refunding bonds was a new problem for Drum and his associates. West Coast financial machinery had not then been developed to a point deemed adequate to absorb so large an issue. It was decided to seek the solution in New York. Frank B. Anderson, a P. G. and E. director, accompanied by Treasurer A. F. Hockenbeamer, went East in December, 1911. They knocked at the Wall Street door of J. P. Morgan and Company and were admitted. Although the negotiations were protracted, agreement finally was reached. J. P. Morgan underwrote $20,000,000 in the new P. G. and E. bonds at 85, and through the firm of N. W. Halsey & Company and Harris, Forbes and Company the securities were offered to the public at 92½.

Acceptance of the bonds by the House of Morgan was further proof that the California utility had grown to full stature in the national market.

* * *

In those early years of P. G. and E. development came an innovation that was to wield a powerful influence upon all public utilities in California. Under the Public Utilities Act of

1911, the State Railroad Commission, on March 23, 1912, assumed regulation of utility rates and other utility actions in all parts of California outside incorporated cities and towns. After three years' trial, the act was extended to cover all utility systems in the state wherever their service was given. The effects were far reaching. With these two strokes the legislature cut off the utilities from political control by city councils and county supervisors. The old abuses of unrestrained competition, wanton multiplication of pipe and pole lines, and deadly rate wars no longer were possible.

* * *

Financing continued to be the major problem of P. G. and E. In 1913 it became apparent that new funds would be required. Millions were being spent for additions to plants and expansion of the system to meet the rising demand for gas and electricity.

President Drum was opposed to any further bond issue, although N. W. Halsey's Cyrus Peirce was arguing for bonds instead of stock sale. The National City Company of New York, subsidiary of the National City Bank, which had succeeded Halsey & Company as the Company's Eastern representative after N. W. Halsey's death in 1911, agreed with Drum. "We are going to solve this problem," said Drum, "by selling our own stock," which was something that had never been attempted on a large scale by a utility company.

The decision brought into prominence a new figure in P. G. and E. history—August F. Hockenbeamer, a young man from the New York office of N. W. Halsey & Company, whose first knowledge of the California company was gained in New York by writing the prospectus for the 1907 bond issue. Sent to San Francisco late in 1907 to report on the properties, he remained as a member of the P. G. and E. staff. His grasp of financial detail was so expert that he was elected treasurer of the Company, August 13, 1908.

A. F. Hockenbeamer had a background of years of experience in railroading. Fresh out of business college he went to work in Logansport, Indiana; for the Pennsylvania lines as a messenger in the office of L. F. Loree, division engineer. For a monthly wage of $15 he swept out the offices, filled the kerosene lamps, cleaned and refueled the coal stoves and during the day worked on the books, took dictation, and ran errands. Seventeen years later, he was assistant to the president of the Rock Island–Frisco railway system, who happened to be his first boss, L. F. Loree.

After a year in that position, Hockenbeamer joined the investment firm of N. W. Halsey & Company as an expert in railroad and corporation investments. Arriving in San Francisco on what appeared to be a temporary assignment, he could not have guessed that he would remain, eventually to become president of P. G. and E.

President Drum felt that the Company's financial scheme was off balance—too much funded debt in the form of bonds and not enough equity holdings in the form of shares of stock in the public's hands. His discussions with Hockenbeamer led to a revolutionary method of obtaining capital funds, which became known as the "customer ownership plan." This was simply the sale of P. G. and E. stock over the counter direct to the public from the Company's treasury. Nothing like that had ever been attempted by any utility company in the United States. Hockenbeamer, who in 1910 had been elected vice-president, comptroller and treasurer, worked out the details of the campaign and to him credit has been given as originator and developer of the plan.

Introduction of "customer ownership" was precipitated by threatening economic conditions in 1914. The European political pot was boiling, American industry and the financial market were at low ebb. Capital was timid and difficult to obtain. Despite the overhanging clouds, P. G. and E. executives made a public offering of 125,000 shares of 6 per cent first preferred capital stock, July 14, 1914, only a fortnight after the assassination at Sarajevo on June 28 had plunged Europe into World War I.

The offer of P. G. and E. stock to its customers and employees was supported by a carefully devised program. Full information about the Company and its properties was provided. The mutual interest of consumers and the company was stressed. Advantages to the customers in becoming part owners of their service were emphasized. Employees and customers were offered shares on an installment-payment plan.

The result of the campaign proved its worth. In 11 months $10,177,300 par value of first preferred shares were sold. Of this total, 1,630 Company employees and 2,054 customers subscribed for 41 per cent, or $4,122,693. The remainder was purchased by those who already owned P. G. and E. stock. Success of the plan enabled the Company to continue its plant expansion and to meet the wartime demand for essential gas and electric service. The Company continued the customer ownership plan for many years. By 1941, a total of $81,601,225 in par value of preferred stocks had been sold over the counter to 83,319 purchasers. By the end of 1951 the number of owners reached a total of 188,463, of whom 65.86 per cent are residents of California.

Customer ownership spread rapidly throughout the country. Year after year other utility companies adopted this plan. Member companies of the National Electric Light Association reported for the year 1928 the direct sale of $208,107,000 par value stock to more than 200,000 investors.

Benefits of the movement went far beyond the supplying of needed capital to gas and electric utilities. More lasting were the social advances accomplished when the utilities took into partnership large numbers of customers and gave to employees the incentive and interest of part ownership. The result, in effect, was public ownership of the utilities, with every customer-stockholder entitled to a vote and a share of the proceeds of the business.

* * *

Although acute financial problems absorbed the attention of the president and directors of P. G. and E. in its early years, other steps of only a little less importance were taken. The program of unifying the system under single corporate ownership continued.

Purchase of the Mutual Electric Light Company was completed November 27, 1911. The Mutual, organized in 1894, had been a sharp competitor for business in San Francisco. In 1906 Fred T. Elsey, John A. Britton, Cyrus Peirce, C. W. Conlisk, and others of the P. G. and E. group had obtained stock control. From that time on it was no longer a competitor but continued to be operated separately until purchased by P. G. and E.

Another San Francisco competitor was removed in November, 1911, by purchase of the Metropolitan Light and Power Company. Originally, this was the San Francisco Coke and Gas Company, established in 1899 by Professor T. S. C. Lowe and his son for the purpose of producing coke. When demand for coke declined, the plant was converted to generation of oil gas. It continued to be a small thorn in the side of the San Francisco Gas and Electric Company until its purchase by P. G. and E.

Rudolph Spreckels, veteran of past battles for and against the San Francisco Gas and Electric Company, reappeared in the utility field February 27, 1912, when he organized the Universal Electric and Gas Company and launched sharp competition for electric customers in the area near the Claus Spreckels Building, now called Central Tower, at Third and Market Streets. This company was an outgrowth of the Spreckels Building generating plant installed in 1900. Spreckels found an old city ordinance that permitted the running of wires on a competitor's poles and thus was able to make extensions. In 1922 the Universal properties and business were purchased jointly by P. G. and E. and Great Western Power Company, which by that time had gained a strong foothold in San Francisco.

As the population of Northern California communities increased, numerous small electric companies were organized to distribute power from steam-operated plants. The consolidation of these little systems, which had started in the earliest days, was continued by P. G. and E. In 1911 small electric properties in Sebastopol, Hayward, and Live Oak were purchased. There were to be many more such purchases until the Northern California territory was served, as it is today with few exceptions, by the one operating company.

During the administration of President Drum and General Manager Britton, the P. G. and E. organization was built into a strong operating force. Increasing attention was given to personnel problems. On May 6, 1913, the Company experienced its first and only system-wide strike, when 1,625 of its workers went out. There was some violence which was met by vigorous action by the Company. The strike was quickly ended. In nearly half a century, P. G. and E. and its component systems have suffered only five labor strikes, four of them affecting only small groups of employees. None is recorded since 1924.

Establishment of a pension system for employees was given early consideration. In the first years of the Company small monthly pensions were given to old employees of predecessor systems on an individual basis. Grants were made to such employees when, in the judgment of the Company, they required aid. As the organization grew, this was found to be an impractical method and the first formal pension system was established February 1, 1916. By the end of the year, 27 employees had been retired on pension. In 1937 a more scientific method was adopted, providing for retirement of both men and women employees at stated age limits and payment of pensions by two national insurance companies which underwrote the plan. The pension fund is accumulated by premium payments from employees and the Company, the latter bearing the larger share of the burden. In 1945 the Company set up a pension trust fund of $13,600,000 for payment of annuities for service prior to 1937. Under the combination plan, P. G. and E. employees accumulate substantial funds from which they are assured an annual income after retirement.

Probably the pioneer disability fund of the Company's corporate predecessors was established in 1877 by the San Francisco Gas Light and Mutual Aid Benevolent Society. All went well until a lamplighter fell ill and, instead of succumbing in a reasonable time, lived on for so many years that his biweekly benefits bankrupted the treasury. The society was the earliest known predecessor of the successful and effective Pacific Service Employees Association which, with 14,800 members, administers disability and death benefits, a credit union, hospitalization plan, wage benefit plan, and complete educational, social, and recreational programs.

* * *

The tradition of long service of employees which had been established by Peter Donahue's San Francisco Gas Company and its successors was carried on by P. G. and E. There was D. H. Foote, who joined the California Gas and Electric Corporation in 1903 as assistant secretary and cashier, was appointed secretary of P. G. and E. in 1907, and remained active until his retirement as vice-president, secretary and treasurer in 1943. It was his boast, if so modest and reserved a man ever boasted, that he had lived to retire two bond issues of the Company for which he had prepared the papers 30 years before. David Howard Foote died in San Francisco, December 8, 1951, at the age of ninety.

W. B. Bosley, general counsel, was another of the Company's staff who gave nearly half a century of service to the utility company. A Yale graduate in law, assistant professor at Hastings College of Law in San Francisco, and lecturer at the University of California in Berkeley, he became general attorney of the California Gas and Electric Corporation in 1903. When P. G. and E. was formed in 1905, he became its attorney and then general counsel. At the time of his retirement in 1948, after 43 years spent in guiding the complex legal affairs of the Company, he bore the title of special counsel. In his eighty-eighth year, he resides at this writing in San Francisco.

The troubled years of the 1910–1920 decade were passing and with them some of the leading characters in the P. G. and E. drama. N. W. Halsey, the New York investment banker who had guided the incorporation of the P. G. and E. in 1905 and later was elected chairman of its board of directors, died July 1, 1911. Since 1908, Halsey gradually had withdrawn from the affairs of the Company, although his firm had continued as underwriter of several of its bond issues.

Eugene J. de Sabla, Jr., and John Martin, the doughty enterprisers who had parlayed the little $500,000 Nevada County Electric Power Company of 1892 into the $30,000,000 P. G.

and E. of 1905, dropped their official connection with the Company midway in the 1910–1920 decade. After the 1906 disaster they continued as members of the board of directors until 1914, when they retired to give their time to other enterprises.

De Sabla, still the incorrigible promoter, sought new investment fields. He became interested in and president of a number of corporations outside the utility business. During that period de Sabla maintained offices in San Francisco and London where he spent several months each year. Eventually he moved to New York where, in his eighty-eighth year, he now resides.

Martin also turned to other activities. At the time of his death Martin headed the Mid-Continent Utilities Corporation which operated public utilities in Middle Western and Southern states. His extraordinarily active and useful life came to an end May 23, 1928.

* * *

As time slipped by, Frank G. Drum began thinking of seeking relief from the heavy responsibilities he was carrying. He had not relinquished management of the vast Tevis-Haggin properties and other business interests when he became president of P. G. and E. in 1907. One of his extra tasks had been to act as receiver for the Western Pacific railroad when that company underwent reorganization. The burden of business was beginning to take its toll.

But when the United States entered World War I, new problems arose and Drum felt he must go on. Although the Company's power supply had been materially increased, it was hard pressed to meet the wartime demand. Government restrictions prevented the use of materials needed for construction of new plant facilities. There was a manpower shortage because of the loss of employees to war service and a severe influenza epidemic. Drum stayed at his post until July 28, 1920, when failing health compelled his resignation. Wigginton E. Creed was elected to succeed him. A new era in P. G. and E. progress was about to begin.

Frank G. Drum continued to hold his membership in the board of directors and the board's executive committee. He died August 28, 1923, only a few months after his sixtieth birthday. For 13 years he had piloted P. G. and E. through storm and stress.

His associates, in an official resolution of the executive committee of the board of directors, paid him tribute as "a wise counselor and a courageous leader, sound in judgment, firm in decision . . . with a modesty and self-effacement that placed accomplishment above self-aggrandizement."

CHAPTER 25

Power for New Population

CALIFORNIA'S population was booming. In the decade from 1900 to 1910 the state had gained nearly 900,000 new residents, an increase of 60 per cent. There was proportionate growth of demand for gas and electric service. In 1911 more than 26,000 new gas, electric, and water customers were added to the P. G. and E. system in addition to 17,000 gained by purchase of other systems.

The time had come for construction of the first major hydroelectric project of P. G. and E. In 1911 the plant system consisted of 11 hydroelectric powerhouses and five steam-operated stations with an aggregate capacity of 141,590 kilowatts. Only one small water-power generating station had been built since P. G. and E.'s organization—the Deer Creek Plant, placed in commission in 1908.

The first site selected for the new development was on the Bear River in Placer County, where the water resources of the old South Yuba Water Company stood waiting to be applied to the generation of electric power. Engineers Frank G. Baum and James H. Wise had begun laying plans for the project in 1905 when they visited Lake Spaulding on the South Yuba River at an elevation of 4,875 feet in Nevada County. John Spaulding had built a rock-fill dam there for the water company in 1892. A new barrier lower down in the gorge would flood some 800 additional acres and increase manyfold the lake's storage capacity.

Work was started July 1, 1912, under the supervision of Wise, then assistant general manager and chief engineer of P. G. and E. Construction involved the building of a concrete dam half a mile downstream from the old one and a 4,400-foot tunnel outlet from the dam to connect with 8½ miles of canal which would transport the water of the South Yuba to a forebay above the Drum Powerhouse site on the south bank of the Bear River.

The dam, originally planned for a height of 305 feet, was built to a height of 225 feet in 1913. In 1916 it was raised to 260 feet, and to its present height of 275 feet in 1919.

Drum Powerhouse was placed in operation November 26, 1913, with its first two units installed. Other units were added later to bring its generating capacity to its present rating of 52,000 kilowatts.

The Spaulding-Drum development is a splendid example of economic employment of water resources for generation of electricity. Here in one widespread water system the waters of Lake Spaulding, the Yuba and Bear Rivers and tributary streams now drive in succession the generators of eight powerhouses, with an aggregate capacity of 118,000 kilowatts. They are Spaulding Nos. 1, 2, and 3, Drum, Alta, Dutch Flat, Wise, and Halsey (named in memory of N. W. Halsey).

Wise Powerhouse was named in commemoration of James H. Wise, the young chief engineer in charge of planning and building Spaulding Dam and Drum Powerhouse, whose career was cut short by his accidental death, September 16, 1912.

Not all of the water used to power these generating stations comes from the Lake Spaulding watershed. Under contract with the Nevada Irrigation District, a substantial flow from the district's water sources empties into Lake Spaulding and is passed through powerhouse turbines and water wheels before it is returned to the district's canals to irrigate some 45,000 acres of orchard and farm lands at lower elevations. As in other hydroelectric regions, the water used to produce electricity is only borrowed; eventually it serves its ultimate purposes for agricultural, industrial, and domestic use. P. G. and E. operates five domestic water systems in Placer County and serves 12 other towns in other parts of its system.

The Spaulding-Drum project was completed by Frank G. Baum after Wise's untimely death. Men who later were to round out distinguished careers with Pacific Gas and Electric Company were members of his engineering staff. Among them was Paul M. Downing, who received his training in electrical engineering at Stanford University, graduating in 1895. In his senior year he was a star tackle and captain of the famous Stanford football team of which former President Herbert Hoover was business manager. At the beginning of his professional life Downing was in charge of the little Blue Lakes plant on the Mokelumne River when Prince Poniatowski launched his Standard Electric Company and built the first Electra Powerhouse in the same region.

Downing joined John Martin in 1898 in his work of selling and installing products of the Stanley Electrical Manufacturing Company. From there it was a natural step to Martin's and de Sabla's Bay Counties Power Company, California Gas and Electric Corporation, and thence to P. G. and E.

I. C. Steele was another young civil engineer who had a hand in the Spaulding-Drum project, especially in the problems of dam design. Steele, a graduate of the University of California in 1909, entered P. G. and E. a few days after he had received his degree. He started as a laborer at 25 cents an hour and 10 years later was placed in charge of the Company's division of civil engineering.

When Spaulding Dam was raised to its present height, Steele directed the numerous studies and investigations required before the job could be completed. Great hydroelectric projects since that time on the Pit, Mokelumne, Feather, and Yuba Rivers bear the marks of his engineering skill. In rock-fill dam design, he became a specialist with a national reputation. In 1947 Steele, who was then chief engineer of P. G. and E., was elected vice-president and chief engineer, a position he held until his retirement, January 1, 1952.

Other engineers of the Spaulding-Drum development were J. P. Jollyman, R. G. Clifford, G. C. Noble, and H. C. Vensano.

A steel-tower transmission line carried Drum power output at 110,000 volts to Cordelia, a main switching station 110 miles distant in Solano County near San Francisco Bay. From Cordelia, in 1915, a line was run to San Rafael in Marin County and thence to Lime Point on the north bay shore opposite San Francisco. From Lime Point, two cables were laid across the tide-swept bay entrance for delivery of electric power from Drum Powerhouse to the metropolis.

Construction of the Drum transmission line was under the supervision of E. H. Steele, who retired from the Company in 1942 as engineer in charge of line construction. Steele recalls the adventures of line building 40 years ago. One of the early problems was how to obtain gravel for the concrete tower footings without long hauls over the rough trails of the Sierra foothill country. Solution was found in the Liberty Mine, an accessible hydraulic gravel deposit. Large sluice boxes were constructed and fitted with "grizzlies," iron gratings to screen the gravel to the desired size. On the floor of the boxes, mining riffles were installed to catch any gold that might be contained in the gravel. Then a miner's monitor and nozzle were used to wash the gravel bank into the boxes. By agreement the mine owner kept for himself the $800 in gold recovered. The line builders obtained 2,500 cubic yards of sized gravel for the concrete footings of the steel towers erected in the mountain section of the line.

Those were primitive days when work horses still did the hauling, the grading, and the lifting. Steele drove the only automobile in the line construction camp. Two hundred and fifty men and 160 horses did the work. Men were paid a daily wage of $2.50, their board cost 25 cents per day, and meat was supplied at 7 cents a pound.

* * *

A December day in 1951 is drawing to a close in Northern California. As the darkness of early winter creeps in, the lights are flashing on in a million and a half homes, factories, offices, and stores. Few of those light users ever have asked, "How does it happen that our wires always are charged with electricity? When millions of lamps are turned on within an hour, how does the Company manage to supply the sudden demand?"

The answer lies in what the power men call "central load dispatching" and "interconnection." The dispatcher of an electric system controls the operation of generating plants and the transmission of power much as a railroad dispatcher directs the movement of trains. The present highly efficient system is the result of a half century of development.

The first electrical systems had only individual powerhouses which served single communities or areas. Control of the generating schedule was simple, but when two or more powerhouses were operated by one company to provide power to other communities, a dispatching system became necessary. This occurred, for example, when, in 1899, de Sabla and Martin built a line from Colgate Powerhouse in Yuba County to Sacramento. Two small generating stations supplied power to that line. Colgate was designated as the master plant, and Richard E. Tremaine was placed in charge. It was his duty to know the power requirements and to supply them, to direct the operations of the two powerhouses, and to control frequency and voltage.

When transmission was extended to Oakland in 1901, the first switching center was established at Davis in Solano County to assist operation control. It was in charge of Charles Porter, former operator at Colgate. In the same year another switching point was installed at South Tower where the Colgate-Oakland line crosses Carquinez Strait. By June, 1906, after P. G. and E. had been organized, more powerhouses had been added to the system. The Standard Electric Company, with its Electra generating plant on the Mokelumne and transmission lines to San Francisco and Oakland, had been merged with P. G. and E. The two transmission systems were interconnected by a line between South Tower and Herdlyn station. South Tower was designated as the control center, and F. R. George was given the responsibilities of coordinating and directing operations of the combined systems.

P. M. Downing then was P. G. and E. engineer in charge of electrical operations. He made a study of control methods and planned a better organized dispatching system. F. R. George was transferred in October, 1906, from South Tower to an office in Station B in Oakland. He was the first to be given the title of Load Dispatcher. As the work increased, W. D. Skinner and C. B. Pierce were added to his staff. Three years later a wooden dummy-switchboard or system-operating chart, 7 feet high and 18 feet long, was installed to assist the dispatcher. It bore a chart showing powerhouses, switching stations, and transmission lines.

F. R. George was advanced in the electrical operations department until in 1929 he was appointed engineer in charge of electrical operation, a post he held until his retirement in 1946, after 44 years of service. His death followed, June 1, 1948.

Two more changes in location were made before the dispatching center was established on June 23, 1923, in the P. G. and E. office building at Seventeenth and Clay Streets, Oakland, where it still is operated. A new metal, electrically operated chart board was installed, 10 feet high and 40 feet long. Vari-colored lights indicate the status of the system at any moment, presenting to the dispatcher a complete picture of powerhouses in operation, the transmission network, substations, and switching centers. By 1923 the organization had grown to a staff of 12 men working in three shifts.

Since 1923 the dispatching system constantly has been extended and elaborated. The organization now is headed by the Office of Power Control in the headquarters building of the Company in San Francisco, where a staff under General Superintendent I. W. Collins maintains a daily record of operational statistics, such as water supply, powerhouses and lines in operation, power output, "outages" or failure of lines from any cause.

In the Oakland headquarters of the system dispatcher is a staff of 14 men working in three shifts. They constitute the heart of the electric system, their duty to keep power flowing through every artery and vein of the vast system of 58 hydroelectric powerhouses, 17 steam-operated plants, and 57,800 miles of transmission and distribution lines.

A master pendulum clock, coordinated with time signals from the Arlington Station at Washington, D.C., and an electric clock stand in the dispatcher's room. Similar clocks are in every major powerhouse. A designated powerhouse governs frequency for the entire system. When the operator of the governor station notes that his electric clock varies from Arlington time, he slows or speeds the generators to bring the frequency of the system's power output back to an average of 60 cycles per second. Every electric clock in Northern California, Southern Oregon, and Central Nevada depends for its accuracy upon the frequency of the electric current which drives it.

When ice clogs the canals, a small steel and aluminum boat is used as an icebreaker. At times flame throwers and dynamite have been used to break the jam.

P. G. and E. "mountain men" face sub-zero weather and deep snow to patrol and repair the power lines in winter.

Linemen in winter often use "sno-cats." In January, 1952, one of these tractors brought food and medical supplies to a snowbound train high in the Sierra.

A lineman on winter patrol hooks into a phone circuit above a mountain lake.

But frequency and voltage control is only one of the dispatcher's functions. He knows every variation in demand for electricity. He is the man who prepares for the sudden lighting demand on a dark December evening, the surge of the call for power when factory motors start humming at eight in the morning. He knows that irrigation pumps will need enormous quantities of power in the summer months. He knows by his charts the hour of peak or maximum demand day or night, summer or winter, and provides power accordingly. He is informed in advance of expected weather changes which affect water supply or demand for power. The dispatcher also must be ready for unexpected jumps in the load demand as, for instance, when in the middle of the night storm or fire or other cause of alarm impels thousands of persons to turn on their lights simultaneously. He must move fast at such times to increase the power supply.

To meet all these requirements, the system dispatcher must be in constant communication with powerhouses and switching centers which control their local areas under his direction. His office is equipped with keyboards of two telephone systems—the Company's own 11,000 miles of private lines and those of Pacific Telephone and Telegraph Company. These are supplemented by carrier-current telephone and micro-wave communication channels.

In 1951 the Company installed its first micro-wave circuit, newest of communication systems. Tall towers were erected on the roof of the Oakland office building where the dispatcher's central station is located and at Newark power-switching center. Between these two points, a micro-wave high-frequency circuit is maintained with five voice channels and a connection at either end with telephone lines to five important generating stations. With this system the dispatcher can be placed in instant communication with vital power resources at all times.

Field crews working in remote sections are equipped with two-way radio telephone sets and are constantly in touch with their bases. More than 35 base radio stations and 370 mobile units are now operating in urban and rural areas of the system.

Messages can thus be relayed from station to station when telephone lines fail.

Another important function of the system dispatcher is to maintain continuity of service. When a storm levels poles, tears transmission lines apart, or disables a powerhouse, when the weight of snow in the mountains breaks power wires, when an eagle alights on a pole and his spreading wings cause a short circuit that burns out a line, or when a motorist shatters a high-tension pole on a highway, the dispatcher supervises the moves necessary to maintain or restore service. Even before line crews have been called out to find and repair the damage, the dispatcher has taken steps to limit the interruption of service to a minimum of time and area. He localizes the trouble by switching power to other lines around the "down" section. If a main transmission line is out or a powerhouse is disabled, he calls upon other parts of the system to supply the deficiency in power supply.

Repairs in isolated mountain regions sometimes require many days of arduous labor. The saga of the linemen and ditch tenders who patrol the Sierra transmission lines and water conduits in winter is a tale of heroic battles against snow and ice under conditions that call for maximum skill, courage, and physical endurance. The credo of these men is simple—the lines must be kept open, the powerhouses must be supplied with water. They face the perils of sub-zero weather and deep snow. They travel on skis and haul their heavy tools and materials on toboggans. In later years they have used "sno-cats," small tractors designed for snow travel.

Sometimes line crews have been marooned for days by storm or impassable drifts. Food has been dropped to them by plane and helicopter. Portable short-wave radios have made communication possible. Modern devices also have helped the ditch tenders. When ice clogs the canals and stops the flow of water into powerhouse penstocks, flame throwers and dynamite have been used to break the jam. Recently a small steel and aluminum motor-driven boat has been used successfully as an icebreaker.

P. G. and E. "mountain men" many times have turned from their work of line and conduit maintenance to perform notable acts of mercy. They have aided in the delivery of babies in isolated cabins that could not be reached in time by a physician. They have rescued lost or injured persons.

In January, 1952, when a Southern Pacific streamliner was snowbound high in the Sierra, three of them labored for days without rest in blinding snow storms to bring food, medical supplies, and a doctor to the suffering passengers. One of them, Pershing J. Gold, died from a heart attack brought on by his heroic efforts. He and his mates, Charles T. Swing and Roy Claytor, drove a sno-cat on repeated trips through the deep snow to accomplish their mission of relief.

* * *

The electric industry made great strides in the years 1910 to 1920, and one of the most significant was the establishment of interconnections between separately operated area systems. Interconnection may be of two kinds—the integration of a system such as the P. G. and E., where all electric components, generating plants, and transmission lines over an area of 89,000 square miles are tied together, or the interconnection of separately operated-and-owned systems for interchange of power.

The first move toward Pacific Coast interconnection was made January 8, 1919, when the northern lines of Northern California Power Company, Consolidated, a predecessor of P. G. and E., were connected with the southern lines of the California-Oregon Power Company. This was followed by interconnection with the lines of the San Joaquin Light and Power Corporation, which operated a separate system in the south.

In later years P. G. and E. made connection with the Southern California Edison Company for interchange of power and with the Sierra Pacific Power Company of Nevada. From these interconnections and similar ties north and south of California emerged during World War II the Southwest and the Northwest Power Pools, which by cooperative agreement did a magnificent job of coordinating the distribution of electric power to the war industries throughout the Pacific Coast. Today the electrical network is continuous from the Mexican border to British Columbia.

* * *

Drought, the ever-present threat to hydroelectric operation in California, brought about state action in 1918 to assist the utilities in their effort to supply adequate power for essential industries during World War I. When production of electric power in the mountain plants fell off, the State Railroad Commission appointed H. G. Butler power administrator to allocate the available power output to meet requirements. Priorities were established and use of electricity for nonessential purposes was sharply curtailed. New business was discouraged, unnecessary lighting was forbidden, and all customers were called upon to reduce their use of power. The "dry" cycle covered a period of eight years, starting in 1916. One of the results was acceleration of P. G. and E. power expansion. As soon as wartime restrictions were lifted, the building of more plants was resumed.

* * *

An important change from the old method of computing monthly bills for electric service was completed in 1912. Meters which measured the kilowatt hours of electricity used by a customer were installed and the outmoded "flat rate" system of billing finally was abandoned.

S. J. Lisberger, P. G. and E.'s engineer of electric distribution, directed the meter change-over. Crews of college students were recruited and trained for the work in San Francisco and Oakland. The magnitude of the job is indicated by the fact that in 1912 there were 116,500 customers on P. G. and E. electric lines.

S. J. Lisberger had been graduated from the University of Wisconsin in 1903 and in the following year joined the Oakland Gas Light and Heat Company. Coming to P. G. and E. after the 1906 disaster, he rose rapidly in the engineering department, finding time in 1907 to obtain a Master's degree from Johns Hopkins University. When he retired in 1946 after 42 years of service he bore the title of chief of the division of electric distribution.

CHAPTER 26

Great Western Invasion

A MAJOR battle for the electric power business of San Francisco and Northern California loomed in 1908 when Great Western Power Company began transmitting kilowatts from the Feather River to the terminus of its high-voltage line in Oakland. The contest with Pacific Gas and Electric Company was to continue for more than a score of years.

When E. T. and Guy C. Earl succeeded in sending the output of Big Bend Powerhouse on the Feather River to the eastern shore of San Francisco Bay, they had completed only the first of their carefully drawn plans. By the end of the following year, they had placed in operation their Oakland steam-operated generating station to make "firm" the continuity of their power supply.

Having no distribution lines or other outlet through which electricity could be sold to customers, they were compelled at first to wholesale their power to Pacific Gas and Electric Company. They stood at the gateway to San Francisco with no means to span the few miles of Bay waters that separate Oakland from the city. Also, when and if their lines reached San Francisco, no customer outlets were available there. The wires and conduits of long-established electric companies already crowded the city's streets.

Great Western found a way to break the barrier—purchase of the San Francisco system of the City Electric Company on July 1, 1911. The City Electric Company had been incorporated January 14, 1907, by Mortimer and Herbert Fleishhacker and Walter Arnstein. The time was favorable for a strong competitor, and by 1911 City Electric had obtained considerable business. As has been noted, it bought for a few thousand dollars the underground conduits of Martell Power Company to increase its downtown distribution.

Great Western Power Company, through Western Power, its New Jersey holding company, transferred to the Fleishhacker interests, in exchange for City Electric Company, $2,670,000 in common stock of the holding company, $3,000,000 in bonds, and $1,000,000 in preferred stock of its subsidiary, California Electric Generating Company. City Electric's funded debt also was assumed.

The Fleishhackers were bankers but they also were experienced in electric utility promotion through organization of the American River Electric Company in 1903. Mortimer Fleishhacker had become president of Anglo California Trust Company, and Herbert president of Anglo and London Paris National Bank, predecessors of the present Anglo California National of San Francisco. After sale of City Electric Company, the Fleishhackers were elected Great Western directors and were appointed to executive positions. In 1912, Mortimer Fleishhacker was elected president of Great Western Power Company, a position he held for the next 12 years. Herbert was made a vice-president.

Great Western Power's position in San Francisco was fortified on January 29, 1912, when its first transbay cable began delivering power from Big Bend into the city. The cable was laid from the Oakland Bay shore to a landing at Folsom Street in San Francisco. Eventually the Company had five underwater cables. The second was laid in 1915; the third, by way of Yerba Buena Island, in 1916; and later two more from Richmond north of Oakland.

The Big Bend–Oakland transmission line passed Oroville, Marysville, and Sacramento en route to the bay. Lacking local distribution systems, Great Western Power sought mining and agricultural customers in the territory adjacent to its lines. Large industrial users of electricity were solicited in Oakland, Sacramento, and San Francisco. The company sold power to the United Railroads in San Francisco and to a big cement plant in Contra Costa County.

The load continued to grow. Small independent electric companies were taken over wherever they could be found—one in Sacramento, another in San Leandro near Oakland, one in South San Francisco and in Half Moon Bay on the coast. A line was run from South San Francisco to Half Moon Bay and nearby towns which gave access to a large peninsular area.

Great Western Power Company was the first of the utility companies to find its activities limited by the Public Utilities Act of 1911. The company wished to extend its business into Solano, Napa, Sonoma, and Marin Counties by running branches from its main transmission lines. But the new law required a showing of "convenience and necessity" for these extensions. Consequently, on May 6, 1912, less than two months after the act went into effect, Great Western applied to the State Railroad Commission for a certificate of approval of its plans. Pacific Gas and Electric Company opposed the application, asserting that the territory already was adequately served. But the commission disagreed and on June 18, 1912, granted the requested permission.

* * *

While Great Western Power was continuing to grow, its engineers resumed studies of the original plan to convert the Big Meadows basin into a great water-storage reservoir.

After its completion in 1908, Big Bend Powerhouse was operated by the natural flow of the north fork of the Feather River. Additional hydroelectric development along the river would require a large reserve of water for regulation of the stream flow during the dry months and years. Such a reserve was to be provided by throwing a dam across the gorge at the downstream outlet of Big Meadows and flooding the wide basin during the next spring runoff.

The reservoir so created was called Lake Almanor, a name devised by Julius M. Howells by combining syllables from the names of the three daughters of Vice-President Earl—ALice, MArtha, EleaNOR. It was Howells who, years earlier, had seen in Big Meadows and its vast watershed an ideal site for hydroelectric development; who had first brought the idea to E. T.

and Guy C. Earl; and who soon was to design the dam which was to transform the cattle ranch country into a big and beautiful mountain lake.

Construction of the dam was attended by difficulties that grew in volume as the work proceeded. Consulting engineer John R. Freeman, in 1904, had proposed a Cyclopean masonry dam; but by 1910, when it was decided to start the project, a multiple arch design prepared by John S. Eastwood and Ralph Bennett was accepted.

Work had not proceeded far before the builders ran into unexpected trouble. Five of the 22 concrete arches and foundations for others had been completed during excavation of the remaining portion of the stream bed. Then the diggers found they had to go much deeper for a solid rock foundation than exploratory borings had indicated. A thick seam of clay lay beneath the stratum of lava on which the buttresses were to rest.

The situation became more serious when news leaked from the camp that all was not well with the dam project. Rumors spread that the structure would be unsafe if completed according to the original plan. In Oroville and Marysville citizen committees were appointed to investigate. In San Francisco, President Fleishhacker was quoted in denial of the rumors:

"We have had three boards of engineers examine this project and they have all reported favorably. . . . The mere assumption that this company, projecting an enterprise which will cost millions of dollars, would put in a dam which had the least possibility of breaking, is ridiculous. . . ."

When the controversy continued, a public hearing of the facts was held by the State Railroad Commission, which was cut short when Guy C. Earl announced that the multiple arch type of dam would be abandoned. Construction ceased in November, 1912.

A decision was made to build a hydraulic-fill dam upstream from the abandoned works. Julius M. Howells designed the new barrier, which was to be constructed by sluicing into the area between the canyon walls large quantities of gravel, sand,

and clay, forming a clay core supported by sand and gravel on the outside slopes.

The dam was completed in June, 1914. Its crest, 85 feet wide, extended 650 feet from one canyon wall to the other. Its height was 72 feet from the stream bed to the crest. Its massive base was 550 feet thick. Along the crest was a county road, relocated because its former route lay on the land to be flooded. The first Lake Almanor had a capacity of 220,000 acre-feet, less than a fifth of its ultimate size.

Julius M. Howells, one of the originators of the hydraulic-fill type of dam construction, served as consulting engineer for the project; R. F. Krafft, who today is a veteran member of the P. G. and E. engineering staff, was an assistant to the resident engineer.

Construction of Lake Almanor Dam was but a part, although the major part, of the project. Much of the Big Meadows land was heavily forested, and the Red River Lumber Company, operated by T. B. Walker of Minnesota, was called upon to clear the wide area. A rail line was constructed and a sawmill erected to handle the logging job which produced some 300,000,000 board feet of lumber. Before water flooded the area, the partly burned remains of the old mining town of Prattville were cleared away.

Roads had to be relocated above the water line of the lake and a 12-mile road constructed from the town of Greenville to the dam site for the hauling of materials, which were transported through Greenville from Keddie, a station on the Western Pacific railroad, a total distance of 26 miles. When an enterprising freighter brought in a fleet of motor trucks to supplement and eventually to replace the six- and eight-mule teams that had provided transportation during the first few months, a storm of protest arose. The 10-ton trucks churned the dirt road into a sea of dust; their sirens frightened the horses and mules still driven by the mountain people; they held up traffic by monopolizing the narrow, winding road, which had few turnouts for passing. Petitions were circulated demanding a county ordinance to limit operation of the gasoline-powered freighters to the night hours. In the end the moderns defeated the old-timers. It was estimated that each truck did the work of 23 horses, making the 52-mile round trip in 10 hours, while the horse- or mule-drawn wagons required three days.

In 1916, flashboards were installed on the spillway crest of Almanor Dam, increasing the capacity to nearly 300,000 acre-feet. The dam then served its purpose successfully for another 10 years until increased demand for Great Western power necessitated the building of more hydroelectric generating facilities. To supply the requisite water power, a new and higher hydraulic-fill dam was built in 1925–1927 to increase fourfold the water storage in the lake. The new barrier was placed just below and joined to the old. Its crest ran 1,200 feet from bank to bank, 75 feet wide and 130 feet above the stream bed. The massive structure is 1,350 feet thick at its base. Its increased height raised the possible maximum storage capacity to 1,308,000 acre-feet, although that total never has been reached.

Construction of the new Almanor Dam was supervised by W. G. B. Euler, Great Western general superintendent; Charles M. Mardel, chief engineer; Julius M. Howells and John D. Galloway, consulting engineers; and R. F. Krafft, resident engineer.

To prepare for the higher level of the lake provided by the new dam, the power company again was compelled to relocate roads at higher levels and remove more standing timber and buildings. A causeway for a logging railroad and state highway was constructed across an arm of the land to be flooded. The Prattville cemetery and three Indian burying grounds were moved above the new water line.

* * *

The story of Lake Almanor Dam would not be complete without mentioning briefly the adventures of the Oro Electric Corporation. Oro Electric was incorporated March 11, 1911, to take over some gold-dredging companies and the properties of the Oro Water, Light and Power Company, which served gas, electricity, and water to the town of Oroville in Butte County.

Oro Electric Corporation announced ambitious plans of development. A $10,000,000 hydroelectric plant was to be built on Yellow Creek at the point where it flows into the north fork of the Feather River. A dam was to be thrown across Yellow Creek to provide water storage. Transmission lines were to be built through several counties of the Sacramento Valley and eventually to San Francisco Bay cities. Through a subsidiary, the Oro Development Company, irrigation pumping was to be developed on a grand scale in all the rural areas.

In order to obtain additional water for their project, the Oro engineers threw a diversion dam across the adjoining Butt Creek which flows into the Feather River just below Almanor Dam. At this point Great Western Power entered the fray. Great Western had installed a small generating station on Butt Creek to provide power for dam construction. Its engineers declared the Oro company had no claim to the flow of the creek where Great Western held long-established water rights. When the Oro men persisted, Superintendent J. W. Bumgarner led a crew of his men to the Butt Creek diversion dam and blew it to splinters with dynamite.

Court action and State Railroad Commission hearings followed. The controversy continued from 1911 to 1917, when P. G. and E. ended the fight by buying control of Oro Electric and taking over its utility properties.

* * *

In 1915, seeking to promote agricultural development, Great Western organized the Western Canal Company which acquired rights and properties of two canal companies and built about 40 miles of main canal and laterals to irrigate some 20,000 acres in Butte and Glenn Counties. Water for the canal system was diverted from the Feather River 3 miles below Oroville. An important part of the flow comes from the company's Lake Almanor storage system.

Western Canal Company was established as a mutual company but later was declared legally to be a public utility. The system was acquired by P. G. and E. through purchase of Great Western Power Company properties. Since then it has been operated as a part of the extensive P. G. and E. water system, providing irrigation water for thousands of acres of productive land.

* * *

Lake Almanor was the key that opened the door to the Feather River's treasures of hydroelectric power. Caribou Powerhouse, situated 12 miles downstream from Lake Almanor Dam, was the second plant built by Great Western.

The name Caribou was an accidental misnomer. The old mine and canal after which the plant had been named had been christened "Cariboo" by some homesick British Columbian, after the northern town and mountain range bearing that name. When it was suggested that the new power plant be given the historic appellation, the name makers mistakenly assumed that the word referred to the cousin of the horned reindeer of the North and the power plant has been called *Caribou* ever since.

Work was started in 1919; the new powerhouse was first operated on May 6, 1921. Three generators, with a capacity of 73,000 kilowatts, produce power for transmission to the San Francisco Bay region. The power output is transmitted at 165,000 volts over a steel tower line 196 miles to Golden Gate substation near the city of Richmond on San Francisco Bay. From there a 7-mile underwater cable carries the current to San Francisco.

Because of the scenic beauty of its surroundings and a comfortably appointed clubhouse, Caribou Powerhouse long has been a favorite spot for the entertainment of Company guests. The clubhouse, which is maintained primarily for the bachelor operators of the plant, is known to hundreds of distinguished visitors. And all of them remember Gee Yuen, the smiling and skilled Chinese cook ("chef" would be a more deserved title) who regarded himself as host to every arrival from "outside." Gee came to Caribou after service in France during World War I. Following nearly 30 years of honorable performance of duty at the power plant, he was retired on pension in 1950.

* * *

Great Western Power Company added to its corporate family in 1915, and itself was reorganized to place it in position to undertake the building of Caribou and other hydro plants. On February 2, 1915, Consolidated Electric Company, a wholly owned subsidiary, was organized to bring together a number of San Francisco and Oakland electric companies that had been formed since 1908 by R. G. Hanford, F. M. (Borax) Smith, W. S. Tevis, and others. They were Consumers Light and Power Company, Equitable Light and Power Company, Southside Light and Power Company, and Central Oakland Light and Power Company.

By 1910 all of these ventures had been placed under the control of United Light and Power Company of California. When they lost their right to do business by failing to pay franchise and license taxes, Fleishhacker obtained control of the properties for Great Western Power under the new Consolidated Electric Company's name.

On November 22, 1915, the old Great Western was superseded by Great Western Power Company of California, with a capitalization of $30,000,000 in common stock and $30,000,000 in 7 per cent cumulative preferred shares. Taking the place of the original New Jersey holding company, the Western Power Corporation was organized under New York laws to hold all but directors' shares of the Great Western Power Company's common stock.

Great Western continued to wage a determined battle for business. Customers in San Francisco were increasing at such a rate that in 1916 a new steam generating station was built at 530 Bush Street to provide additional power supply and live steam for use in downtown office buildings. The Bush Street plant, converted to service as Substation R, still is in operation as part of the P. G. and E. system.

Great Western Power had become a powerful factor when the 1920 decade opened. The company had extended its distribution lines until it was serving 31,615 domestic, agricultural, and industrial customers in some 15 counties of Northern California.

During the preceding years there had been many rumors that Pacific Gas and Electric Company and Great Western Power were to be merged. The rumors had a certain basis in fact.

Soon after Great Western completed Big Bend Powerhouse, the subject of consolidation of the two systems became a recurring topic of conversation between representatives of the two companies. The talks had never crystallized into definite action but conditions were shaping toward that end.

CHAPTER 27

Decade of Consolidation

TO WIGGINTON E. CREED, a young lawyer untrained in gas and electric utility operation, fell the task of piloting P. G. and E. during the early 1920s. Frank G. Drum, before his resignation, was deeply concerned over the selection of a successor, and it was he, upon suggestion from his brother, John S. Drum, who recommended Creed's appointment. John Drum had come into contact with the young lawyer during business conferences in Oakland and at hearings before the State Railroad Commission and had acquired a deep respect for his capacity and talents.

Creed was only forty-three when he assumed the presidency of P. G. and E. on July 28, 1920. A graduate of the University of California and a regent of the university during a term as president of its alumni association, he first earned distinction as a practicing attorney in Oakland. In 1913 he was retained to guide the reorganization of the People's Water Company of Oakland, which resulted in the founding of the East Bay Water Company. During two years as president of the water corporation, he gained his first intimate knowledge of public utility problems and of state regulation by the Railroad Commission.

Other executive experiences followed: president of Columbia Steel of Pittsburg, Calif.; president of C. A. Hooper and Company, wholesale lumber; president of the Contra Costa Bank at Pittsburg; director of Wells Fargo Bank and Union Trust Company of San Francisco, Associated Oil Company, and East Bay Water Company.

The new president early evinced a keen interest in two major factors of utility administration—the Company's staff organization and its relations with the public it serves and with its employees. P. G. and E. had been formed from the consolidation of two widely differing organizations—one entirely a San Francisco body, the other a young utility company composed of many older subsidiaries, owning or controlling properties scattered throughout Northern California. Its business was administered by district managers, each reporting to the central office.

Within a few months after he came to the Company, Creed effected a reorganization further to fuse the system into a single unified body. He divided the area served by P. G. and E. into geographical divisions, each with a headquarters office in the principal city of its territory. Each was placed in charge of a division manager, under whom were superintendents of electric and gas operations, district managers, and managers of sales and other local departments. Division managers were granted full authority within their territories, subject only to direction from the central office in San Francisco. The system thus established is still maintained, there now being 13 divisions through which all local business of the Company is transacted.

Reorganization of the Company's general staff followed. John A. Britton continued as vice-president and general manager; A. F. Hockenbeamer, vice-president and treasurer; and D. H. Foote, secretary—all veterans of the Company's first years. Six new vice-presidencies were created by promotion of men with long records of service. They were P. M. Downing, in charge of electrical construction and operation; F. A. Leach, Jr., public relations and service; W. G. Vincent, executive engineer; A. H. Markwart, in charge of engineering; W. S. Yard, engineer of gas construction; R. E. Fisher, in charge of sales.

Not long after this reorganization, one of the leaders came to the end of his long career in utility service. John A. Britton died June 29, 1923, in his sixty-seventh year. For 49 years he had labored in the utility field, starting with the Oakland Gas Light Company as a collector. His talents for administration and his interest in the human side of business had brought him to the post of general manager of P. G. and E. in 1907, where he remained throughout his career.

Micro-wave tower at Newark power-switching station is part of micro-wave circuit which puts system dispatcher in instant touch with vital power resources of P. G. and E.

Wigginton E. Creed added many valuable utility properties to Pacific Gas and Electric Company during his presidency, 1920 to 1927.

A. Emory Wishon, distinguished son of pioneer utility man A. G. Wishon, became vice-president and general manager of P. G. and E. in 1943 and executive vice-president in 1947.

A. F. Hockenbeamer, president from 1927 to 1935, brought about final major consolidations—Great Western and San Joaquin power systems—by which P. G. and E. fulfilled its destiny.

Paul M. Downing, veteran electrical engineer, was P. G. and E. vice-president and general manager from 1929 to 1943 and executive vice-president from 1943 to 1945.

The general office building of Pacific Gas and Electric Company at 245 Market Street, San Francisco, was completed in 1925, annex (right) in 1948.

John A. Britton was succeeded as general manager by Frank A. Leach, Jr., then in charge of public relations.

After the death of Britton, President Creed found he needed someone to share his heavy executive burdens. In 1923 he appointed as assistant to the president John P. Coghlan, then serving as attorney and manager of the claims department. Four years later Coghlan was elected vice-president and assistant to the president and later a director of the Company. He has occupied the same position under three presidents, and at this writing, still at his desk, he exerts an unobtrusive but potent influence upon the conduct of the Company's affairs.

Son of a pioneer hydraulic miner, John P. Coghlan was born at North Columbia on the San Juan ridge in Nevada County, not far from where John Martin and Eugene de Sabla built Rome Powerhouse, their first venture in hydroelectric development. His first schooling was at the little schoolhouse where a single teacher guided the children of the remote community through the elementary grades.

When Coghlan was fourteen, his father moved his family to San Francisco and the boy went to work to help in their support. His first job was as a $4-a-week copy boy and messenger on the *Evening Post*. In the evenings he continued his education at night school. From copy boy he progressed to reporter, later covering state and Federal courts for the *Bulletin* under Fremont Older, its famous editor. Long night hours were spent in study of the law.

Admitted to the bar, Coghlan turned from journalism to active practice, and in 1904 was appointed assistant to the city attorney of San Francisco. In 1908 he joined P. G. and E. as attorney in claims and compensation cases. During this service, he organized the Company's first claims and safety departments, set up a central safety committee, and established a system-wide program of accident prevention.

As assistant to the president, Coghlan has been especially interested in the Company's publicity program, its relations with the public, and its promotion of employee welfare. A considerate and understanding executive, his door is always open to employees with problems that need solution. Coghlan was largely responsible for establishment of *P. G. and E. Progress* in 1923, a plain, unpretentious eight-page monthly publication designed to inform customers, stockholders, and employees of the utility's affairs, its development and problems. With readers in every part of the world, *Progress* now has the extraordinary circulation of approximately 1,250,000 copies.

In the first issue of *Progress* in 1923, President Creed expressed in a single meaty sentence an ideal of public relations that best describes the policy that has been developed over the years. "The aim of the Company," he said, "has been to win the public good will by *deserving* the public good will."

Pacific Gas and Electric Company continued to grow in the 1920s. Its service of gas and electricity was firmly established. Its system had become completely integrated with the economy of Northern California. By the end of 1925, its report of progress showed these advances as compared to 1915:

Gain in gross revenue	157.6 per cent
Gain in sales of electricity	173.6 per cent
Gain in sales of gas	94.6 per cent
Gain in number of customers	101.6 per cent
Gain in number of stockholders	382.5 per cent

One consequence of this growth was the construction of a new general office headquarters building at 245 Market Street, San Francisco. The solid, gray 17-story structure was occupied in 1925 by the officers of the Company and departmental staffs. It served adequately until 1948, when a 13-story wing was added to house the enlarged personnel.

* * *

The process of utility consolidation was continued through the Creed presidency by purchase of stock control of four established gas and electric systems which added large segments of service area to the P. G. and E. domain. By the end of 1927, the Company in seven years had nearly doubled the total number of customers served, which then approached the million mark. Electric capacity also had been nearly doubled, providing electricity to more than 300 Northern California communities.

First of the independent companies to be absorbed by P. G. and E. at this time was the California Telephone and Light Company which had been organized November 23, 1911, to bring under one banner 37 small electric and telephone utilities in Lake, Sonoma, and Mendocino Counties. Lakeport, Kelseyville, Cloverdale, Calistoga, and extensive rural areas were among the communities served. An agreement was reached April 17, 1923, to transfer its properties to P. G. and E.

California Telephone and Light Company's properties were operated as a unit until 1929 when integration and interconnection with the P. G. and E. system was completed. Two years earlier the telephone properties were sold to the Sacramento Valley Telephone Company.

Acquisition of Western States Gas and Electric Company, Coast Valley Gas and Electric Company, and Sierra and San Francisco Power Company in 1927 and 1928 by exchange of stock was a deal of greater magnitude. The seller was Standard Gas and Electric Company, which was a wholly owned subsidiary of H. M. Byllesby & Co. of Chicago, a utility investment firm which owned many operating utilities in the Middle West and on the Pacific Coast.

Western States Gas and Electric Company had been incorporated November 30, 1910, by the Byllesby company to join under one management utility companies in the widely separated cities of Stockton, Eureka, and Richmond—the Stockton Gas and Electric Corporation, the Eureka Gas Works, and the Richmond Light and Power Corporation. The Western States corporate background consisted of 26 predecessor and component companies. Its service area included eight Northern California counties and parts of three others.

The Coast Valleys Company and Sierra and San Francisco Power Company had been acquired by the Byllesby firm when in 1925 it obtained control of the United Railroads in San Francisco. Coast Valleys had been organized March 18, 1912, by the consolidation of several older utilities in Monterey and San Benito Counties. The company served gas and electricity to the towns of Salinas, Monterey, and King City and to farm areas in Monterey and San Benito Counties. Water systems in

King City and Salinas were included in its holdings. Among the constituent companies were the California Consolidated Light and Power Company and the pioneer Salinas City Gas and Electric Company.

Acquisition of Sierra and San Francisco Power Company involved only the legal formalities of transfer of ownership, as the physical properties had been operated under lease by P. G. and E. since January 1, 1920. The Sierra and San Francisco company was the result of the pressing need for hydro power to operate the streetcars of San Francisco. When the Stanislaus Electric Power Company became involved in financial troubles in 1908 after completing a large powerhouse and flume on the middle fork of the Stanislaus River, the San Francisco street railway operators grasped the opportunity to obtain the electric power source they long had been seeking. United Railway Investment Company, their New Jersey holding organization, formed the Sierra corporation May 28, 1909. Properties of the bankrupt Stanislaus Power company were purchased and a steel tower line was built to transmit energy from Stanislaus Powerhouse to Bay Shore substation, which supplied the United Railroads in San Francisco.

When P. G. and E. became owner of the Sierra company's properties, it fell heir to a large number of water properties in Stanislaus and Tuolumne Counties that had been handed down from the earliest gold-rush days. Forty-nine constituent and predecessor corporations were included in the Sierra company's holdings. Among these one finds names and places reminiscent of the time when Mark Twain and Bret Harte wrote and lived in the camps in the vicinity of historic "Jimtown" (Jamestown), Columbia, and Sonora. There are the Woods Diggins Water Company (1851), Tuolumne Hydraulic Association (1852), Gold Mountain Water Works and Mining Company (1854), Tuolumne County Water Company (1852), Nil Desperandum Water Company (1860), and dozens more.

Stanislaus Powerhouse drew its water supply from sources high in the mountains above it through a wooden flume 16 miles long. The timber structure, which clung to the precipitous walls of the middle fork canyon, served its purpose for 31 years until it was replaced in 1939 by 11 miles of tunnel.

* * *

Purchase of the three systems—Western States, Coast Valleys, and Sierra—concluded April 27, 1927, brought territorial strength to P. G. and E. None of the three was in direct competition with the older company. Their service areas filled in the gaps in many parts of the P. G. and E. systems. They added valuable properties, power and water sources, and some 83,000 customers to the Company's holdings. This acquisition was nearly the last important accomplishment of President Creed.

Wigginton E. Creed died August 6, 1927, after a brief illness. He was only fifty years old.

One of Creed's favorite promotions was cooperation with the irrigation districts. He had made a contract with the Nevada Irrigation District for use of its water for generation of power in the Company's Placer County plants before it was sent on its way to the foothill farm lands. A few weeks before his death the Melones Powerhouse in Tuolumne County was placed in operation, June 1, 1927. The project was one in which he had been deeply interested. Melones Dam and Powerhouse had been built by the cooperative efforts of P. G. and E. and the Oakdale and South San Joaquin Irrigation Districts. The utility company erected the powerhouse to generate electricity before release of the water into the district's irrigation canals. Melones Powerhouse still is in operation, an excellent example of cooperation between the electric utility and the irrigationists to secure maximum benefit from water resources.

CHAPTER 28

The Pit—Magical Hydro River

LONG BEFORE the Armistice brought World War I to an end, it was apparent that P. G. and E. again must seek additional electric power sources. The demand of war industries, the ever-growing use of electricity by communities in the Company's broadening field of service, and the beginning of a cycle of short-water-supply years made the need acute.

Even before the end of hostilities made materials and equipment available, the engineers started plans for a great power project on the Pit River in Shasta County far to the north of San Francisco. Conceived in the time of President Frank G. Drum, construction was started and completed in the first years of W. E. Creed's administration as chief executive.

Of all the streams of the Sierra and Cascade mountain ranges, none was better designed by nature than the Pit River for the generation of electricity. Hydro engineers for years had looked forward to the time when development of its resources should become economically feasible. Only its remote location, far from centers of population, had deferred realization of their hopes.

The Pit country is a wild and beautiful region, once peopled by warring tribes of Indians, the Pits and the Wintoons. The name of the river and the native tribe is believed to have come from the custom of the Indians of digging deep pits on the bank of the stream for roasting fresh-water mussels. History of the region is filled with tales of adventure told by early explorers, Hudson's Bay trappers, and pioneer settlers. The Modoc Wars added a chapter of battles in which Civil War Generals Philip H. Sheridan and John B. Hood fought when they were only obscure lieutenants, and in which General E. R. S. Canby was murdered by Indians when they tricked the Americans with a false flag of truce. The Lassen Trail, traveled by some of the immigrants of 1849, traversed the Pit region. To the north and a little westward stands Mt. Shasta, the mountain Joaquin Miller, the poet, described as "Lonely as God and white as a winter moon." Into this remote land came the twentieth-century builders, seeking water power for their turbines and electric generators.

The Pit River rises in the Cascade Mountains in the extreme northeastern corner of California in Modoc County, cuts across Lassen County, and traverses Shasta County to empty into the Sacramento River. Its vast watershed, 4,900 square miles in extent, formed by volcanic action and prehistoric lava flows, is honeycombed with subterranean channels and perennial springs fed by the melting snow and winter rains which sink through the porous ground instead of running off the surface. From these underground storage pools the Pit draws the constant flow which makes it ideal for the operation of electric generating plants.

Gathering volume as it flows through the lava beds of Modoc County, the river drops into its canyon, hemmed in by mountain walls, just below the point where it is joined by its tributary, Fall River. From there for more than 75 miles the stream runs fast and full-bodied, falling rapidly in elevation as it hurries to its confluence with the Sacramento.

J. R. Scupham, a civil engineer who explored the region in 1875 searching for a possible route for the Central Pacific railroad's California-Oregon line, first noted the hydroelectric virtues of the Pit. He built a boat at Fall River Mills and, with a German naturalist, attempted to float down the river to its mouth. The German lost his life when he attempted alone to run one of the many perilous rapids that roughen the upper reaches. Scupham made his way out safely. In 1883 he prepared a report on the river's hydro potentials and outlined a plan for their development.

For more than 20 years the source lay dormant. Economical transmission of power for the 250 miles that lay between the

Pit and San Francisco Bay cities was the obstacle. Then mining engineer John Hays Hammond became interested. With his financial backing the Mt. Shasta Power Company was organized in 1909 to build a power plant at a spot on the lower river called Big Bend. Hammond's plan followed the familiar pattern—a diversion dam at the head of the bend in the river's course, a tunnel cutting across to the lower point of the arc, and a powerhouse there to receive its water supply dropped from the tunnel outlet. Preliminary work was started on the project but was discontinued.

In the meantime, the Northern California Power Company, which was distributing electricity to Red Bluff, Redding, and a number of other towns in the northern Sacramento Valley, had chosen a site not far from that of the Mt. Shasta company's project. G. R. Milford, who in later years was to become a leading figure in P. G. and E. operations in Shasta County, completed surveys for a powerhouse on the Big Bend of the Pit River. With J. H. Stutt he had fixed the location of the diversion dam almost at the exact spot where many years afterward P. G. and E. built a dam for its Pit 5 Powerhouse. Tunnel construction was started; then, because of financial difficulties, work was suspended.

The years passed. P. G. and E. engineers long had looked to the Pit River as their next major construction job. Plans were drawn, not for one powerhouse but for six, located like steps of a stairway at intervals along the river's downhill course. But, first, possession of water rights was essential, and to this end, November 16, 1917, Pacific Gas and Electric Company completed, through stock purchase, the acquisition of the Mt. Shasta Power Company's properties. Similar action was taken with the Northern California Power Company, Consolidated, which was added to the P. G. and E. system August 29, 1919. The purchases cleared the way for Pit River development.

First of the chain of generating plants was to be Pit 1 near the head of the canyon 5 miles below Fall River Mills. While preparations for construction were going forward, two smaller powerhouses on Hat Creek, a nearby tributary of the Pit, were erected primarily for the Red River Lumber Company which needed power for its extensive logging operations. Hat Creek Powerhouses 1 and 2, completed August 22 and September 28, 1921, were operated by P. G. and E. under a lease agreement until 1945, when they were purchased from the lumber company.

Construction of Pit 1 in its isolated location was a challenge to the engineers. Speed was necessary because of the cry for more power in Northern California. In the deep snow of midwinter, surveying parties mapped a railroad line 33 miles between the plant site and the terminus of the McCloud River Railroad, a lumber carrier which connected with the Southern Pacific's main line. Graders and rail layers followed the surveyors as soon as weather permitted, and 120 days later the first of tens of thousands of tons of materials and equipment began to arrive at the powerhouse site.

Although Pit 1 Powerhouse stands on the bank of the river for which it is named, its water power comes from the Fall River, a tributary of the Pit. The flow is diverted near the town of Fall River Mills into a short tunnel which carries it to the powerhouse penstock pipes and turbines.

Pit 1 Powerhouse, which produces 57,000 kilowatts of energy at present rating, is like a castle of the Rhineland transplanted to a mountainside in a California wilderness. Its lofty and imposing façade and turreted towers are in sharp contrast to the functional, rectangular simplicity of today's powerhouse design. The structure was designed by Ivan Frickstad, then head of the Company's architectural department.

Planned by Engineer Frank G. Baum and built under the supervision of P. M. Downing, vice-president in charge of electrical construction and operation, and O. W. Peterson, construction engineer, the first of the Pit River plants was placed in operation September 30, 1922. Power was transmitted at 220,000 volts over one of the earliest lines of that high tension to Vaca-Dixon Substation, 202 miles away, and thence at 110 volts via Oakland to Newark Substations for switching into P. G. and E.'s interconnected system. The voltage and distance marked a long stride from the time in 1895 when transmission at 11,000 volts 22 miles from Folsom to Sacramento was hailed as a history-making achievement.

This addition to the power resources of the north was considered so important to the region's economy that the chambers of commerce of the Sacramento Valley arranged a celebration to commemorate the event. Five hundred persons made the long trip to the powerhouse to watch President Creed start the generators. Five thousand gathered at the Vaca-Dixon Substation, where General Manager John A. Britton telephoned the signal that all was ready to receive and distribute the new supply of energy from the Pit River.

Development of the Pit's resources continued. The 1923–1924 winter season was the eighth in succession in which rainfall was deficient. Construction of a second plant on the Pit was started soon after Pit 1 was completed. Pit 3 Powerhouse, capacity 70,000 kilowatts, was placed in operation July 15, 1925, downstream from Pit 1. Lake Britton, formed by a low dam across the stream above the plant, serves as a forebay for regulation of the flow to the penstocks and turbines.

Nearly 20 years passed before the builders returned to erect a third and greater plant on the Pit, and even then the water power resources of the stream were not exhausted. Soon the engineers will go there again to take more of its energy for hydroelectric production.

* * *

When control of Northern California Power Company, Consolidated, was purchased by P. G. and E., six water-powered generating plants with a capacity of approximately 30,700 kilowatts were acquired, together with a transmission and distribution system and a considerable electric, gas, and water business. Northern California Power Company was serving a territory about 100 miles long and 50 miles wide in six northern counties beyond the limits of the P. G. and E. service area.

Northern California Power Company, Consolidated, traced its origin to 1900 when H. H. Noble, a San Francisco financier, organized the Keswick Electric Power Company. Noble's first purpose was to supply electricity to the Mountain Copper Company at Keswick. In 1901 he built Volta Powerhouse in Shasta County, using old sawmill ditches and the flow of North Battle Creek for his water supply.

From the beginning, Noble's project made progress. He extended his lines. He absorbed gas, electric, and water companies in Red Bluff, Redding, Corning, Orland, Willows, and Williams; built a second powerhouse, Kilarc; and over his own 60,000-volt transmission line to Chico sold power to the California Gas and Electric Corporation.

The name of the Keswick company was changed in 1902 to Northern California Power Company, with a later addition of the word "Consolidated." Noble was joined in financing the reorganization by a syndicate which included San Francisco capitalists Edward Coleman and Antoine Borel.

In 1919 when control passed to Pacific Gas and Electric Company, Northern California Power represented the consolidation of 19 antecedent companies and systems. It was serving mines, gold dredges, irrigation districts, a large agricultural area, and many industries that had been promoted because of the availability of electric power.

The first interstate electric connection with Oregon was made by Northern California Power when, in 1918, its lines were connected to those of the California-Oregon Power Company at Delta. Power interchange facilities with the Oregon system have been continued ever since.

Northern California Power and its employees were involved over the years in a long series of disputes. The city of Redding was the scene of one of these disagreements. Town officials complained that the arc lamps that lighted the streets were obsolete and inefficient and demanded that the street lighting be modernized. President Noble refused. The situation became so tense that in 1913 agitation was started for municipal ownership of the electric distribution system, and this was said to have been the origin of the movement which resulted in Redding's going into the electric business in 1921. The city has managed its own system ever since that year, purchasing its power supply from P. G. and E.

The farmers fought constantly for what they considered their rights to the waters of Battle Creek and other streams used for the generation of electricity. The company's days were punctuated by rifle shots, destruction of water diversion dams, cutting of wires, arrests, alleged misappropriation of water, and almost constant litigation.

G. R. Milford, now "G. R." to most Northern California habitants, came close to death several times as a member of the company's staff. Once a whining rifle bullet missed him by inches when he found that a gate in a stream had been illegally opened to flood a rancher's land.

At another time Milford was threatened by Molly Flood, a ranch woman, who attempted to split his head open with an ax when he stopped her from diverting water which was the property of his company. From this and similar incidents arose the famous Smith and Asbury water suits which occupied the courts of Shasta County from 1912 to 1920. Milford was once forced to take a loaded shotgun away from an irate rancher who threatened to shoot him if he interfered with the rancher's attempt to divert water from one of the company's sources of supply.

P. G. and E. ended the fighting and litigation when it purchased all conflicting rights. Mrs. Flood used the money she received in settlement of her claims to purchase P. G. and E. stock. Three of her four sons and a son-in-law became employees of the Company.

Milford became general manager of all Northern California Power companies' properties, and in 1920 he was appointed manager of the Shasta Division of the P. G. and E. system. In that position he gained distinction for his extensive knowledge of the hydrography of the region and its electric resources. He was also an active civic leader and, as hobbies, a naturalist with an expert's familiarity with the wildlife of the land and a seismologist deeply learned in the volcanic history of Lassen Peak. "G. R." retired in 1948 after 45 years spent in utility development in Northern California.

CHAPTER 29

One Company—One System

INEXORABLY in the 1920s the economic pressures of gas and electric utility operation were bringing nearer to consolidation the three principal systems of Northern California—P. G. and E., Great Western Power, and San Joaquin Light and Power. The long-established principle that public utility service is best provided by a natural, regulated monopoly was slowly but surely drawing the three systems together.

Definite action came in 1922 when P. G. and E. President Creed reported to the board of directors that he had received a tentative proposal that his Company purchase all the capital stock of the Western Power Corporation of New York, the holding company which controlled Great Western Power Company of California. Harley P. Wilson, veteran promoter and one of the founders of Great Western, was at that time president of the New York holding company. Although Creed urged acceptance of the offer, the directors, after consideration by the executive committee, rejected the proposal on the grounds that Great Western's funded debt was overlarge and would impose too heavy a burden upon the purchaser.

Wilson, in his New York office, considered the California situation. The Great Western system had been a costly one to build. If P. G. and E. did not wish to buy, something else should be tried to strengthen the position of the California company. Why not purchase control of San Joaquin Light and Power Corporation and the Midlands corporation and so create a strong combination that would have for its service area a large part of Northern California from the Tehachapi in the south to the upper tier of counties in the north?

There were many good reasons to support Wilson's suggestion. The San Joaquin company, which had no real competition in its field, received a large part of its revenue from sale of power for agricultural purposes. Its electric irrigation pumping load, with peak demand in the summer months, would give to the combination a balanced, diversified business throughout the year. Interconnection of the two systems would strengthen both by making the combined generating resources available to both and providing an additional outlet for Feather River power not yet developed. Economies in administration and operating costs could be effected. Also, the two dominating figures of the San Joaquin company, W. G. Kerckhoff and A. C. Balch of Los Angeles, were nearing their time of retirement. After thirty years of constant activity in gas and electric developments by their numerous companies, they would be receptive to an invitation to sell their stock control.

* * *

Opening of negotiations in 1924 between Western Power and San Joaquin Light and Power brought into prominence a young Californian whose rise in the utility field had been spectacular. He was James B. Black, vice-president and general manager of Great Western Power Company.

After graduation in 1908 from the California School of Mechanical Arts (Lick School) in San Francisco and the University of California in 1912 with a degree of B.S. in mechanical engineering, Black went to work for Great Western Power Company, first as a service inspector and then in the sales department. Promotions came in rapid-fire order—assistant to the general agent, manager of the San Francisco Division, and then in 1918 manager of the sales department when he was only twenty-eight years old. From that position he advanced to general manager in 1922 and to vice-president and general manager a year later at the age of thirty-three with the maturity of judgment and intensity of purpose of a much older man.

And so it happened that when H. P. Wilson decided to explore the possibilities of acquiring control of the San Joaquin utility, he consulted Guy C. Earl, president of Great Western, and James B. Black, the young vice-president. Conversations were opened with A. C. Balch, president of San Joaquin Light and Power, and with Director Ben R. Meyer.

Conferences were held in Los Angeles, in San Francisco, and at last in H. P. Wilson's offices at 50 Broad Street, New York. Agreement was reached November 29, 1924, when Western Power Corporation signed a contract to purchase a controlling interest in the San Joaquin system and the Midland Counties Public Service Corporation. The Fresno City water system, owned by the San Joaquin company, was included in the purchase.

Majority control of the San Joaquin corporation and its system was obtained by purchase of the stock holdings of Kerckhoff, Balch, Meyer, L. T. Haggin, Gordon Blanding, Harry L. Tevis, Louise T. Sharon, and the Mercantile Trust Company of San Francisco. To this group was paid in return for their shares about $6,900,000 in cash and 25,000 shares of the Western Power Corporation's preferred stock with a par value of $100 per share. The consideration amounted to a total of approximately $9,400,000.

Consolidation of ownership of the two systems was not followed by their merger into a single organization. The three companies—Great Western, San Joaquin, and Midlands—were left undisturbed and their management and operating personnel continued in charge as before. A. G. Wishon became president of San Joaquin, and his son A. Emory was elected vice-president and continued in charge as general manager. Physical operation of the systems was coordinated by the building of a connecting transmission line 103 miles between Great Western Power Company's Brighton substation near Sacramento and the San Joaquin trunk lines at Wilson substation in the vicinity of Merced.

While negotiations for the purchase of the San Joaquin properties were going forward in 1924, Wilson had become aware of another and larger New York investment company's interest in California utility properties. This was The North American Company which, among other interests, controlled utilities in St. Louis, Milwaukee, and Cleveland. Frank L. Dame, president of North American, had approached Wilson with a suggestion that his company might be interested in obtaining control of the Western Power Corporation and thus gain ownership of Great Western of California.

"But we are already negotiating for purchase of San Joaquin," said Wilson. "Perhaps we should hold off on that deal until you have time to consider making an offer."

"No," replied Dame, "go right ahead. North American would be more interested in the two systems than in the one."

Consequently, before the first transaction was completed, Wilson and Dame were studying a new shuffling of stock control of the two California systems. The result was an agreement arrived at September 4, 1925, under which North American obtained stock control of Western Power Corporation and, through that medium, control of Great Western Power Company of California, San Joaquin Light and Power Corporation, and Midland Counties Public Service Corporation. The consideration was an exchange of shares by which stockholders of Western Power Corporation received stock in North American for their holdings.

Under North American ownership the two California companies retained their corporate identity but management became more centralized. By February, 1927, A. Emory Wishon had been appointed vice-president and general manager of both the Great Western and San Joaquin companies and had instituted measures to coordinate the operation of the entire system as one organization. James B. Black, who up to that time had served as vice-president and general manager of Great Western, was called to New York where he became a vice-president of The North American Company and of its new subsidiary, the Western Power Corporation, retaining also a vice-presidency in Great Western.

* * *

The wheels of corporate consolidation kept turning. Frank L. Dame pondered his next step, which appeared to be acquisition of Pacific Gas and Electric Company to make com-

Super-Inch pipe line, built over desert, valleys, and mountains, brings natural gas from Texas to California. It is part of P. G. and E.'s 14,000 miles of gas pipe lines.

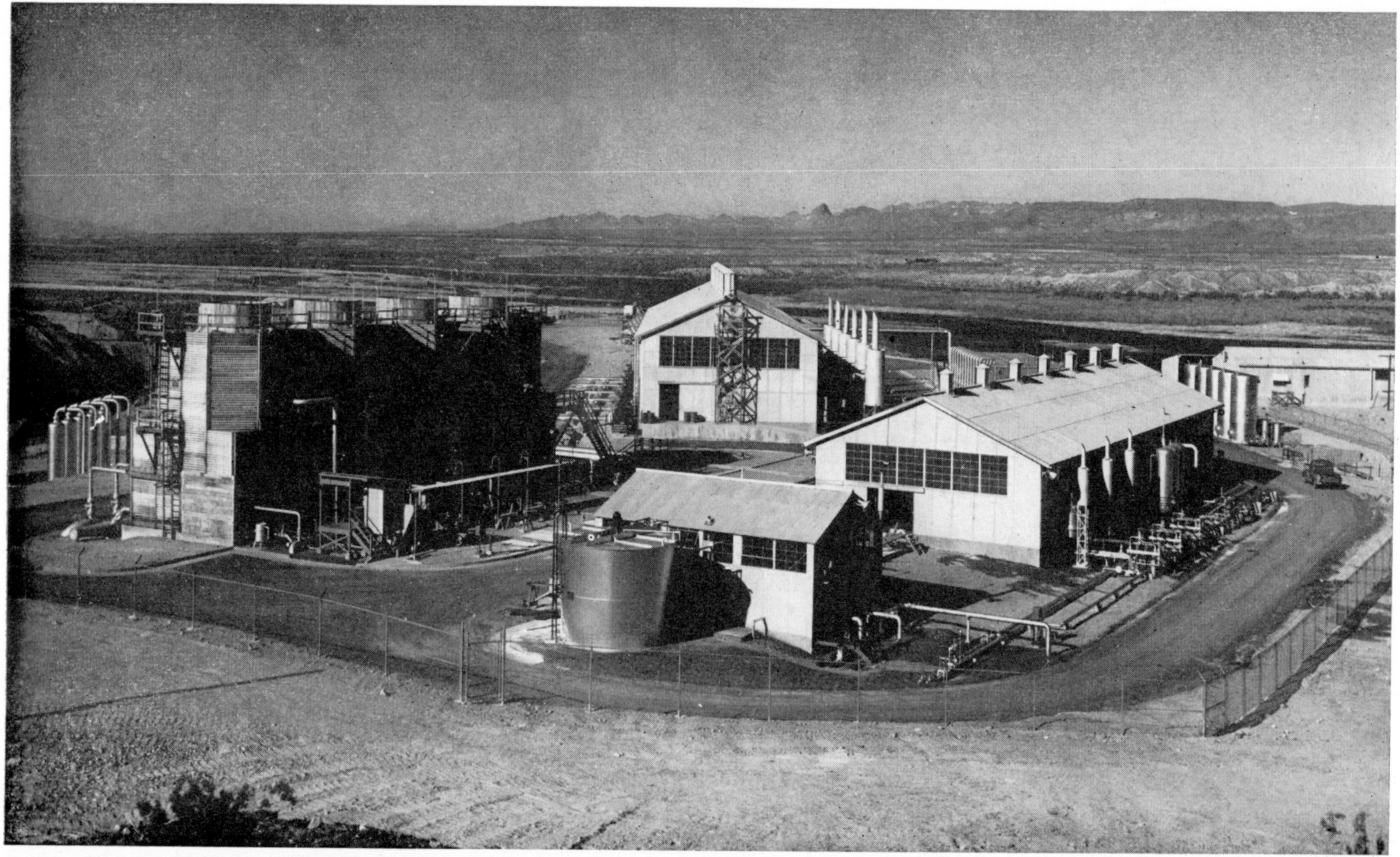

Topock Gas Compressor Station is one of three pressure boosters that keep natural gas
flowing under required pressure in Super Inch pipeline.

These strange-looking cylinders are "scrubbers" at Hinkley Compressor Station on the Super-Inch natural gas pipe line.

James B. Black has been president of Pacific Gas and Electric Company since 1935. He was only forty-five years old when he was elected to the presidency.

John P. Coghlan has served as vice-president, assistant to the president, and director of Pacific Gas and Electric Company nearly 25 years.

plete his mastery of the Northern California situation. He discussed the idea with Black, who told him that he could not hope to obtain control of P. G. and E. as he had of San Joaquin and Great Western. P. G. and E. was too strong. A better way would be to exchange his company's holdings in the California companies for P. G. and E. stock, to be held as an investment. Dame agreed.

Black made frequent trips to San Francisco while he was a vice-president of The North American Company. Always he would drop in for a chat with A. F. Hockenbeamer, who had become president of P. G. and E. following the death of W. E. Creed. The two men discussed a possible merger of the three big systems—Great Western, San Joaquin, and P. G. and E. Eventually Hockenbeamer indicated a desire to consider the idea seriously. Negotiations were carried on by the two in San Francisco in September, 1929. The market crash in October interrupted the conversations. They were resumed later in the year and again were discontinued.

Then one day, Hockenbeamer and A. Emory Wishon were walking together to their respective offices in San Francisco after some civic affairs meeting. They stopped to look in a store window, and as they inspected the display that had attracted them, Hockenbeamer remarked that he hoped Black would see him again about their deal. Wishon lost no time in telephoning Black and informing him of the situation, but Black, using some of Hockenbeamer's favorite horse-trading methods, replied that this time he thought the P. G. and E. president should come to see him in New York. Hockenbeamer went East, accompanied by E. J. Beckett, his financial assistant. He returned to California with a memorandum agreement for purchase by P. G. and E. of The North American Company's majority stock holdings in Great Western Power Company of California, San Joaquin Light and Power Company, Midland Counties Public Service Power Corporation, and the Fresno Water Company.

The formal agreement was signed March 29, 1930, in San Francisco by Black and Hockenbeamer. It provided that P. G. and E. would deliver to The North American Company 1,825,-

000 shares of its $25 par value common stock and receive in return stock control of the companies involved and cancellation of $19,000,000 of their indebtedness to The North American Company. Par value of P. G. and E. stock, both common and preferred, had been reduced from $100 to $25 January 3, 1927, to make it more easily available to all classes of investors.

The properties thus added to the P. G. and E. system included the three hydro plants and five steam-operated plants of Great Western, with aggregate generating capacity of approximately 250,000 kilowatts, and transmission and distribution facilities in 10 counties including the city and county of San Francisco. From the San Joaquin system were acquired 11 hydro plants and three steam stations, with an aggregate capacity of about 165,000 kilowatts, and gas and electric business covering 10 counties including the coastal territory served by Midlands Corporation. The Fresno Water Company, also acquired, was sold later.

The exchange was concluded on June 12, 1930, when P. G. and E. delivered to The North American Company a single sheet of paper, a certificate for 1,825,000 shares of P. G. and E. common stock, representing at the current market price about $114,000,000.

By this final major consolidation, P. G. and E. had fulfilled its destiny. It had reached the peak of its long climb to a point when it could give to all Northern California, with only minor exceptions, the benefits of gas and electric service by one integrated system, administered by one company. Those benefits under state regulation were to be the economic advantages of adequate supply of light, heat, and power to communities, to industry, and to agriculture, provided with maximum efficiency at minimum cost to the customer.

* * *

Acquisition of the three companies did not result in immediate merger of all properties and personnel. There was still outstanding a considerable amount of stock in the San Joaquin company held by minority interests, and until all of these shares were obtained by purchase or exchange, the system was continued under its old management. In 1930 A. Emory Wishon was elected president of San Joaquin, succeeding his father A. G. Wishon, who was made vice-chairman of the board, a position he held until his death in 1936. The younger Wishon also was appointed a vice-president and assistant general manager of P. G. and E. Dissolution of the company and merger of its extensive system as the San Joaquin Power Division of P. G. and E. was not accomplished until 1938.

Absorption of Great Western Power Company was a simpler undertaking, as P. G. and E. had received in the exchange all of Great Western's common stock, although the corporation was not dissolved until 1935. Guy C. Earl, president of Great Western, James B. Black, and Edwin Gruhl, representing The North American Company, were appointed to P. G. and E.'s board of directors.

Purchase of the Great Western and San Joaquin companies brought to P. G. and E. a group of active and well-trained men who were to prove their worth to their new employer, many of them in high places. Among those who came from Great Western were:

W. G. B. Euler, now executive vice-president.

J. A. Koontz, chief of division of hydroelectric and transmission engineering at the time of his retirement on January 1, 1951.

G. H. Hagar, now manager of electric operation.

O. R. Doerr, now vice-president in charge of sales.

And from the San Joaquin organization came:

J. S. Moulton, now vice-president and executive engineer.

D. D. Smalley, now vice-president in charge of operations.

The late Al C. Joy, veteran newsman and manager of the publicity and advertising department.

Did space permit, a score more names might be added to the list of Great Western and San Joaquin men who joined the P. G. and E. staff and left a lasting record of achievement.

* * *

When P. G. and E. purchased the Great Western Power Company and San Joaquin Light and Power Corporation properties, it added to its generating plants some notable producers of electricity. Among them was the new A. C. Balch hydroelectric plant, placed in commission February 20, 1927. Balch Powerhouse, situated on the north fork of the Kings River in Fresno County, has a rating of 34,500 kilowatts. It receives its water power under a static head of 2,336 feet, a vertical drop of nearly half a mile from penstock head to the water wheels that drive the single generator.

Great Western also had added new plants to its system just before its consolidation with P. G. and E. Bucks Creek, the third plant to be built on the Feather River, was completed March 4, 1928. Although the powerhouse is on the Feather, it draws its water supply from a watershed high above that river, draining into a series of reservoirs and lakes and through tunnels and creek beds to the head of the penstock pipe line.

Bucks Creek Powerhouse is distinguished as having the highest head of any hydro plant in the Western Hemisphere. From the forebay where the flow enters the penstock pipes, the water drops a vertical distance of 2,561.6 feet to the powerhouse. The powerhouse stands at streamside on the Feather 26 miles above Big Bend generating station and 21 miles below Caribou plant. Its capacity is 60,000 kilowatts.

Great Western's second new plant was a large steam-operated station on the shore of San Francisco Bay near the present U.S. navy yard at Hunters Point. Now known as Station P, the plant was placed in operation December 3, 1929. Its initial capacity was 42,000 kilowatts, designed primarily for stand-by service. In 1948-1949 the powerhouse was enlarged as a modern high temperature, high pressure steam-operated plant, with a capacity of 262,000 kilowatts. Through underground conduits its power output is transmitted at 110,000 volts to Mission Station in the heart of San Francisco for distribution throughout the city.

CHAPTER 30

Natural Gas

LATE IN the 1920s, Northern California witnessed the beginning of a remarkable utility development which brought cleaner, cheaper cooking and heating to housewives, low-cost space heating to hotels and office buildings, and the many advantages of a more efficient fuel to industry. This was P. G. and E.'s successful piping of natural gas from distant fields to the principal cities in its service area.

One of the oldest fuels known to civilization, natural gas had already made a grand entrance in other parts of the country, where in Cinderella-fashion it had been transformed from a scorned stepchild of oil field operation into a desirable member of the family of fuels. But despite many explorations over the years, no source of the gas could be found in the P. G. and E. territory near San Francisco.

The Company itself in 1921 drilled to 5,200 feet in the Montezuma Hills of Solano County, where geologists had reported signs of a possible gas structure. But to no avail. While gas wells were multiplying in other sections of the country, a dependable and adequate supply of natural gas remained as elusive in the Company's northern domain as good uranium ore.

As related in Chapter 4, water-well diggers unexpectedly struck enough natural gas in Stockton in 1864 to heat and light the courthouse. Stockton was thus the first California city to establish natural gas service. A small number of private wells were drilled in the area, and in 1888 the Stockton Natural Gas Company came into being to serve the city's business district.

Not until 1907, six years after oil and natural gas were found in quantity near the town of Santa Maria in Santa Barbara

County, was the first natural domestic gas service established by the newly formed Santa Maria Gas and Electric Company.

Two years later, oil-well drillers struck a bonanza in the sands of the Buena Vista Hills of Kern County. The first company to utilize the large-volume, high-pressure production of natural gas was the West Side Gas Company, formed in 1910 to serve the oil-field cities of Maricopa, Taft, and Fellows. At about the same time, the California Natural Gas Company built a pipe line from the Midway-Sunset oil fields and extended it to the city of Bakersfield and the Kern River oil field.

The crowning achievement of this oil-boom period, however, was the construction in 1913 of a pipe line across the steep Tehachapi Mountains to feed some 24 million cubic feet of natural gas daily from Buena Vista to Los Angeles, 107 miles away. The job was done by the Midway Gas Company, founded by William G. Kerckhoff, then president of the San Joaquin Light and Power Company. The Midway company bought the gas at the field and delivered it to Los Angeles and its environs for resale by local distribution companies. Consumers actually received a "reformed" natural gas, a mixture with artificial gas that lowered the heating rating but was more economical for the companies to distribute.

By 1924 Southern California cities were being served by 28 gas and oil fields, but no economical source had yet been found for the San Francisco Bay area. The nearest major wells were at Elk Hills and Ventura. Not only was their production insufficient to provide the reserve and continuous supply necessary, but the fuel could not be piped to distant markets at a low enough cost to enable it to compete with oil, coal, or manufactured gas.

Then in 1926 the picture changed abruptly. Probing for oil in the vicinity of Elk Hills, the Milham Exploration Company, organized and owned by Ogden Mills and John Hays Hammond, brought in a big gas well at Buttonwillow, 28 miles west of Bakersfield and 250 miles southeast of San Francisco. Tests revealed the existence of a large underground supply of "dry" (or oil-free) gas under high pressure and having a heating value of 1,000 to 1,150 British thermal units, about twice that of gas made from oil. The discovery, plus the "surplus" gas then available from Ventura and the parallel development of electrically welded, large-diameter steel pipe, made it possible for P. G. and E. to consider seriously the introduction of natural gas into its territory.

P. G. and E. President A. F. Hockenbeamer entered into negotiations with the Milham Exploration Company and the Southern California Gas Company for purchase of gas and for construction of a pipe line that would link Ventura, Buttonwillow, and San Francisco. Southern California fieldmen had already surveyed a portion of the projected line and a contract was soon drawn up. But it was destined to remain unsigned. For the very morning the document was placed on his desk, Hockenbeamer opened his newspaper to a one-paragraph item announcing that the day before, October 6, 1928, the Milham company had brought in an apparently bigger gas well in the Kettleman Hills, 49 miles northwest of the one at Buttonwillow.

The contract was held up, and as things turned out, the president's caution was well justified. Within a month, the well, known as the Elliott 1, was completed to a depth of 7,236 feet and was shown by tests to be one of the greatest high-pressure gas producers in the country, with a daily flow of 90 million cubic feet of "wet" gas. "The pressure was so tremendous," reported one well tester, "that the noise of the escaping gas made me deaf for nearly a week."

Hockenbeamer made a tour of the new wells and decided to tap both the Buttonwillow and the Kettleman Hills discoveries —a job that called for initial expenditure of $13,000,000 for the construction of the longest pipe line in the West. In a public announcement the president explained:

"This undertaking will prove the greatest contribution of this generation to the growth and development of the Bay area. Natural gas is a cheap and efficient fuel which will not only attract new industries but keep the old ones here. . . . Domestic consumers will also profit. Natural gas has greater heating value than artificial gas. With increased heating values and with rate adjustments we propose to make, consumers in the Bay area will save $3,000,000 a year in their gas bills." This promise, as we shall see, was more than well kept, the annual saving proving to be ten million dollars instead of three.

The Company entered into contracts with the Milham Exploration Company, the Texas Company, and the Standard Oil Company of California for purchase of gas from the two fields. In January, 1929, construction of the pipe line was begun. The job was completed seven months later. The pipe line, 250 miles long, consists of a 16-inch main from Buttonwillow to a compressor station in the Kettleman Hills, a 22-inch line to Panoche Junction (west of Mendota) in Fresno County, and a 20-inch line which swings through Panoche Pass to Tres Pinos and thence to the metering station at Milpitas, on the southern tip of San Francisco Bay. At Milpitas, a branch runs along the eastern shore of the Bay to Oakland and Richmond, while the main stem continues 44 miles to San Francisco. Capacity is approximately 100 million cubic feet per day.

During construction of this line, P. G. and E. began to look ahead to expansion in the north. Plans were drawn to build another large transmission line from the oil fields up the west side of the San Joaquin Valley to the oil refinery cities of Martinez and Richmond on the eastern shore of San Francisco Bay. A branch line through the Livermore Valley from Tracy would tie into the station at Milpitas, while another line would serve the cities of Stockton, Lodi, and Sacramento. The entire network would thus not only bring natural gas into all the cities of the Bay area but provide a complete loop which could be tapped to supply all the Company's territory in Northern and Central California.

Work on the Valley line, as it was called, was begun, but plans were changed when P. G. and E. learned that Standard Oil of California intended to build a line of its own to its Richmond refinery. To avoid duplication, the two companies agreed to join forces to construct and operate a line of greater capacity than originally contemplated. This line, which ends at Richmond by way of Antioch and Pittsburg, was completed in 1930, and in July of that year the two companies formed a new corporation known as Standard-Pacific Gas Line, Inc., which owns and operates it.

Natural gas arrived in San Francisco and Oakland on August 16, 1929, and was first used at the Potrero steam-electric station to fire the boilers. The advent of natural gas had been quiet but it was not unnoticed.

"It passed so silently," commented an editorial in the San Francisco *Chronicle,* "that few were aware of the event. There was none of the shrieking of motor cops' sirens or other manifestations that usually herald the approach of a king, a queen, a grand lodge convention or a movie star. Instead, the visitor came in unobtrusively and it was not until the Pacific Gas and Electric Company announced the fact, that San Francisco knew that at last the Kettleman Hills field had been tapped and natural gas is now in the mains of the city."

Within a few months, however, nearly everyone in San Francisco was to have direct knowledge of the new fuel. Up to then, San Franciscans had been using the services of two manufactured-gas plants supplying approximately 8½ billion cubic feet of artificial gas during 1928. But the physical and chemical characteristics of manufactured and natural gas differ so widely that P. G. and E. faced the considerable task of adjusting the gas appliances of the city's 183,000 consumers, along with thousands of customers in the outside territory reached by natural gas mains.

The San Francisco area was divided into 11 districts, each successively to be cut off from the main gas line by a specially placed valve. The installation of these valves took six months. Standpipes were then erected to draw off the manufactured gas. At the same time, the valve was opened to permit natural gas to flow through the district's lines.

The appliance change-over was handled with military dispatch. The public had been prepared for the event by newspaper stories, but to prevent misunderstanding, every consumer received a letter notifying him when to expect the arrival of natural gas and what to do about it before a P. G. and E. man visited his premises. At the Company offices, 600 men were given a month's training and divided into crews of 35, each headed by a captain who operated out of a district headquarters.

Crews set out on the morning of February 24, 1930, and the last appliance was adjusted exactly five months later. Most of the domestic cutovers involved only minor adjustments of the stove or water heater to reduce the size of the air openings. But special procedures had to be worked out for firms using more complex equipment. Coffee houses utilizing time-controlled roasters, for example, required special handling to prevent a slight drop of temperature that might spoil the roast. In such cases, the Company installed a new set of burners on days when operation of the plant was suspended. Individual procedures were also worked out for hospitals, newspapers, and canneries. The first establishment (outside of P. G. and E.) to use natural gas was the Illinois Pacific Glass Company, then on Fifteenth and Folsom Streets, where a new 8-inch line was constructed to feed this company's large furnaces.

By the year's end, nearly all of P. G. and E.'s Bay area customers were receiving natural gas, and a $2,000,000 job involving the adjustment of 1¾ million appliances had been successfully completed with scarcely an interruption in service.

And what about the Company's 21 manufactured-gas plants? Eight of the smaller ones were immediately retired and four were used to supply fuel to communities too far from natural-gas distribution facilities. The rest were utilized as stand-bys in case of disruption of service or a sudden unexpected demand for additional gas. Taking advantage of a timely development, P. G. and E. later converted some of the larger plants which had been making gas from fuel oil to the use of Diesel oil, a process that increased the plants' manufacturing capacity and provided a product that can be mixed with or substituted for natural gas.

Seeking further economies in the 1930s, P. G. and E. shared in the Pacific Coast development of gas fuel made by mixing butane or propane with air. Tried first in Grass Valley and Nevada City for stand-by service in 1935, this method proved to be so superior to the oil-gas technique that it was soon adopted in Colusa. In recent years propane air service has been extended to Red Bluff, Redding, and King City for round-the-clock operation.

The Company now maintains 12 gas plants for service during emergencies and to aid in meeting demand when cold weather causes gas consumption to shoot up by millions of cubic feet. These plants have an aggregate daily capacity of 160 million cubic feet.

Introduction of natural gas brought with it a major problem—how to meet the daily variations in demand. The customer cannot store gas on his premises like oil or coal, to be dipped into at will. He depends entirely on the amount available in the pipe line, and this, in turn, depends on the Company's ability to anticipate the demand. P. G. and E.'s early practice was to consult the U.S. Weather Bureau for forecasts at various points in the system. If these reports indicated the approach of cold weather, an anticipated increase in the demand for heating was met by boosting the pressure on the lines and thereby packing them with more fuel than they normally carried. This method worked so well that in 1938 the Company decided to employ a full-time meteorologist whose job is to predict the weather 36 hours in advance. The importance of the meteorologic function is pointed up by the fact that for each degree's difference in daily mean temperature below 65 degrees—the temperature at which most people begin to heat their homes—the demand for natural gas jumps 26 million cubic feet per day.

The full effect of natural gas was realized just two years after the change-over. "The extent to which retail users have benefited by the introduction of natural gas," said the Company's annual report for 1932, "may be inferred from the fact that the revenue received from commercial and domestic consumers in 1932, while greater than in either of the two preceding years, was still $1,946,519 or 9 per cent less than in 1929, the last year of artificial gas, notwithstanding the enlarged usage reflected in the delivery of 78 per cent more heat units. More than 85 per cent of the $2,539,658 derived from sales of natural gas to industrial consumers represents business added during the last three years which could not have been secured with manufactured gas. We estimate that the use of natural gas is saving all classes of customers about $10,000,000 per annum at the present rate of consumption."

In 1936 P. G. and E. met an increased demand for natural gas in San Francisco and its environs with an additional 45-mile, 22-inch line from Milpitas, covering a region not previously within reach of the distribution lines. Using natural gas from new fields as well as from the Kettleman line, the Company also expanded its service in the southern part of the San Joaquin Valley. Other extensions of trunk lines were built to serve Stockton, Sacramento, and scores of smaller towns in the Central Valley. Today natural gas is delivered by P. G. and E. to points as far north as Eureka (where gas was found in local wells) and to Marysville, Woodland, Chico, Willows and Healdsburg. Additional lines also supply the counties south and east of San Francisco.

The search for new gas wells was also pressed. Two discoveries in the early 1930s were the McDonald Island field near Stockton and the Ten-Section field in Kern County. In 1937 gas from a group of wells in the Montezuma Hills near Rio Vista proved to be so substantial that the Company invested a million dollars in new transmission lines. Now regarded as one of the most important gas sources in the P. G. and E. system, the Rio Vista field supplies more than 300 million cubic feet a day to the Company.

During World War II the natural gas business skyrocketed. In 1941 defense activities boosted gas sales to over 89 billion cubic feet, almost four times the sale in 1930, and by the end of 1945 this had increased more than 150 per cent. War's end brought the question of future natural gas supply. The tremendous drain during the war had cut deeply into the declining reserves; there had been no discoveries of new major sources within the state.

For the first time the Company turned its attention outside California. On August 11, 1947, after completion of a new 1,000-mile line from the rich oil fields of Texas and New Mexico to Los Angeles, P. G. and E. made a contract with the Southern California and Southern Counties Gas Companies to purchase 75 million cubic feet of this gas daily in 1948 and 100 million cubic feet thereafter until 1953.

This was followed by a preliminary agreement with the El Paso Natural Gas Company of Texas for an additional 100 million cubic feet of gas per day to be delivered at a point on the California-Arizona border where P. G. and E. would take over with a new line of its own. In November, 1948, the Company began preparation to build the 502-mile main which now connects with the El Paso network at the state line.

The project was an ambitious one. Since economies increase as the size of the pipe is increased, the Company's plan called for construction of the biggest pipe ever used for a gas transmission line—a 34-inch main now generally known as the "Super-Inch." This meant the development of new kinds of construction machinery. The terrain presented another problem, for the line had to cross the Mojave Desert, the Tehachapi Mountains, the San Joaquin Valley, and the Coast Range Mountains. Recently completed, the job cost the Company $62,000,000 for pipe line and compressor stations.

Plates for the pipe line were rolled at the Geneva Steel Company's mill in Utah and formed into pipe at the South San Francisco plant of Consolidated Western Steel Corporation, both subsidiaries of U.S. Steel. A special contracting organization—comprising the Bechtel Corporation of San Francisco, the Conyes Construction Company of San Pablo, Calif., and the H. C. Price Company of Bartlesville, Okla.—laid the line. P. G. and E. engaged in 2,000 transactions to obtain the right of way.

Construction began on June 29, 1949, at the northern end of the line 29 miles south of Hollister. The schedule was arranged to avoid winter rains in the north and to make possible the crossing of the Mojave before the blistering heat of the following summer. An 80-mile section of the main was completed by early December and was joined to the Company's 20-inch Bay area line to transport and store an additional 50 million cubic feet a day from the Kettleman Hills.

Men and machines were then moved swiftly to Topock on the California-Arizona border and the major portion of the line was begun. It was a dramatic operation placed against a backdrop of sandstorms, burning heat, and steep grades. Bulldozer crews prepared the route by cutting and clearing a 54-foot swath along the right of way to permit the 32½-ton trenching machines to scoop out a 5½-foot ditch a mile a day. Behind these monster machines came "baby" bulldozers, known as "doodlebugs," equipped with drags to brush the bottom and leave it smooth. It was not always that easy. There were stretches of rocky ground where the pipe layers had to drill and blast before the trench could be completed.

Meantime the pipe, delivered to the trench by truck and trailer, was welded into long sections and lifted off the ground by a line of special side-boom tractors each weighted to handle up to 39 tons at a radius of 6 feet. Then came the pipe-cleaning crew with a self-propelled rotary wire brush and pumps to flood the pipe surface with primer paint. In odd contrast to the giant machines all about them, teams of men next preceded the self-propelled wrapping and coating machine, flicking off remaining dust with feather dusters to ensure a clean surface and firm bond when the wrapping of asphalt-impregnated rag felt and paper was applied. Finally the pipe was lowered and the trench backfilled. The fittings were then installed and, as a spectacular windup, the line was purged by flowing gas through at sufficient pressure to whip out the dust. Later a plane reseeded the barren land of the right of way to restore the range grass that formerly had carpeted it.

At the end of 1951, pressure "booster" stations at Topock, Hinkley, and Kettleman Hills, costing $11,000,000, were completed to forge the last link in the giant project that now supplies daily 400 million cubic feet of natural gas from Texas and New Mexico to the populous Northern California area.

In 20 years, P. G. and E., starting with a single natural gas line from the Kettleman Hills, had come to control a network of 14,300 miles of gas pipe line branching into 33 California counties.

CHAPTER 31

Through Fires of Depression

SEVERE economic depression was to test the Greater P. G. and E. soon after it had been created in 1930 by acquisition of the Great Western and San Joaquin power systems. That the Company emerged with undiminished strength proved the soundness of its financial structure and the competence of its organization.

A. F. Hockenbeamer, the young man from Indiana who had come to the struggling P. G. and E. in 1907, had moved into the president's chair August 16, 1927, after the death of W. E. Creed. As vice-president and treasurer of the Company, he had become well versed in every phase of its operations. "Hock," as his familiars called him, was a different kind of utility president. Plain in exterior and unpretentious in manner, there was little about him to give hint of his broad knowledge of corporation finance and his grasp of the practical facts of utility operation. He had a prodigious appetite for detail, and no task was too small for his personal attention. There were vital decisions to be made during his brief term as president; he accepted the challenge with assurance and determination.

There was, for example, the extensive Mokelumne River development, involving construction of a big dam, miles of concrete flume, and two powerhouses at an approximate cost of $19,000,000. There was also the introduction of natural gas in 1929 and 1930. On the heels of this major undertaking came the sweeping consolidation with Great Western and San Joaquin, by which virtually all the major gas and electric systems of Northern California were brought under one administration. P. G. and E. then included in its service area 46 of the state's 58 counties, with a population of 2,750,000. The customer roll, gas, electric, water, and steam, which had passed the million mark in 1928, had risen to a total of 1,267,000 in 1931.

The most severe effects of the business recession which swept the country were felt in the years 1931 to 1934. New building and expansion of industry declined almost to the vanishing point. Use of gas and electricity, especially for industrial purposes, was curtailed. Revenue of the Company fell off. To combat the downward trend and to conserve its resources, P. G. and E. temporarily reduced common stock dividends, stopped all but indispensable new construction, and enforced all possible economies in operating expenditures. Much of the burden of the economy program fell upon the shoulders of P. M. Downing, who in 1929 had succeeded Frank A. Leach, Jr., as vice-president and general manager.

The depression was only one of the problems the Company faced during the critical days of the early 1930s. The State Railroad Commission, which had been investigating gas rates, ordered a reduction in 1933 that meant a $2,000,000 loss in revenue. For the first time in the 22 years the commission had exercised regulatory power over gas and electric rates, the Company felt itself obliged to contest the action of the commission in the courts. An injunction restraining the commission's order was granted December 14, 1933, and the case was in litigation until 1938, when after two conflicting decisions had been handed down by the U.S. Supreme Court, the state commission's order was upheld. It then became necessary to refund the excess amounts collected from customers, approximately $6,000,000. Meanwhile, in 1936, business conditions having improved, the Company voluntarily reduced gas rates to the extent of $2,500,000 annually.

In November, 1935, only a few days after attending a directors' meeting, A. F. Hockenbeamer remarked to one of his associates that he was tired and would remain at home for a brief rest. He never returned to his office, and on November 11, 1935, he died at the age of sixty-four after 28 years of faithful and often burdensome service to his company.

Pit No. 5 Powerhouse, largest hydro plant of the P. G. and E. system, was rushed to completion in 1944 to supply power for expanding war industries.

W. G. B. Euler, executive vice-president of P. G. and E., started utility career as division superintendent with Great Western Power.

N. R. Sutherland, vice-president and general manager of Pacific Gas and Electric Company since 1950.

Rock Creek Powerhouse, commissioned in 1950, was the latest of five important P. G. and E. hydro plants to be built on the Feather River.

Moss Landing steam plant, on Monterey Bay, has a unique submarine pipe line through which oil tankers pump fuel to the steam plant's storage tanks.

The year brought two other severe losses to the organization. Guy C. Earl, one of the founders of the Great Western Power system in 1902, later president of Great Western and, since its sale, a director of P. G. and E., died June 25, 1935. And on September 17 occurred the death of Frank B. Anderson, chairman of the board of the Bank of California. For 32 years he had been a director of P. G. and E. and its predecessor, California Gas and Electric Corporation.

The lives of two more of the pioneers came to an end in succeeding years. W. H. Crocker, director for 31 years, died September 25, 1937, and Fred T. Elsey, a member of the board for 24 years, passed away February 28, 1938.

* * *

When Prince Poniatowski and W. H. Crocker completed their Electra plant on the Mokelumne River in 1902, they had tapped only a small part of the region's hydroelectric resources. The original plant barely had been made a part of the P. G. and E. system before the engineers had plans ready for additional powerhouses on the Mokelumne. In 1926 and 1927 preliminary steps were taken to launch the long-deferred program.

The Mokelumne development was based upon construction of a dam and storage reservoir near the river's headwaters at a point called Salt Springs. Here the rock walls of the canyon were blasted down to provide material for a huge rock-fill dam across the river channel. The dam when completed was 328 feet high and 1,270 feet wide along its crest. The reservoir created by the dam and fed by lakes at higher elevations held some 142,000 acre-feet of water to provide the constant flow required for operation of two new powerhouses below it.

Salt Springs Powerhouse, erected at the downstream base of the dam, was equipped to produce 12,000 kilowatts of electric power. From Salt Springs 20 miles of concrete flume and tunnel were constructed to a second plant erected at the confluence of Tiger Creek and the main river with an installed capacity of 58,000 kilowatts.

The two plants were officially placed in operation August 1, 1931. Vice-president A. H. Markwart, in charge of engineering, was responsible for design of the project; O. W. Peterson supervised construction.

Even then the hydroelectric potential of the Mokelumne had not been exhausted. In 1948 a new Electra plant and a powerhouse at West Point increased the available capacity to 107,000 kilowatts, and as this is written still another development is nearing completion. It is the Bear River project which will bring the waters of a tributary of the Mokelumne and its Alpine watershed through separate penstock pipes to drive a new 29,000-kilowatt generator installed in Salt Springs Powerhouse and to increase the water supply to the downstream plants. When this installation is completed early in 1953, P. G. and E.'s five plants on the Mokelumne River will have a total generating capacity of 206,000 kilowatts.

* * *

James B. Black was elected president of P. G. and E., November 20, 1935. He possessed extraordinary qualifications for the position he was about to assume. He was a Californian. He knew the state's mountains, its cities, and its people. He was the first president of the Company to hold a degree in engineering. During his college years he had worked in vacations as a lumberjack, a mule "skinner," a structural-iron worker, and as a laborer for the Stone & Webster Engineering Corporation. He entered the utility business as a service inspector for the Great Western Power Company. He was just out of college and began at the bottom. He spent 15 years with the Great Western Company, rising from service inspector to vice-president and general manager. As a vice-president of The North American Company in New York, and a member of the P. G. and E. board of directors, representing North American interests, he had gained invaluable experience in utility finance. And he was young—forty-five years of age—at the time of his election to the presidency.

Some other historian in later years will record the progress of P. G. and E. during this closing decade of its first hundred years. Events and persons of the decade are now too close to the present to be described with complete objectivity. Yet the reader of these pages should be acquainted with the man who for the past 17 years has led the Company's advance to the top of the nation's gas and electric utilities.

James B. Black works without fanfare. He seldom appears as a public speaker. The same absence of display characterizes his daily routine, a fact that becomes obvious when a caller enters his office. His workshop is a little room in the far corner of the executive floor next to the directors' room. Here one finds a cheerful, small office, a moderately sized desk in the corner, a few visitors' chairs, a bright painting of a California scene on the wall. No stacks of papers are visible on his desk which at the end of a day is invariably clear.

The P. G. and E. president has an accurate and retentive memory for facts and figures. He seems always to have a clear picture in his mind of the complex and intricate details of the Company's operations. He thinks in terms of millions—capital, bonds, stocks, kilowatts of generating capacity, cubic feet of gas, prospective demand, economic trends—with clarity and definite conclusion. He delegates responsibility to officers and heads of departments. He listens to or reads carefully reports and estimates and has a faculty for getting swiftly to the core of a subject. Having done so, he makes his own decision.

Yet with his calm, reasoning mentality, he has a very human personality. He is interested in people and in the world about him. Since his college days he never has lost his enthusiasm for athletics and sports. He has found time to serve as chairman of the Finance Committee and the Board of Management of the Golden Gate International Exposition from 1935 to 1940, as president of the San Francisco War Chest, as a director or trustee of many other organizations, of the San Francisco Symphony Association, the California Palace of the Legion of Honor, and St. Luke's Hospital. He served on the President's Advisory Committee on the Merchant Marine in the year 1947. He is a trustee of Stanford University, a member of the Advisory Council of the University of California's School of Business Administration, a member of the Business Advisory

Council of the United States Department of Commerce, and holds membership in social clubs in San Francisco and New York.

In his business life he is a director of United States Steel Corporation, Southern Pacific Company, Equitable Life Assurance Society of the United States, Shell Oil Company, Firemen's Fund Insurance Company, Del Monte Properties Company, California Pacific Title Insurance Company.

* * *

The business curve turned upward in 1934 after four years of depression. Volume of the Company's sales of gas and electricity mounted and the number of customers multiplied. In 1936 and 1937 voluntary reductions in electric rates resulted in annual savings for customers of approximately $7,000,000. Gas rates, as has been noted, also were reduced. The drop more than offset the disputed reduction in rates ordered by the State Railroad Commission in 1933, which still was in the courts for settlement.

When P. G. and E. acquired other gas and electric companies, consolidation of the physical properties usually was accomplished quickly, but sometimes the acquired corporations could not be dissolved for a number of years. In 1936, 15 subsidiaries were liquidated, leaving only the San Joaquin corporation and its associate, Midland Counties Public Service Corporation, to be fully merged. This was brought about two years later, and P. G. and E. at last could be regarded as a fully consolidated company with all its operative properties held under one corporate name.

At about this time the question of subsidiaries came up in a different manner. The Federal Public Utility Holding Company Act of 1935 placed under regulation of the Securities and Exchange Commission all gas and electric companies which were subsidiaries of registered holding companies. The act laid down the dictum that if 10 per cent or more of a utility's voting stock were owned by a holding company, the utility would be regarded as a subsidiary of the holding company and subject to regulation by the commission unless it was found the holding company did not exercise a controlling influence upon the subsidiary.

P. G. and E. asked for exemption on the ground that no such controlling influence was exerted upon its affairs. About five years after its application was filed, hearings were held before an examiner. The issue was whether The North American Company's holding of 17 per cent of P. G. and E.'s voting stock made P. G. and E. a subsidiary of North American. Most of this stock had been acquired by sale of the Western Power properties in 1930.

Directors of the California company testified that three-fourths of its stockholders were residents of the state; that North American was represented by only two members of the Company's board of 15 directors; that North American could not possibly win control of P. G. and E., either through the board or by proxy contest. The trial examiner recommended that P. G. and E.'s application for exemption be granted.

The commission, however, refused to issue an order declaring P. G. and E. *not* a subsidiary of North American. The Company sought a reversal of this position by an action in the Federal courts. The case finally was carried to the U.S. Supreme Court, and on March 12, 1945, the Court held, by an evenly divided opinion, that P. G. and E. *was* a subsidiary of the New York holding company.

The situation was only temporary. Before the year was out North American had sold to underwriters for public resale 700,000 shares of its P. G. and E. holdings. That action was followed by periodic distribution of P. G. and E. common stock to North American stockholders in the form of dividends. By the end of 1948, North American had divested itself of all its holdings and no longer was a P. G. and E. stockholder.

Standard Gas and Electric Company, the H. M. Byllesby & Company subsidiary, which still held 177,000 shares of P. G. and E. stock, a part of the amount received in exchange for its California gas and electric properties, also sold its holdings during this period. As a result of these two large dispersals of stock the number of P. G. and E. shareholders was substantially increased. By the end of 1948 the total was 154,259.

* * *

During the early years of President Black's administration, a change was made in the form and content of the Company's annual report to stockholders. For many years this document had consisted chiefly of tabulations of revenue, expenditures, liabilities and assets, and other statistics from which the stockholder was expected to gain information about his investment. Gradually more of the story was told each year, but the presentation still was an uninspiring collection of data, bound in a plain gray cover. It remained for E. J. Beckett, who retired January 1, 1952, as treasurer after 36 years of service with the Company, to inject new life into the report. Beginning with the 1940 edition, gradual improvements were made until today, as many other American companies do, P. G. and E. now presents to its stockholders an accounting that describes all phases of the Company's operations and reports in simple, understandable language what has been done and what is planned for the future. Attractive format, typography, and illustrations in color add interest to a publication designed to give the shareholder full information about his company.

* * *

When the Pearl Harbor attack plunged the United States into battle in December, 1941, all hands and minds were turned to defense and support of the armed forces. P. G. and E. speeded its construction program to provide additional power resources to meet the constantly mounting demand.

Construction had been started in the late 1930s on three steam-operated plants on the shore of San Francisco Bay. These were to be operated on a novel plan for the conservation of fuel and for lower production costs. Each was built alongside an oil refinery—Avon, adjoining the Tidewater–Associated Oil Company's refinery; Martinez at the Shell Oil Company's plant; and Oleum side by side with the Union Oil Company's refinery, all in Contra Costa County. Avon was completed December 16, 1940; Martinez, June 13, 1941; and Oleum, January 15, 1942. The three plants had a total rated capacity of 137,000 kilowatts, which since has been increased to 187,000 kilowatts. The feature of their planning was the use of waste fuels from the refineries and large savings in operating costs by exchange of steam, water, and power between the oil refineries and the power plants.

Two other plants were completed by P. G. and E. before war restrictions were imposed upon the use of materials. The Narrows plant, a 12,000-kilowatt installation on the Yuba River in Nevada County, went into operation December 29, 1942. Dutch Flat Powerhouse on the Bear River in Placer County was commissioned March 29, 1943, with a rated capacity of 22,000 kilowatts. Plans for two new hydro projects on the Feather River were abandoned because of inability to obtain a satisfactory license from the Federal Power Commission.

But there was one extensive powerhouse project, already under construction months before Pearl Harbor, which was given official sanction. This was Pit 5 Powerhouse, largest hydro plant of the P. G. and E. system with a present generating capacity of 152,000 kilowatts. At a time when shipyards, aluminum and magnesium plants, and hundreds of wartime industries were using more and more electric power, the addition of 152,000 kilowatts of available energy would be a valuable defense measure.

Pit 5 Powerhouse was built at Big Bend, 41 miles downstream from Pit 1 Powerhouse. Here work was started July 1, 1941. When the United States entered the war, efforts were redoubled to complete the job in record time. From 1,000 to 2,000 men worked night and day building a diversion dam, driving a 5-mile tunnel across the neck of the wide bend in the river channel, and erecting penstocks and powerhouse at the lower end of the project.

There was a time when completion of the tunnel was threatened by that nemesis of tunnel men, "heavy" or moving ground. The great tube, 19 feet in diameter, was only half finished when the excavators encountered a stratum of heavy earth. The enormous pressure of the moving mass crushed like matchsticks the

16-inch timbers set side by side to hold it back. As fast as the earth could be removed to make room for the concrete forms, more was pressed in. P. M. Downing, then executive vice-president, and O. W. Peterson, in general charge of construction, spent worried days studying the problem. Engineers expert in tunnel construction were brought in for consultation. At last the ingenuity of the builders won the battle. With steel and fast-setting concrete, the bore was driven through the dangerous ground and completed safely.

Pit 5 Powerhouse was placed in operation April 29, 1944. Because of the importance of the new power source to the defense program, the occasion was celebrated with a formal dedication. High-ranking officers of the armed forces attended, accompanied by civic officials. Governor Earl Warren spoke. And as he spoke, power flowed from Pit 5 at 220,000 volts down to the San Francisco Bay area, 250 miles away, to speed the building of ships and the manufacture of war materials.

Construction of Pit 5 was under the general supervision of O. W. Peterson, engineer of construction, and H. W. Haberkorn, assistant engineer. The plant was designed under direction of I. C. Steele, chief engineer. For P. M. Downing, who had been so keenly interested in the project, it was the last task of a lifetime spent in electrical development. He died December 11, 1944, a few months after the generators of Pit 5 Powerhouse began to play their part in the P. G. and E.'s great interconnected system.

* * *

V-J Day, 1945, marked the end of World War II. P. G. and E. had done its share in support of the nation's defense. Its honor roll listed 2,835 employees who entered military service. Gold stars commemorated 68 who lost their lives. When the war ended, the men who had been in service, with few exceptions, resumed their employment with the Company.

With nearly 3,000 of its employees engaged in military service, the utility got along during the war as well as it could with a shortage of manpower and material. Under government restrictions every effort had been devoted to maintaining maximum service of power and gas for the use of defense industry and at the same time to provide essential services to the civil population.

When hostilities ended, P. G. and E. turned to the future, assembling materials as rapidly as they could be obtained, training extra men to handle the large backlog of work that had accumulated during the war years, planning new plant facilities to provide new sources of power and gas.

The postwar period had commenced.

CHAPTER 32

Government Ownership

DURING the past half century, P. G. and E. has found itself involved from time to time in opposition to the proponents of government ownership of electric power. In the latter half of the nineteenth century, when the electrical industry was still experimental, municipal enterprises arose to challenge the private utilities. This movement, which never achieved more than a beachhead in Northern California, was followed in the early 1920s by a proposal to place the state in the electric business in competition with the Company. Then during recent years came the Federal government's attempts to construct a competitive power system in connection with the well-known Central Valley Project.

P. G. and E.'s position at all times has remained essentially the same—that of a staunch defender against political invasion of a business successfully created and maintained by individual initiative and developed according to the needs of a growing state.

The Company also has contended, with proof, that the people of Northern California are opposed to politically owned and managed power systems. In 1947 President James B. Black, testifying before a Congressional committee, pointed out that "in 25 years there has been only one public utility power system organized in the territory served by the P. G. and E." There have been dozens of proposals, Black said, but all but one have been turned down by the voters.

Advocates of municipal lighting and power in California began to appear in the latter part of the nineteenth century while the electrical industry was still in swaddling clothes. The year 1887 saw the birth in Alameda of Northern California's first municipal power system. This city set a pattern by issuing bonds with which to buy the existing generating and lighting system owned by a private electric company. Other cities followed Alameda's example, starting with Palo Alto in 1898. When P. G. and E. was formed in 1905, municipal systems were being operated also by Healdsburg, Ukiah, and Biggs. During the next two decades sporadic local movements added to the list Santa Clara, Gridley, Roseville, Redding, Lodi, and Lompoc.

In two places, the private company continued business in competition with the publicly owned system. This occurred in Palo Alto, where P. G. and E. remained in the field up to 1929, and in Modesto Irrigation District, the first California setup of its kind, where competition lasted deep into the 1940s. At Modesto the problem was settled through an agreement whereby the district purchased the Company's facilities within the district and agreed to buy from P. G. and E. all energy needed to supplement its own supply.

Around the turn of the century, the California power industry successfully interconnected hydroelectric plants and steam-operated powerhouses and thereby paved the way for the widespread regional power systems of today. Small towns soon found that they were unable to produce power in local stations as cheaply as they could buy it from the large systems, with the result that they soon restricted their power operations to distribution only. Today, there are 14 municipal and district enterprises in Northern California which buy all or most of their power at wholesale from P. G. and E.

Despite these developments, the proponents of municipal ownership continued to plead their cause in two cities of Northern California—Sacramento and San Francisco.

In the state capital the government ownership issue was introduced in 1923, when after years of agitation, organization of the Sacramento Municipal Utility District was authorized by vote of the people. The boundaries of the district included the city of Sacramento and adjacent rural territory. The announced purposes of the district were to develop a mountain water supply for the capital city from Silver Creek, a tributary of the American River, to generate power, and to acquire an electric distribution system within the district. The emphasis at that time was centered upon the water plan.

Beginning in 1927, three elections were held for authorization of bonds to finance the Silver Creek project and each time the proposal was defeated. Finally, during the depression of the thirties, the issue was settled in favor of the municipal-ownership side. In November, 1934, the people voted authority to the Sacramento Municipal Utility District to issue general obligation bonds for acquisition or construction of an electrical generating and distribution system, the original Silver Creek water plan long since having been put aside. Negotiations to purchase the P. G. and E. local distribution system ensued, but it was not until 1946 as a result of a condemnation suit that the district was able to take over the Company's property. The district paid $13,917,000 as compensation and contracted to buy substantially all its power from the Company until June 30, 1954.

Controversy over government ownership in San Francisco also was long drawn out. The contest differed from others because of Federal government intervention. San Francisco generates electricity in two hydroelectric plants connected with the municipal Hetch Hetchy Water Project, which is governed by a 1914 Act of Congress, known as the Raker Act. This law prohibits the city from selling water or energy to any individual or corporation (except a municipality or a public irrigation district) for resale to others. For a number of years the output of the city's plants was distributed by the Company as the city's agent, according to a contract under which the Company paid the city some $2,400,000 annually. The arrangement was so satisfactory that on eight different occasions the city's voters rejected bond proposals that would have given San Francisco authority to acquire or build its own electric distribution system.

During the 1930s, however, Secretary of the Interior Harold Ickes declared that the agency contract did not comply with provisions of the Raker Act and brought the matter into the Federal court. The U.S. District Court for Northern California ruled in his favor and the case eventually went to the U.S. Supreme Court, which upheld the lower court. An injunction was issued, but its enforcement was postponed from time to time until the city could find a way to dispose of its power. In 1945, the city made an agreement with the Company under which the city uses its power for such municipal purposes as streetcar and bus operation, public building and street lighting, for sale to two irrigation districts and for sale to two former Company customers—the Permanente Cement Company and the Kaiser Aluminum Corporation. The city leases a transmission line from the Company to deliver power to these two plants and the Company transmits energy from the terminus of the city's lines near Newark to San Francisco for the city's various municipal functions. The Company also agreed to sell the city any supplementary power it may require and to buy any municipal surplus energy that might otherwise be wasted.

In the early 1920s, an attempt was made to pass an amendment to the state constitution that would have authorized the state to establish a competitive power system. The movement was based upon the Marshall Plan, a comprehensive scheme for water conservation devised by Colonel Robert B. Marshall, chief geographer of the U.S. Geologic Survey. Its principal feature was a proposal to transfer part of the flow of the Sacramento River to the upper San Joaquin Valley. The idea later was adopted in the design of the present Central Valley Project.

In 1921, legislative approval was sought for a measure that provided for a bond issue of $500,000 to investigate the feasibility of the Marshall Plan. The goal was adoption of the plan itself. The measure was defeated, although another bill was passed providing $200,000 for investigation of the possibilities of storing and controlling the state's waters.

A group of wealthy "progressives" thereupon drew a constitutional amendment known as the Water and Power Act, which provided for issuance of up to $500,000,000 in bonds to finance a statewide water and power project. Although ostensibly the act was predicated upon the Marshall Plan, there was a radical difference—Colonel Marshall's proposal was in all essentials a *water* plan while that of the "progressives" was in substance a *power* plan. The Water and Power amendment was brought before the people in the election of 1922 and was soundly defeated. However, its proponents kept the issue alive. In two subsequent elections, those of 1924 and 1926, the people again voted down the proposal.

Although the Company had fought hard to preserve itself from government competition, it always willingly gave cooperation to worthy public water projects. As early as 1924, for instance, the Company contracted with the Nevada Irrigation District for joint utilization of the water supply in the Lake Spaulding area. Under this contract the district built Bowman Reservoir and a connecting canal to Lake Spaulding. In the mutual interest of the district and the Company the contract provides that Lake Bowman water shall be used through Company facilities for power generation and then turned into the district's canals for irrigation used by its farmer members.

Two years later, a similar mutually beneficial agreement was made with the Oakdale and South San Joaquin Irrigation Districts. Under it, the districts constructed Melones Dam for irrigation purposes and the Company built a generating plant below it to use the water before it flows into the irrigation canals. Several other similar contracts have been made and today the Company buys power or water from a number of public agencies, thus providing a revenue-producing outlet for these agencies that might not otherwise have been available and without which the irrigation reservoirs could not have been constructed.

The water problems of the Central Valley became pressing as irrigation expanded. In 1930, the State Water Plan was presented to the legislature. It was the first detailed inventory of the water resources of California. It not only dealt with floods, soil erosion, power, and irrigation, but it also offered a plan for the "maximum conservation, control, distribution, and application of all the waters of the State." Essential features of this plan were incorporated in the Central Valley Project Act of 1933.

When the legislature, urged by proponents of government ownership, added provisions to build transmission lines and a steam plant and rushed the bill through in the closing hours of the last session, the Company in self-defense endeavored to defeat the measure when it was submitted to a referendum.

The Company regarded the proposal as another Water and Power Act—a plan infeasible to construct at the stated cost, a position that was sustained by later events. But this time the populace was gripped by depression. To many the possibility of a work program financed by the Federal government seemed too good to pass up, and so in 1933 the bill became a law. Basically the bill provided for a gigantic water project to be paid for by the issuance of $170,000,000 in bonds. But because of the depression, the bonds were never issued. A year later the state appealed to Washington for assistance under the newly passed National Industrial Recovery Act, which included a provision for the financing of public works.

The Public Works Administration took no action on this request, but in September, 1935, President Franklin D. Roosevelt allocated to the Bureau of Reclamation money provided for emergency relief, to start construction of the project. In December, the President approved the project as a Federal reclamation undertaking. In the 1935 Rivers and Harbors bill Congress gave its first recognition to the project, when it authorized expenditure of $12,000,000 for construction of Shasta Dam.

P. G. and E. prudently prepared for the early absorption of the large power output expected from the project's Shasta and Keswick power plants. As early as 1936, when power from Hoover Dam became available in the south, P. G. and E. contracted to purchase energy from Southern California Edison Company, instead of building additional plants as it would otherwise have had to do to meet the increase in Northern California load. Since a number of Southern California Edison's plants are located near the P. G. and E. operating area, power produced by them was delivered to the Northern California system while Southern California Edison replaced it with an additional supply from Hoover Dam.

The Company's contract with Southern California Edison was designed to end as soon as Shasta power became available. In effect, the Company was doing on a larger scale what it had accomplished for several irrigation districts in the 1920s. It was preparing a market for Shasta power; it was clear that the greatest economic advantage to the people of California and the nation would accrue if the power were eventually coordinated with the P. G. and E. system.

On February 11, 1937, James B. Black, president of the Company, addressed a letter to the State Department of Public Works, then representing the Federal Bureau of Reclamation, in which he outlined the principles of Company cooperation with the Central Valley Project. The letter read in part:

"It is and has been the fixed policy of our Company to aid and cooperate in the development of all worthy public projects which mean the building and growth of California. As California grows, so will our Company grow and benefit. We recognize the desirability and the necessity of conserving and putting to maximum beneficial use the waters of the State and we are anxious to assist in every possible way the final realization of this worthy objective."

In the same year, Congress reauthorized the project, providing among other things, "that the entire Central Valley Project, California, heretofore authorized and established under the appropriation of the Emergency Relief Appropriation Act of 1935 . . . is hereby reauthorized and declared to be for the purpose of improving navigation, regulating the flow of the San Joaquin River, controlling floods, for the reclamation of arid and semiarid lands . . . and other beneficial uses and for the generation and sale of electric energy as a means of financially aiding such undertakings and in order to permit the full utilization of the works constructed to accomplish the aforesaid purposes" and providing further that the project dams and reservoirs "shall be used, first, for river regulation, improvement of navigation, and flood control; second, for irrigation and domestic uses; and, third, *for power.*"

While this language clearly indicates the intent of the lawmakers to make power secondary to irrigation, the Bureau of Reclamation in 1941 asked Congress for funds to construct a steam electric plant that would "firm" the fluctuating power

Contra Costa steam plant, twin of Moss Landing Powerhouse. Capacity of both plants will be raised in 1953 to 575,000 kilowatts.

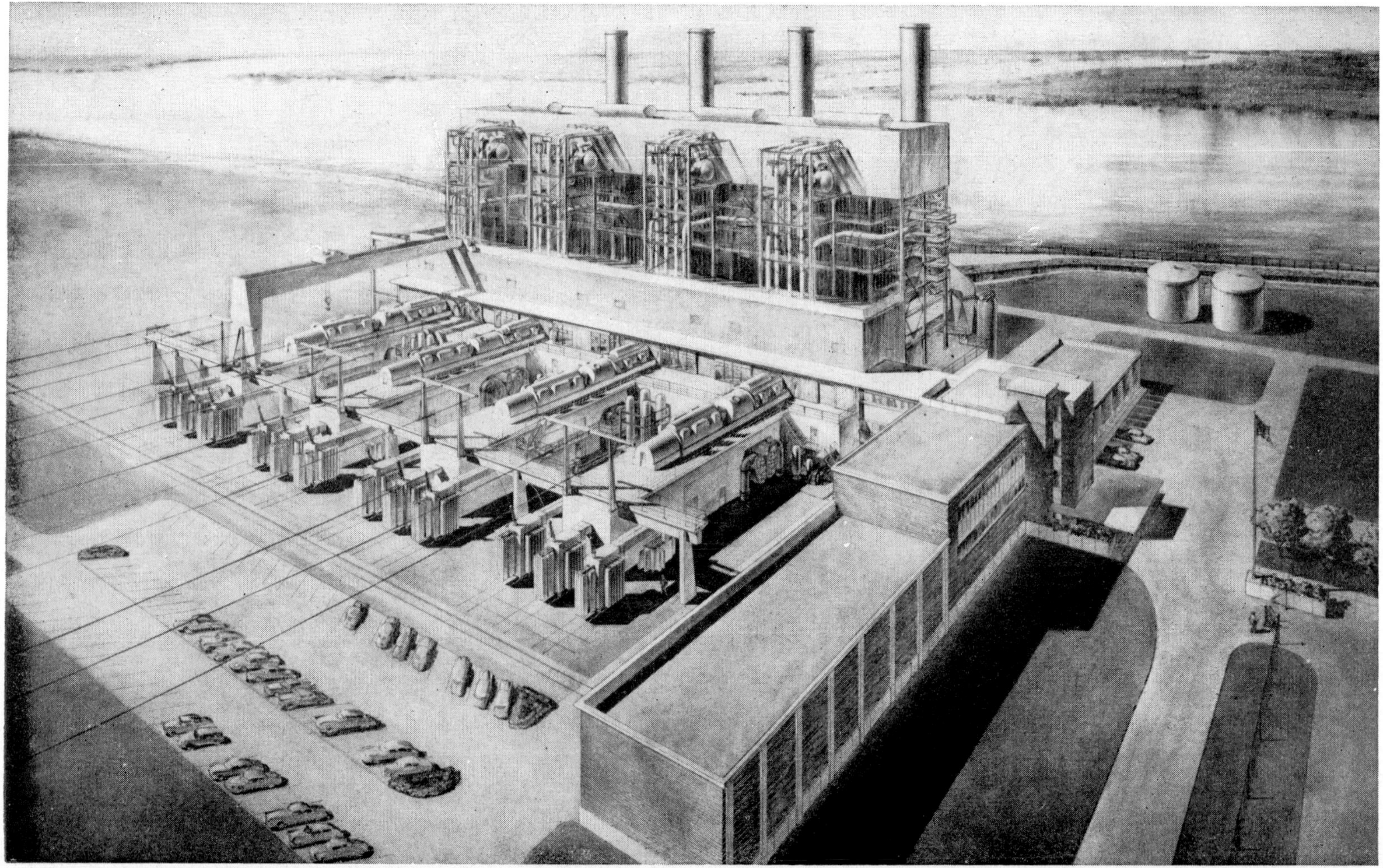

supplied by Shasta Dam and thereby make the generation and transmission of power one of its prime purposes.

Prior to this move of the bureau, President Black in January, 1941, wrote a letter to John C. Page, Commissioner of Reclamation, in which he informed him that the Company would provide the steam support necessary for Shasta as well as for the P. G. and E. system.

Despite this offer, the Bureau of Reclamation requested funds for a steam electric plant at Antioch and for transmission lines down the Sacramento Valley. P. M. Downing, then general manager of the P. G. and E., appeared before a Congressional committee to oppose this request, pointing out that the area was already well served by P. G. and E. and that additional generating capacity was not necessary. Congress refused to appropriate funds for the steam plant.

Later in a statement to the Legislature's Joint Committee on Water Problems, Downing indicated his objections to the government's request for a steam plant to supply power for the area:

"There is no independent market at present," he said, "and the only way of getting one is to carve it out of the Company's system by uneconomic piecemeal condemnation, which would take many years, or to duplicate facilities and enter into destructive competition. Neither method will produce the revenue from power sales desired to bring to a minimum the cost of water to farmers. Acceptance of the Company's offer (to purchase power at Shasta) would produce revenue at the earliest possible moment at the best price obtainable, would avoid the necessity of expenditure for firming power or transmitting it and would enable both the project and the Company to escape the ills of competition."

In March, 1942, when the Congressional hearings on the 1943 appropriation were held, Black restated the P. G. and E. position that a steam plant and transmission lines were unnecessary and a waste of government funds. The House thereupon refused to make an appropriation for transmission lines and a steam plant. In a subsequent hearing the Senate decided to put a temporary halt to the controversy and recommended that the

Secretary of the Interior and the Company get together on a contract "for the duration of the war and a reasonable time thereafter for the complete pooling of all public and private power facilities that will result in delivering the greatest amount of power to war industries. . . . Any such contract should provide for the recapture without prejudice of any advantage which temporarily may accrue to either party." However, the contract recommended by the Senate was not executed until some time later.

In 1943, the bureau requested funds for a 100-mile line from Shasta Dam to the Company's system at Oroville. Congress denied this and the lawmakers allowed $400,000 for a "transmission line to Shasta Substation only." Despite this Congressional direction, Secretary Ickes ordered the construction of the remaining 75 miles of line through to Oroville out of "unexpended balances" in Central Valley funds. More than ever it appeared that the Bureau of Reclamation was determined to inch its way into the competitive power business.

At the further prodding of Congress, a year later, a five-year contract between the Company and the bureau was executed. The Company agreed to take delivery at its Shasta Substation of all Shasta Dam power, and leased the bureau's line to Oroville as a "tie-line" to carry either Company or bureau power between the Company's Pit River and Feather River transmission systems.

The bureau then demanded that P. G. and E. "wheel" power to "preferred" agencies. ("Wheeling" meant that the Company should deliver power over its lines to the bureau's customers and receive the equivalent in government power at Shasta Substation.) The contract did not so provide and wheeling was not then undertaken. When the contract expired, the bureau refused to renew, preferring to sell Shasta power to the Company on a day-to-day basis until a long-term contract which would provide for wheeling or exchange service to preference customers could be drawn up.

In Washington, the controversy was renewed after World War II was over. From 1945 on, Black appeared each year before House and Senate committees to oppose the bureau's requests for a steam plant and transmission lines. The P. G. and E. president reiterated his proposals for buying project power at Shasta Substation at bureau-fixed rates, which, he pointed out, would give the government maximum net revenue. Congress consistently turned down the bureau's requests for a steam plant but finally authorized construction of a line east of the Sacramento River from Oroville to Tracy, for direct service to the project's pumps. This was followed by authorization to construct two similar lines from Shasta Dam to Tracy along the west side of the river, thus giving the bureau three 230,000-volt "backbone" lines between the power plants and the pumping plant at Tracy.

Meantime, the bureau was busily engaged in trying to sew up outlets for its power among the preferred public agencies. The bureau offered rates that were lower than those of P. G. and E., but the Company promptly met this competition by reducing its own rates 7 to 9 per cent to those agencies that would sign five-year contracts with the Company. Three months later, all the cities involved except Roseville had accepted the P. G. and E. offer. Roseville signed with the Company in 1951.

In Redding, which owns its distribution system, the question of whether the city should make a contract for power with the Bureau of Reclamation was the subject of a special election in the fall of 1949. The people voted down the bureau contract and elected to continue purchasing power from the Company.

In Washington, the basic difficulties between the bureau and the Company were coming to a head. At the 1949 Congressional hearing members of the Senate committee expressed a desire to see a plan worked out which would provide for joint use of Company and bureau facilities to serve preference customers. P. G. and E. indicated a willingness to comply with the committee's views and agreed to endeavor to negotiate an exchange or wheeling contract with the bureau.

Proposals and counterproposals were made until the early months of 1950, but an agreement was not reached. In April of that year, the bureau again asked for funds to construct a transmission system and a steam plant, backing its request with objections to the proposed P. G. and E. wheeling contract. But

Congress again refused to appropriate funds and repeated its desire that the parties continue to endeavor to get together.

In April, 1951, the end of the road appeared to be in sight when a 10-year "wheeling contract" was finally drawn and agreed upon. This contract was followed in October by a "sale and interchange" agreement, under which the Company purchases project power that the bureau does not need. It also provides for integrated operation of the project and the Company system so as best to meet the combined load requirements of both parties, and it obligates the Company to provide power to make up deficiencies in the output of project plants.

CHAPTER 33

Billion-dollar Expansion

PACIFIC Gas and Electric Company wrote in staggering figures of expansion the closing chapter of the story of its first hundred years. In six postwar years, 1946 to the end of 1951, the Company invested $800,000,000 in new system facilities. By the end of 1953 this total will have passed the billion-dollar mark—the greatest construction program ever undertaken by any gas and electric utility in the United States.

California's population swelled to new highs during the war. Migrants streamed in from the Middle West and the Southwest, attracted by employment in the shipyards and other war industries. Farm workers poured into the sun-drenched valleys where crop production had been stepped up to provide food and cotton for the nation's needs.

Men who studied the situation at the beginning of the postwar period, late in 1945, found two uncertainties which would seriously affect the state's economy. Would the new population drain quickly back to home sources? And would the war industries convert their plants to the manufacture of peacetime products and so moderate the severity of the expected slump in employment?

Pacific Gas and Electric Company chose the more optimistic view. In his review of the year's developments in 1946, President Black said:

"Last year we observed that the war served to accelerate an already significant westward movement of population and industry. It is now even more apparent that much of the war time growth is of a permanent character, and that the industrial, commercial and agricultural development of this region will continue on a far higher plane of activity than before the war.

"Some measure of the magnitude and diversified character of this growth is afforded by the statement that in 1946 alone, more than 1,200 industries announced plans for new or expanded facilities in the Company's service area.

"Latest estimates place the population of the forty-six California counties in which the Company operates at 4,600,000, a gain of 1,300,000 or 40 per cent over the 1940 census figures."

P. G. and E. plunged into the task of catching up with accumulated demand for gas and electric service. A towering backlog of applications for service had piled up. Wartime restrictions on new construction were responsible. When work could be resumed, there were shortages of pipe, wire, poles, and insulators, and of men experienced in installation work. Supplies were bought wherever they could be found, as far away as the Middle West where the demand had been less urgent. Government surpluses of material and equipment were hunted down and secured. Schools for linemen were established to train new crews in construction and maintenance of electric transmission and distribution lines. In six years, beginning in 1946, the Company built thousands of miles of electric line extensions.

Population figures continued month after month and year after year to confuse the pessimists who had predicted recession. According to the census of 1950, California's population was 10,586,223, the second largest in the Union. In the preceding decade its people had multiplied by 53.3 per cent. In 1951 alone P. G. and E. gained 134,000 customers, to bring the total in all branches of its operation to 2,520,211. All estimates of postwar growth had been exceeded.

Construction of powerhouses started late in 1945 and 1946. The first completed was Donbass in Eureka, a salvaged halfship that had been beached, its power plant adapted to commercial use. Its output, made available in December, 1946, helped meet the urgent requirements of the northern lumber city.

In 1948 three new powerhouses went into operation. They were the Kern plant, steam-operated, and Electra and West Point hydro plants on the Mokelumne. The Kern plant, situated near Bakersfield, was rushed to completion to provide more power for irrigation of the vast acreages in the southern San

Joaquin Valley that had been planted in cotton and other crops. So great was the need for speed in construction that tons of machinery parts were flown in by air to save time.

An extended winter drought in the 1947-1948 season accentuated the necessity for more power resources. Hydro plants could be operated only at reduced capacity and fuel-operated powerhouses were called upon for full-time service. In order to meet the most pressing power demands and to conserve water in storage, rules to curtail use of electricity were set up by the State Public Utilities Commission and were kept in force during the period between February 24 and April 12, 1948, when late spring rains relieved the situation.

On the Feather River two big hydro powerhouses were added to the three already in service there. They were Cresta and Rock Creek Powerhouses, placed in service in 1949 and 1950, respectively. The five plants of the Feather River power development, which had been started with construction of Big Bend Powerhouse more than 40 years ago, now have an aggregate capacity of 383,000 kilowatts.

During postwar expansion a marked change was brought about in the planning of new installations. Since pioneer days California had turned to water power for production of electricity because of the lower cost of operation on the streams of the Sierra. Steam-operated powerhouses were built and maintained chiefly for stand-by service during periods of short water supply, peak loads, and emergency. In recent years, however, the engineers planned more and larger steam-operated stations. The primary reasons were that generation by steam plants was becoming more efficient and could be established economically in centers of population and industry; also that available sites for large hydro projects were diminishing in number.

Revolutionary advances were being made in the design of steam plants. Turbo generators driven by steam at 950 degrees Fahrenheit temperature and 1,300 pounds pressure were producing power with greater and greater efficiency. (New steam units now being built will develop 1,000 degrees temperature and 1,800 pounds pressure.) Today more than twice as much electricity is generated by the use of one barrel of fuel oil as was possible 30 years ago. A steam plant can be operated almost continuously at full capacity merely by supplying it with fuel, while the hours of operation of a hydro plant are limited to the available water supply.

In the past, steam plants had represented 25 to 40 per cent of the system's power capacity. Their capability had been increased by 1951 to a point where steam resources were approaching a 60-40 ratio.

These were some of the reasons behind construction of two steam-operated plants, Moss Landing, on the shore of Monterey Bay, and Contra Costa, near the town of Antioch where the San Joaquin River empties into the Bay. Each plant had an initial capacity of 340,000 kilowatts, larger than any other operated by P. G. and E. Moss Landing was placed in commission in 1950. It is distinguished by the equipment installed for filling its four 120,000-barrel oil fuel tanks. A submarine pipe line extends on the Bay bottom from the shore 3,200 feet to an ocean anchorage where oil tankers are moored to pump their fuel cargoes to the tanks alongside the powerhouse. Contra Costa Plant, a twin of the Moss Landing Powerhouse in design, was placed in operation in 1951.

In the six years from V-J Day, the Company built 11 powerhouses, counting as new construction a large addition to Station P in San Francisco. In that brief period more than 1,400,000 kilowatts were added to the P. G. and E. system. Plant capacity had been almost doubled. In addition, the Company at this time has available some 550,000 kilowatts of power from other producers.

Powerhouse building was not all of the expansion program. Thousands of miles of power lines were erected to bring the total in service December 31, 1951, to about 58,000 miles. Scores of substations were constructed, existing plants were improved, new buildings erected, all at an additional cost of many millions of dollars. Approximately $62,000,000 was spent for the "Super Inch" natural gas line and three compressor stations to deliver gas from western Texas and New Mexican fields to Northern California, and other millions were spent on additions to the Company's gas facilities. It is already proposed to increase the capacity of the Texas natural gas line.

Even when plans were considered adequate for the near future, the amazing growth of the state and its industries compelled further expansion. As this is written, work has been started on another and larger steam-operated generating giant. It is at Pittsburg on the bay shore in Contra Costa County in the heart of a wide industrial area, only 7 miles from the Contra Costa plant. Here four generators with an aggregate capacity of 600,000 kilowatts will be installed.

Architecture of the structure represents a departure from the past practice of providing a building for the turbine generator units. The Pittsburg plant is of the semi-outdoor type which does away with the turbine-room superstructure, including its walls and roof. Pittsburg plant, to be in partial operation in 1953 and completed in 1954, will be the largest in California.

Both Moss Landing and Contra Costa plants will be enlarged in 1952 and 1953 to bring their capacity close to that of Pittsburg. Two generating units will be installed in each plant, and when the work is done each will have a capacity of 575,000 kilowatts.

Looking still farther ahead, the Company announced early in 1952 its plans for construction of two more hydro plants on the Pit River in Shasta County at an estimated cost of $45,000,000. Two new steps will be added to the stairway of water power that starts at Pit 1 Powerhouse, at the head of the river canyon, and ends now at Pit 5 plant, 41 miles downstream.

The new powerhouses will be Pit 4, capacity 84,000 kilowatts, and Pit 6, 60,000 kilowatts. When they are placed in operation in 1955 and thereafter, the Pit River chain of powerhouses will then have an aggregate capacity of 440,000 kilowatts.

Development of remaining hydro sources will be continued. Four new powerhouses will be added to the Feather River system, which then will consist of nine plants with a total generating capacity of nearly 750,000 kilowatts. Powered by the stored waters of Lake Almanor, Butt Valley reservoirs, and the flow from the north fork of the Feather and its tributaries, the new powerhouses will have an aggregate capacity of 364,-

000 kilowatts. Construction will involve the driving of some 13 miles of tunnel and will require about 3½ years to complete. The plants will be named *Butt Valley, Caribou No. 2, Belden,* and *Poe*. Their cost is estimated at $114,000,000.

The long-planned King's River project, where the Company is prepared to construct new hydro plants with an aggregate capacity of 240,000 kilowatts, still is tangled in the web of governmental disputes which have delayed required authorization of the development.

When the projects now under way are completed by the end of 1954, the P. G. and E. system will have a total generating capacity of 4,150,000 kilowatts, a fair measure of its progress since the day in September, 1879, when George H. Roe started his little dynamo to light 21 arc lamps.

Financing of the billion-dollar expansion program was accomplished smoothly by succeeding issues of bonds and preferred and common stocks. That this was done successfully, attested both the soundness of the plan and public confidence in the financial integrity of P. G. and E.

An event significant in the financial history of P. G. and E. occurred March 1, 1952. On that day $7,667,000 in noncallable 6 per cent bonds of the old San Joaquin Light and Power Corporation matured. Holders of the bonds were paid. With that payment the last of 65 bond issues of subsidiary and acquired companies had been redeemed since 1920. Maturity of the San Joaquin bonds marked the conclusion of a capital simplification program that had covered three decades. The capital structure now consists only of First and Refunding Mortgage bonds and first preferred and common stocks.

The story of six years of unprecedented building activity would not be complete without recording the names of the men who accomplished the great work. W. G. B. Euler, as general manager and later as executive vice-president, was in general charge of the program. O. W. Peterson, as engineer of construction, had been building dams, tunnels, waterways, and powerhouses for P. G. and E. since 1913. A graduate of the University of California in 1904, he had crowded into his life more construction experience than most men. When he retired

January 1, 1951, he was succeeded by A. J. Swank, who had been his chief assistant. Engineering of the program was supervised by I. C. Steele, who upon retirement was succeeded by Walter Dreyer, formerly chief of the civil engineering department. Hydroelectric construction was in direct charge of H. W. Haberkorn.

The hectic years of the war and construction periods had taken their toll from personnel of the Company. When P. M. Downing was advanced to the post of executive vice-president in 1943, he was succeeded by A. Emory Wishon as vice-president and general manager, who remained in that position until 1947 when he was advanced to executive vice-president. Less than six months later, January 4, 1948, his lifetime of leadership in utility advancement was ended by death.

A man who started his career as a lamplighter in the days when San Francisco streets were illuminated by gas is now vice-president and general manager of the Company. He is N. R. Sutherland, appointed to his present post in 1950. While he was still in school he made the rounds lighting the lamps at dusk and extinguishing them in the early hours after dawn. When he finished his schooling he joined the Company on full time as a junior clerk. From that position he was advanced to the posts of manager of the commercial department and of the San Francisco division, vice-president in charge of public relations and sales, vice-president and assistant general manager and then general manager.

National recognition of the P. G. and E.'s billion-dollar expansion program and of its successful efforts in meeting problems of government competition came in 1952, when the Charles A. Coffin Award was conferred upon the Company.

The Award was established in 1921 by the General Electric Company as a tribute to the memory of the late Charles A. Coffin, founder and first president of the General Electric Company. It is administered by the Charles A. Coffin Foundation. Each year it recognizes "a distinguished contribution to the development of electric light and power for the convenience of the public and the benefit of the industry." The Award is the most coveted recognition of merit in the electric industry.

Presentation of the Award was made to President James B. Black, June 3, 1952, at the annual convention of the Edison Electric Institute in Cleveland, Ohio. The judges' citation declared:

"Confronted, at the close of World War II, with reduced reserve capacity due to war-time restriction, a rocketing demand for electric power accompanying a phenomenal rate of population growth, and an invasion of its business field by a bureau of the Federal government, the winning company acted with decision, vigor and marked ability. . . .

"Basic to the company's achievements has been its billion dollar post-war construction program, unequalled in magnitude in the history of the utility industry. Three-quarters complete in 1951, this well-planned, soundly financed expansion has resulted in the virtual doubling in six years of the company's generating capacity. . . ."

Pacific Gas and Electric Company is awarded the honor, the judges continued, "For its courageous undertaking and able execution of a huge expansion program, for its cooperative and far seeing acts which brought to all the people of the area and to the taxpayers of the nation the great economic advantage in putting to use the electricity generated as a by-product of a major irrigation and flood control project, and for the inestimable value which these great achievements have had in the preservation of the American system of free enterprise and in furthering the progress of the electric industry."

* * *

One hundred years ago far-sighted Peter Donahue saw opportunity in the service of gas to primitive, gold-rush San Francisco. Seventy-three years ago George H. Roe, with equal vision, believed the new electric light might profitably be provided for the city's residents. From their small beginnings, carried on and developed by Martin, de Sabla, the Drums, Miller, the Livermores, Kerckhoff, Balch, the Wishons, Poniatowski, Crocker, Creed, Hockenbeamer, the Earls, down to James B. Black of 1952, has grown the P. G. and E. of today.

The efforts and the dreams of these men and their associates have built a vast instrument of public service, providing light, heat, and power to the millions who in a century of time have populated the land that once held only the thousands brought to California by the lure of gold.

What P. G. and E.'s contribution has meant to the economic progress of the territory it serves cannot be stated statistically. It is self-evident that only with the aid of a progressively improved and adequate service of electric power and gas could Northern California's economy have advanced as it has. Equally true is the corollary that as the territory grew and prospered, so did the utility system grow and prosper.

The Company, inevitably, is of the people and for the people. Its lines enter almost every home. It serves the business and industry and agriculture of an area in which 5,000,000 persons live. With total assets of approximately one and three-quarters billion dollars, the utility is owned by 188,463 stockholders, a majority of whom have less than 100 shares each. In 1951 alone 17,965 new owners were added to the Company's rolls. Sixty-six per cent of the Company's stockholders are Californians.

It might be said, also, that the indirect interest in the Company extends far beyond the ownership of its 188,463 stockholders. It flows out over the country through the security holdings of insurance companies, educational, religious, and other institutional investors. In the words of the 1951 annual report:

"This broad ownership, both direct and indirect, clearly places the Company in the category of a publicly owned institution, operating effectively as a private enterprise under public regulation."

Again if one seeks to define P. G. and E., he may find it in the Company's 17,000 employees—its ditch tenders and lake tenders; its linemen, who risk their lives and endure hardships that service may be maintained without interruption; its operators who stand lonely watches in isolated powerhouses to hold constant the flow of power from the generators; its servicemen whose skill is on call for the aid of customers when gas or electric appliance or motor operation must be restored. They and their fellows are integral parts of the communities in which they live. Many of them are leaders or workers in civic affairs. In each place *they* are the Company.

And if one may brave the cynicism of a materialistic world, he will find in this utility organization, evolved during a century of development, an intangible quality, a spirit and a strength and a purpose of its own that are above and beyond the strength and purpose of individuals. Instead of being merely a corporate body, a thing of bylaws and rules, it has become a living, lasting entity, with a character and a tradition based firmly upon its dedication to public service.

This is P. G. and E. of California.

APPENDIX

THE "FAMILY TREE"
PACIFIC GAS AND ELECTRIC COMPANY

Pacific Gas and Electric Company today represents the amalgamation of approximately 520 predecessor companies and miscellaneous properties by a progressive process of consolidation during the past 100 years. In abbreviated form, the lines of descent of the principal corporate gas and utility groups absorbed into the present Company in past years are here indicated. Each group in turn consisted of many other companies. Numerous individual organizations and systems have been acquired directly by P. G. and E.

The first date after a company name is that of incorporation; the second date is when stock control was obtained by the company's successor. Indentation signifies that the company or companies were antecedents or components of the first named.

PACIFIC GAS AND ELECTRIC COMPANY

Incorporated October 10, 1905

- Calif. Gas and Elec. Corp. 1901-1906
  - Bay Counties Power Co. 1900-1903
    - Nev. County Elec. Power Co. 1892-1900
    - Valley Counties Power Co. 1902-1902
  - California Central Gas and Electric Company 1901-1903
  - South Yuba Water Co. 1890-1905
  - Standard Elec. Co. of Calif. 1897-1904

- San Francisco Gas and Elec. Co. 1896-1906
  - San Francisco Gas Light Co. 1873-1897
    - San Francisco Gas Co. 1852-1873
  - Edison Light and Power Co. 1891-1897
    - California Elec. Light Co. 1879-1891

- Great Western Power Company of California 1915-1930
  - Great Western Power Co. 1906-1915
  - Western Power Co. of Calif. 1902-1906

- Northern Calif. Power Co., Consolidated 1908-1919—
  - Northern Calif. Power Co. 1902-1908

- Sierra and San Francisco Power Company 1909-1927—

- Coast Valleys Gas and Electric Co. 1912-1927—

- San Joaquin Light and Power Corporation 1910-1930
  - San Joaq. Lgt. and Power Co. 1905-1910
    - San Joaquin Power Co. 1902-1905
      - San Joaquin Electric Co. 1895-1902
  - Midland Counties Public Service Corporation 1913-1930

- —Western States Gas and Elec. Co. 1910-1927

- —Calif. Telephone and Light Co. 1911-1923

PACIFIC GAS AND ELECTRIC COMPANY
PREDECESSOR COMPANIES

Component companies of Pacific Gas and Electric Company are listed below. The majority of these were merged into the principal groups named on the preceding page before those groups were consolidated with P. G. and E.; the remainder were acquired directly by Pacific Gas and Electric Company.

In the following table the companies or systems are listed alphabetically by company name. When a company was a part of one of the principal groups, its line of descent is indicated by initials of the parent corporation of that group. When the date is blank, there is no record available. Where the column of descent is blank, the company was acquired directly by P. G. and E.

Names of a number of telephone, mining, water and ditch companies, and of some individuals whose water rights, distribution lines, and other properties were acquired have been omitted from this list.

Key

C. G. & E.	California Gas and Electric Corporation
C. T. & L.	California Telephone and Light Company
C. V. G. & E.	Coast Valleys Gas and Electric Company
G. W. P.	Great Western Power Company of California
M. C. P. S.	Midland Counties Public Service Corporation
N. C. P.	Northern California Power Company, Consolidated
S. F. G. & E.	San Francisco Gas and Electric Company
S. J. L. & P.	San Joaquin Light and Power Corporation
S. & S. F. P.	Sierra and San Francisco Power Company
W. S. G. & E.	Western States Gas and Electric Company

Name and Location (Town or County)	*Descended to P. G. and E. through*	*Date Organized*
Alameda Gas Company	C. G. & E.	1883
Alameda Gas Light Company	C. G. & E.	1877
Amador Canal and Mining Company	C. G. & E.	1873
Amador Electric Light and Power Company	—	1909

Name and Location (Town or County)	*Descended to P. G. and E. through*	*Date Organ-ized*
Amador Electric Railway and Light Company	—	1891
American Gold Dredging Company (Oroville)		1916
American River Electric Company (Eldorado County)	W. S. G. & E.	1903
Arcata Light and Power Company	W. S. G. & E.	1905
Aubin Gas Company (San Francisco)	S. F. G. & E.	1857
Auburn Water Works	C. G. & E.	1888
Bakersfield and Kern Electric Railway Company	S. J. L. & P.	1900
Bakersfield Gas and Electric Light Company	S. J. L. & P.	1890
Battle Creek Power Company (Shasta County)	N. C. P.	1905
Bay Counties Power Company	C. G. & E.	1900
Bear Creek Canal Company	C. G. & E.	—
Bear Creek and Auburn Water and Mining Company	C. G. & E.	1851
Bell Electric Company (Auburn)	—	1889
Bellevue Irrigation Company (Shasta County)	N. C. P.	1899
Benbow Power Company (Humboldt County)	—	1928
Benecia Gas Company	C. G. & E.	1881
Berkeley Electric Lighting Company	C. G. & E.	1894
Berkeley Electric Light Power and Heat Company	C. G. & E.	1892
Berkeley Gas Light Company	C. G. & E.	1878
Berkeley Improvement Company	C. G. & E.	1893
Big Oak Flat (Tuolumne County)	—	—
Blue Lakes Water Company (Amador County)	C. G. & E.	1890
The Blue Lake Water Company (Amador County)	C. G. & E.	1887
Butte and Tehama Power Company	—	1909

Name and Location (Town or County)	*Descended to P. G. and E. through*	*Date Organized*
Butte County Electric Power and Lighting Company	C. G. & E.	1899
Butte County Power Company	C. G. & E.	1901
Calaveras Dredging Company Transmission Lines	W. S. G. & E.	1907
California Central Gas and Electric Company	C. G. & E.	1901
California Consolidated Light & Power Company (Monterey County)	C. V. G. & E.	1911
California Electric Generating Company (Oakland)	G. W. P.	1908
California Electric Light Company (San Francisco)	S. F. G. & E.	1879
California Exploration Company, Ltd. (Calaveras County)	C. G. & E.	1898
California Exploration Company (Calaveras County)	C. G. & E.	1896
California Gas and Electric Corporation	—	1901
California Hotel Company Electric Plant (San Francisco)	S. F. G. & E.	1904
California Power and Manufacturing Company (Shasta County)	—	1911
California Public Service Company (Mendocino County)	—	1926
California Telephone and Light Company (Lake, Mendocino, Napa, and Sonoma Counties)	—	1911
Calistoga-Brookside Telephone Lines	C. T. & L.	—
Calistoga Electric Company	C. T. & L.	1911
Calistoga Telephone System	C. T. & L.	—
Call Building Plant (San Francisco)	G. W. P.	1897
Capital Gas Company (Sacramento)	C. G. & E.	1875
Cataract Gold Mining and Power Company (Oroville)	—	1909
Central California Electric Company (Placer County)	C. G. & E.	1895

Name and Location (Town or County)	*Descended to P. G. and E. through*	*Date Organ-ized*
Central Electric Railway Company (Sacramento)	C. G. & E.	1891
Central Gas Company (San Francisco)	S. F. G. & E.	1881
Central Gas Light Company (San Francisco)	S. F. G. & E.	1882
Central Light and Power Company (San Francisco)	S. F. G. & E.	1897
Central Mendocino County Power Company	—	1922
Central Natural Gas Company (Stockton)	W. S. G. & E.	1899
Central Oakland Light and Power Company	W. S. G. & E.	1909
Charles East Electric Light and Power Company (Humboldt County)	—	—
Cherokee Mining Company (Butte County)	C. G. & E.	1858
Chico Gas and Electric Company	C. G. & E.	1901
Chico Gas Company	C. G. & E.	1874
Chico Gas, Electric Power and Lighting Company	C. G. & E.	1900
Citizens Gas Company (San Francisco)	S. F. G. & E.	1863
Citizens Gas Light and Heat Company (Sacramento)	C. G. & E.	1872
Citizens Gas Light Company (Sacramento)	C. G. & E.	1871
Citizens Natural Gas Company (Stockton)	W. S. G. & E.	1889
The Citizens Natural Gas Company (Stockton)	W. S. G. & E.	1889
City Electric Company (San Francisco)	G. W. P.	1907
City Gas Company (San Francisco)	S. F. G. & E.	1870
The Clear Lake Consolidated Telephone and Telegraph Company	C. T. & L.	1910
Clear Lake Telephone and Telegraph Company	C. T. & L.	1893
Clear Lake Telephone and Telegraph Company (Reorganized)	C. T. & L.	1903

Name and Location (Town or County)	*Descended to P. G. and E. through*	*Date Organized*
The Clear Lake Telephone and Telegraph Company	C. T. & L.	1908
Cloverdale Light and Power Company	C. T. & L.	1902
Coalinga Water and Electric Company	M. C. P. S.	1909
Coast Valleys Gas and Electric Company	—	1912
Colfax Distributing System	—	1904
Columbia and Stanislaus River Water Company	S. & S. F. P.	1855
Columbia Gulch Fluming Company	S. & S. F. P.	1854
Colusa Gas and Electric Company	C. G. & E.	1901
Colusa Gas Company	C. G. & E.	1886
Colusa Light and Power Company	C. G. & E.	1900
Commercial Light and Power Company (San Francisco)	S. F. G. & E.	1898
Commercial Steam Power Works (San Francisco)	S. F. G. & E.	—
Compagnie Française Des Placers (Trinity County)	W. S. G. & E.	1903
Consolidated Electric Company (San Francisco and Oakland)	G. W. P.	1915
Consolidated Electric Light, Gas and Power Company (Woodland)	C. G. & E.	1888
Consolidated Light and Power Company (San Mateo County)	C. G. & E.	1900
Consolidated Stanislaus Water and Power Company	S. & S. F. P.	1904
Consumers Light and Power Company (San Francisco)	G. W. P.	1908
Contra Costa Electric Light and Power Company	—	1903
Copperopolis Electric Distribution	—	—
Cotati-Cotati Junction Telephone System	C. T. & L.	—
Covelo (Clyde W. Henry) (Mendocino County)	—	1925
Crystal Lake Company, Ltd. (Shasta County)	—	1929

Name and Location (Town or County)	*Descended to P. G. and E. through*	*Date Organ-ized*
Del Monte Light and Power Company	C. V. G. & E.	1919
Dixon Electric Power and Water Company	C. G. & E.	1903
Dixon Light and Water Company	C. G. & E.	1891
Downieville Electric Light Company	—	1902
Durham Light and Power Company	—	1906
Dutch Flat Canal System	C. G. & E.	1855
East Berkeley Electric Light Company	C. G. & E.	1887
Edison Electric Light and Power Company (Fresno)	C. G. & E.	1891
Edison Light and Power Company (San Francisco)	S. F. G. & E.	1891
Eel River Power and Irrigation Company	—	1904
Eldorado Power Company	W. S. G. & E.	1921
Eldorado Water and Deep Gravel Mining Company	W. S. G. & E.	1873
Electric Distribution System—City of Lemoore	S. F. L. & P.	—
Electric Improvement Company of San Francisco	C. G. & E.	1887
Electric Improvement Company of San Jose	C. G. & E.	1889
Equitable Gas Light Company (San Francisco)	S. F. G. & E.	1898
Equitable Light and Power Company (San Francisco)	G. W. P.	1909
Eureka Electric Light Company	W. S. G. & E.	1886
The Eureka Gas Company	W. S. G. & E.	1882
Eureka Gas Works	W. S. G. & E.	1882
Eureka Lighting Company	W. S. G. & E.	1894
Eureka Power Company (Butte County)	G. W. P.	1902
Fair Oaks Electric Company (Sacramento County)	G. W. P.	1922
Feather River Canal Company	G. W. P.	1860
Feather River Mutual Water Company	G. W. P.	1912

Name and Location (Town or County)	*Descended to P. G. and E. through*	*Date Organized*
Feather River Pine Mills, Inc. (Butte and Plumas Counties)	—	1927
Feather River Power Company	G. W. P.	1925
Ferndale Electric Light Company	W. S. G. & E.	1896
Folsom Distribution System	—	1901
Folsom Water Power Company	C. G. & E.	1881
Fortuna Lighting Company	W. S. G. & E.	1904
Fowler Gas Company	—	1913
Fresno City Railway Company	S. J. L. & P.	1901
Fresno City Water Company	S. J. L. & P.	—
Fresno City Water Corporation	S. J. L. & P.	—
Fresno Gas and Electric Light Company	C. G. & E.	1888
Fresno Gas and Electric Company	S. J. L. & P.	1881
Fresno Gas Company	C. G. & E.	1881
Fresno Gas Light Company	C. G. & E.	1882
Garden City Gas Company (San Jose)	C. G. & E.	1877
Globe Gas Company of San Jose	C. G. & E.	1877
Gold Mountain Water Company (Tuolumne County)	S. & S. F. P.	1900
Gold Mountain Water Works and Mining Company (Tuolumne County)	S. & S. F. P.	1854
Golden State Power Company (Plumas County)	G. W. P.	1902
Gonzales Electric Distribution	C. V. G. & E.	1908
Grass Valley Electric Light and Motor Company	C. G. & E.	1887
Grass Valley Gas and Electric Light Works	C. G. & E.	—
Grass Valley Gas Company	C. G. & E.	1885
The Grass Valley Gas Company	C. G. & E.	1862
Great Western Power Company	G. W. P.	1906
Great Western Power Company of California	—	1915
Groveland Electric Company (Tuolumne County)	—	—
Half Moon Bay Light and Power Company	G. W. P.	1911

Name and Location (Town or County)	*Descended to P. G. and E. through*	*Date Organized*
Harbor Light and Power Company (San Francisco)	S. F. G. & E.	1894
Hayward Electric Light Company	—	—
Healdsburg and Alexander Valley Distribution Lines	C. T. & L.	1913
Healdsburg Rural Telephone Lines	C. T. & L.	—
Healdsburg Telephone Company	C. T. & L.	1910
Healdsburg Telephone System	C. T. & L.	—
Humboldt Electric Light and Power Company	W. S. G. & E.	1893
Humboldt Gas and Electric Company	W. S. G. & E.	1907
Humboldt Manufacturing Company	W. S. G. & E.	—
Hydrauliques De Junction City (Trinity County)	W. S. G. & E.	1894
Independent Electric Light and Power Company (San Francisco)	S. F. G. & E.	1899
Independent Gas and Power Company (San Francisco)	S. F. G. & E.	1901
Ione Water Works Company	—	1884
Keswick Electric Power Company (Shasta County)	N. C. P.	1900
Kincaid Flat Mining Company (Tuolumne County)	S. & S. F. P.	1867
King City Water, Light and Power Company	C. V. G. & E.	1908
LaGrange Ditch and Hydraulic Mining Company	S. & S. F. P.	1871
LaGrange Water and Power Company	S. & S. F. P.	1907
Lake County Water and Power Company	C. T. & L.	1925
Lakeport, Saratoga Springs and Ukiah Telephone Company	C. T. & L.	1891
Lakeport Telephone System	C. T. & L.	—
Lava Bed Dredging Company (Oroville)	—	1900
Lehe Distributing System (Solano County)	—	—
Lemoore Light and Power Company	S. J. L. & P.	1909

Name and Location (Town or County)	*Descended to P. G. and E. through*	*Date Organized*
Lincoln Water Works	C. G. & E.	—
Live Oak and Encinal Light and Power Company	—	1908
Livermore Water and Power Company	—	1896
Lodi Natural Gas Company	—	1906
Long Valley Light and Power Company (Laytonville)	—	—
Los Gatos Gas Company	—	1895
Los Gatos Ice and Power Company	—	1896
Los Gatos Ice Company	—	1886
Los Gatos Ice, Gas and Electric Company	—	1907
Los Gatos Manufacturing Company	—	1869
Lucerne Water, Light and Power Company (Lake County)	—	—
Madera Electric Company	S. J. L. & P.	1893
Madera Electric Water Company	S. J. L. & P.	1907
Madera Light and Power Company	S. J. L. & P.	1908
Marigold Dredging Company (Oroville)	—	1901
Martell Power Company (San Francisco)	G. W. P.	1900
Marysville and Nevada Power and Water Company	—	1896
Marysville Coal Gas Company	C. G. & E.	1858
Marysville Electric Light and Power Company	C. G. & E.	1890
Marysville Gas and Electric Company	C. G. & E.	1895
McKinley Brothers, Inc. (Lake County)	C. T. & L.	1903
Merced Electric Light Company	S. J. L. & P.	1888
Merced Falls Electric Power Company	S. J. L. & P.	1898
Merced Falls Gas and Electric Company	S. J. L. & P.	1899
Merced Gas Corporation	S. J. L. & P.	1881
Merced Stone Company (Not incorporated)	S. J. L. & P.	1907
Merchants Lighting Company of Santa Rosa	C. G. & E.	1892
Metropolitan Gas Company (San Francisco)	S. F. G. & E.	1863

Name and Location (Town or County)	*Descended to P. G. and E. through*	*Date Organized*
Metropolitan Gas Corporation (San Francisco)	S. F. G. & E.	1911
Metropolitan Light and Power Company (San Francisco)	S. F. G. & E.	1907
Middle Yuba Hydro-Electric Power Company	—	1909
Midland Counties Gas and Electric Company (San Luis Obispo, Santa Maria, and Paso Robles)	M. C. P. S.	1912
Midland Counties Public Service Corporation	—	1913
Midland Power Company (Contra Costa County)	—	1902
Midway Light and Power Company (Kern County)	S. J. L. & P.	1910
Mills Building Power Company (San Francisco)	S. F. G. & E.	1892
Modesto Gas Company	—	1916
Modesto Gas Light, Coal and Coke Company	—	1884
Monterey and Pacific Grove Street Railway and Electric Water Company	C. V. G. & E.	1893
Monterey County Gas and Electric Company	C. V. G. & E.	1903
Monterey County Gas and Electric Company Water Properties	C. V. G. & E.	—
Monterey Electric Light and Development Company	C. V. G. & E.	1891
Monterey Gas and Electric Company	C. V. G. & E.	1902
Mt. Diablo Light and Power Company (Contra Costa County)	S. & S. F. P.	1904
Mt. Konocti Light and Power Company (Lake County)	C. T. & L.	1911
Mt. Shasta Power Company (Shasta County)	—	1909
Mt. Shasta Power Corporation (Shasta County)	—	1912
Mountain King Mining Company	S. J. L. & P.	1903

Name and Location (Town or County)	*Descended to P. G. and E. through*	*Date Organized*
Municipal Light and Power Company (San Francisco)	P. G. & E. and G. W. P.	1906
Mutual Electric Light Company (San Francisco)	S. F. G. & E	1894
Napa City Gas Light and Heating Company	C. G. & E.	1888
Napa City Gas Light Company	C. G. & E.	1867
Napa Gas and Electric Company	C. G. & E.	1899
Napa Thomson Houston Light Company	C. G. & E.	1890
Napa Valley Electric Company	G. W. P.	1907
National Park Electric Company (Yosemite Park)	S. & S. F. P.	—
Natoma Water and Mining Company (Sacramento County)	C. G. & E.	1853
Natoma Water Company (Sacramento County)	C. G. & E.	1851
Natural Gas Corporation of California (Kern and King Counties)	—	1912
Nevada City Gas Company	C. G. & E.	1885
Nevada City Gas Works	C. G. & E.	1865
Nevada County Electric Power Company	C. G. & E.	1892
Nevada County Gas and Electric Company	C. G. & E.	1901
Nevada Hydraulic Mining Company	C. G. & E.	1875
Newcastle Water Works	C. G. & E.	—
Newman Light and Power Company	—	1904
Nil Desperendum Water Company (Tuolumne County)	S. & S. F. P.	1860
North Mountain Power Company (Trinity County)	W. S. G. & E.	1902
North Sacramento Land Company	G. W. P.	1910
Northern California Power Company	N. C. P.	1902
Northern California Power Company, Consolidated	—	1908
Northern Light and Power Company (Sacramento Valley)	N. C. P.	1907

Name and Location (Town or County)	*Descended to P. G. and E. through*	*Date Organized*
Northern Light and Power Company (Humboldt County)	—	1937
Northern Natural Gas Company (Stockton)	W. S. G. & E.	1889
Northwestern Electric Company	C. T. & L.	—
The Northwestern Electric Company	C. T. & L.	1908
Northwestern Telephone Company of Guerneville	C. T. & L.	—
Novato Light and Power Company	—	—
Novato Utilities Company	—	1916
Oakdale Gas Company	—	1913
Oakland Electric Light and Motor Company	C. G. & E.	1887
Oakland Equitable Gas Company	C. G. & E.	1899
Oakland Gas Light and Heat Company	C. G. & E.	1884
Oakland Gas Light Company	C. G. & E.	1866
Oro Development Company (Oroville)	—	1911
Oro Electric Corporation (Oroville)	—	1911
Oro Water, Light and Power Company (Oroville)	—	1905
Oroville Electric Light Company	—	1889
Oroville Gas, Electric Light and Power Company	—	1895
Oroville Light and Power Company	—	1901
Oroville Water Company	—	1878
Pacific Gas Improvement Company (San Francisco)	S. F. G. & E.	1884
Pacific Improvement Company (Monterey County)	C. V. G. & E.	1878
Pacific Improvement Company (Reorganized)	C. V. G. & E.	1880
Pacific Power Company (San Francisco)	S. F. G. & E.	—
Pacific Thomson Houston Electric Light and Power Company (Sacramento)	C. G. & E.	1884
Paso Robles Light and Water Company	M. C. P. S.	1906

Name and Location (Town or County)	*Descended to P. G. and E. through*	*Date Organ-ized*
Paso Robles Water Company	M. C. P. S.	1888
Peninsula Lighting Company (San Mateo and Santa Clara Counties)	C. G. & E.	1896
Peoples Light and Power Company (San Leandro)	G. W. P.	1909
Petaluma Electric Light and Power Company	C. G. & E.	1897
Petaluma Gas and Electric Company	C. G. & E.	1899
Phoenix Water Company (Tuolumne County)	S. & S. F. P.	1859
Pioneer Pulp Company (Placer County)	C. G. & E.	1888
Pittsburg Distributing System (Black Diamond Distributing System)	—	—
Placerville Gold Mining Company	W. S. G. & E.	1911
Pleasant Valley Company	S. J. L. & P.	1916
Point Arena Electric Light and Power Company	—	1919
Power Development Company (Kern County)	S. J. L. & P.	1894
Power Transit and Light Company (Bakersfield)	S. J. L. & P.	1902
Pyramid Power Company	C. G. & E.	1902
Quincy Electric Light Company	G. W. P.	1915
Red Bluff Electric Company	N. C. P.	1889
Red Bluff Gas Company	N. C. P.	1874
Redding Electric Light and Power Company	N. C. P.	1891
Redding Gas Company	N. C. P.	1886
Redding Water Company	N. C. P.	—
The Redding Water Company	N. C. P.	1886
Redwood City Electric Company	C. G. & E.	1892
Richmond Light and Power Company	W. S. G. & E.	1902
Richmond Light and Power Corporation	W. S. G. & E.	1910
Richmond Light and Water Company	W. S. G. & E.	1901
Rio Rancho Company (Butte County)	—	1897

Name and Location (Town or County)	*Descended to P. G. and E. through*	*Date Organ-ized*
Rio Vista Electric Light and Power Company (Solano County)	—	1905
Riverside Road Street Railway—Sacramento	—	—
Rock Creek, Deer Creek and South Yuba Canal Company	C. G. & E.	1850
Russel Robison Water and Electric Company (Pismo and Arroyo Grande)	M. C. P. S.	1906
Russian River Light and Power Company (Sonoma County)	C. T. & L.	1910
C. T. Ryland Electric Properties (Sonoma County)	C. T. & L.	—
Sacramento County Water Company	C. G. & E.	1892
Sacramento Electric Gas and Railway Company	C. G. & E.	1896
Sacramento Electric Light Company	C. G. & E.	1884
Sacramento Electric Power and Light Company	C. G. & E.	1892
Sacramento Gas Company	C. G. & E.	1854
Sacramento Gas Company	—	1914
Sacramento Natural Gas Company	—	1895
Sacramento Railway and Improvement Company	C. G. & E.	1890
Sacramento River Supply Company	C. G. & E.	1906
Sacramento Valley Power Company	N. C. P.	1909
The Sacramento Valley Power Company	N. C. P.	1910
Sacramento Valley Utility Company	—	1936
Salinas City Gas and Electric Company	C. V. G. & E.	1875
Salinas City Light and Water Company	C. V. G. & E.	1896
Salinas Valley Water Company	C. V. G. & E.	1896
Salinas Water Light and Power Company	C. V. G. & E.	1901
San Domingo Gold Mining Company (Stanislaus County)	S. & S. F. P.	1898
San Francisco Coke and Gas Company	S. F. G. & E.	1899
San Francisco Electric Company (Berkeley)	C. G. & E.	1891

Name and Location (Town or County)	*Descended to P. G. and E. through*	*Date Organized*
San Francisco Gas and Electric Company	—	1896
San Francisco Gas Company	S. F. G. & E.	1852
San Francisco Gas Light Company	S. F. G. & E.	1873
Sanger Light and Power Company	S. J. L. & P.	—
San Joaquin Canal and Irrigation Company	S. & S. F. P.	1908
San Joaquin Electric Company (Fresno)	S. J. L. & P.	1895
San Joaquin Electric Light Company (Fresno)	S. J. L. & P.	—
San Joaquin Light and Power Company (Fresno)	S. J. L. & P.	1905
San Joaquin Light and Power Corporation (Fresno)	—	1910
San Joaquin Power Company	S. J. L. & P.	1902
San Jose Brush Electric Company	C. G. & E.	1882
San Jose Gas Company	C. G. & E.	1860
San Jose Gas Works	C. G. & E.	1860
San Jose Light and Power Company	C. G. & E.	1889
San Jose Railroads and Peninsular Railway Distributing System	—	—
San Leandro Gas and Electric Light Company	—	1889
San Luis Obispo Gas and Electric Company	M. C. P. S.	1903
San Mateo Electric Light Company	C. G. & E.	1895
San Mateo Gas Light Company	C. G. & E.	1892
San Mateo Power Company	C. G. & E.	1905
San Miguel Light and Power Company	M. C. P. S.	1905
San Rafael Gas Company	C. G. & E.	1883
San Rafael Gas and Electric Company	C. G. & E.	1887
Santa Clara Municipal Gas System	—	—
Santa Maria Gas and Electric Company	M. C. P. S.	1907
Santa Maria Petroleum and Pipe Line Company	—	1911
Santa Rosa and Mark West Rural Telephone Company	C. T. & L.	—
Santa Rosa Gas Light Company	C. G. & E.	1896
Santa Rosa Lighting Company	C. G. & E.	1888

Name and Location (Town or County)	*Descended to P. G. and E. through*	*Date Organ-ized*
Sawmill Flat Fluming Company (Tuolumne County)	S. & S. F. P.	1861
Sebastopol Light, Power and Water Company	—	1905
Selma Light and Water Company	S. J. L. & P.	1901
Shasta Power Company (Shasta County)	N. C. P.	1904
Shaw's Flat and Tuolumne Canal Company	S. & S. F. P.	1856
Sierra City (Johanna M. Goff)	—	—
Sierra and San Francisco Power Company	—	1909
Sierra Irrigation Company (Tehama County)	—	1910
Sierra Nevada Irrigation and Power Company (Amador and Calaveras Counties)	C. G. & E.	1893
Sierra Nevada Land and Water Improvement Company (Eldorado County)	W. S. G. & E.	About 1885
Sierra Water Supply Company (Eldorado County)	W. S. G. & E.	1907
Snow Mountain Water and Power Company (Mendocino County)	C. T. & L.	1906
Solano Electric Light and Gas Company	—	1896
Sonoma and Glen Ellen Telephone Exchanges	C. T. & L.	—
Sonoma Electric Light Company	C. G. & E.	1898
Sonoma Valley Light and Power Company	C. T. & L.	1903
Sonoma Valley Rural Telephone Company	C. T. & L.	—
South Sacramento Power Company	G. W. P.	1910
South San Francisco Power and Light Company	—	1900
South Side Light and Power Company (San Francisco)	G. W. P.	1910
South Yuba Canal Company	C. G. & E.	1870
South Yuba Water and Mining Company	C. G. & E.	1880
South Yuba Water Company	C. G. & E.	1890
Sperry Flour Company Light Plant (Paso Robles)	M. C. P. S.	—
Spreckels Estate Electric Facilities (San Francisco)	—	—

Name and Location (Town or County)	Descended to P. G. and E. through	Date Organized
Standard Electric Company of California	C. G. & E.	1899
Standard Electric Company of California (West Virginia)	C. G. & E.	1897
Stanford University Lines	—	—
The Stanislaus Electric Power Company	S. & S. F. P.	1905
Stanislaus Milling and Power Company	S. & S. F. P.	1895
Stanislaus Reservoir Company	S. & S. F. P.	1855
Stanislaus Water and Power Company	S. & S. F. P.	1902
Stockton Gas and Electric Company	W. S. G. & E.	1894
Stockton Gas and Electric Corporation	W. S. G. & E.	1907
Stockton Gas Company	W. S. G. & E.	1859
Stockton Gas Light and Heat Company	W. S. G. & E.	1884
Stockton Gas Light and Heat Company (Reorganized)	W. S. G. & E.	1888
Stockton Natural Gas Company	W. S. G. & E.	1888
Stockton Water Company	C. G. & E.	1890
Stockton Water Works Company	C. G. & E.	1867
Street Ditch Corporation (Tuolumne County)	S. & S. F. P.	1856
Suburban Electric Light Company (Alameda County)	—	1901
Suburban Light and Power Company (Alameda County)	—	1908
Suisan and Fairfield Distributing System	—	1900
Sullivan Creek and Tuolumne River Water Company	S. & S. F. P.	1853
Sullivan Creek Water Company (Tuolumne County)	S. & S. F. P.	1851
Sutter and Amador Water Works Company	—	1884
Tehama County Power and Transportation Company	N. C. P.	1903
Tehama Electric Light Company	N. C. P.	1899
Thomson Houston Electric Light Company (Marysville)	C. G. & E.	1889
Tomales Mutual Electric Corporation (Marin County)	—	1921

Name and Location (Town or County)	*Descended to P. G. and E. through*	*Date Organized*
Towle Brothers Company Distribution System (Placer County)	—	1889
Tracy Gas Company	—	1926
Tuolumne County Electric Power and Light Company	—	1896
Tuolumne County Water and Electric Power Company	S. & S. F. P.	1898
Tuolumne County Water Company	S. & S. F. P.	1852
Tuolumne Hydraulic Association	S. & S. F. P.	1852
Tuolumne Hydraulic Mining Company	S. & S. F. P.	1872
Tuolumne River Power Company	S. & S. F. P.	1908
Tuolumne River Water Company	S. & S. F. P.	1854
Tuolumne Transmission Company	S. & S. F. P.	1908
Tuolumne Water Power Company	S. & S. F. P.	1907
Turnback Creek Light and Power Company (Tuolumne County)	—	1926
Union Construction Company (Tuolumne County)	S. & S. F. P.	1905
United Gas and Electric Company (San Mateo and Santa Clara Counties)	C. G. & E.	1902
United Gas Improvement Company (San Francisco)	S. F. G. & E.	1882
United Light and Power Company of California (San Francisco)	G. W. P.	1910
United Light and Power Company of New Jersey (San Francisco)	G. W. P.	1911
United Pacific Power Company (San Francisco)	S. F. G. & E.	1902
United Water and Power Company of California (Placer County)	—	1907
Universal Electric and Gas Company (San Francisco)	P. G. & E. and G. W. P.	1912
Utica Power Company (Tuolumne County)	—	—
Vacaville Water and Light Company	—	1890
Vacaville Water and Power Company	—	1919

Name and Location (Town or County)	*Descended to P. G. and E. through*	*Date Organized*
Vallejo Gas Company	C. G. & E.	1904
Vallejo Gas Light Company	C. G. & E.	1867
Valley Counties Power Company (Butte County)	C. G. & E.	1902
Valley Electric Company (Coalinga)	M. C. P. S.	1905
Washington Electric Gas and Fuel Company (West Sacramento)	—	1903
Waterhouse Electric Company (Marysville)	C. G. & E.	—
West Sacramento Electric Company	—	1911
West Side Lumber Company Electric System (Tuolumne County)	—	1900
Western Canal Company (Glenn and Butte Counties)	G. W. P.	1915
Western Light and Power Company (San Francisco)	S. F. G. & E.	1893
Western Power Company of California (Plumas County)	G. W. P.	1902
Western Refrigerating Company (Petaluma)	C. G. & E.	1887
Western States Gas and Electric Company	—	1910
Williams Water and Electric Company	N. C. P.	1909
Willows Water and Light Company	N. C. P.	1887
Woodland Gas and Electric Company	C. G. & E.	1901
Woodland Gas Company	C. G. & E.	1874
Woods Diggins Water Company (Tuolumne County)	S. & S. F. P.	1851
Yosemite Power Company	S. & S. F. P.	1910
Yuba Development Company	C. G. & E.	1900
The Yuba Development Company	—	1920
Yuba Electric Power Company	C. G. & E.	1899
Yuba Power Company	C. G. & E.	1897
The Yuba River Power Company	—	1896

OFFICERS AND DIRECTORS
PACIFIC GAS AND ELECTRIC COMPANY

From October 12, 1905

Name	*Term (Inclusive)*
	Chairman of the Board
N. W. Halsey	January 2, 1906–April 25, 1908
	President
John A. Britton	October 12, 1905–July 3, 1907
John Martin (who acted during absence of Mr. Britton on leave)	April 12, 1906–June 27, 1906
Frank G. Drum	July 3, 1907–July 28, 1920
W. E. Creed	July 28, 1920–August 6, 1927 *
A. F. Hockenbeamer	August 16, 1927–November 11, 1935 *
James B. Black	November 20, 1935–
	Executive Vice-President
P. M. Downing	August 18, 1943–December 11, 1944 *
A. Emory Wishon	July 1, 1947–January 4, 1948 *
W. G. B. Euler	August 1, 1950–
	Vice-President and General Manager
John A. Britton	July 3, 1907–June 29, 1923 *
Frank A. Leach, Jr.	July 11, 1923–July 31, 1929
P. M. Downing	August 1, 1929–August 18, 1943
A. Emory Wishon	August 18, 1943–July 1, 1947
W. G. B. Euler	July 1, 1947–August 1, 1950
N. R. Sutherland	August 1, 1950–
	Vice-President
Frank G. Drum	January 2, 1906–July 3, 1907
John S. Drum	September 28, 1908–February 16, 1910
John Martin	December 27, 1911–January 20, 1912

* Date of death.

Name	*Term (Inclusive)*
A. F. Hockenbeamer	February 16, 1910–August 16, 1927
J. E. Gladstone	March 16, 1914–April 13, 1915
P. M. Downing	November 1, 1920–August 1, 1929
Frank A. Leach, Jr.	November 1, 1921–July 11, 1923
D. H. Foote	November 22, 1922–July 1, 1943
John P. Coghlan	August 16, 1927–
A. H. Markwart	January 24, 1922–January 25, 1940 *
W. G. Vincent	January 24, 1922–January 29, 1946 *
W. S. Yard	January 24, 1922–August 1, 1935
R. E. Fisher	January 24, 1922–July 1, 1947
A. Emory Wishon	June 18, 1930–August 18, 1943
W. G. B. Euler	January 1, 1944–July 1, 1947
L. Harold Anderson	August 1, 1946–
N. R. Sutherland	July 1, 1947–August 1, 1950
J. S. Moulton	July 1, 1947–
D. D. Smalley	July 1, 1947–
I. C. Steele	July 1, 1947–December 31, 1951
O. R. Doerr	April 21, 1948–
Walter Dreyer	January 1, 1952–

Secretary

Charles W. Conlisk	December 15, 1905–July 15, 1907
D. H. Foote	July 15, 1907–July 1, 1943
Raymond Kindig	July 1, 1943–

Treasurer

Cyrus Peirce	December 15, 1905–July 3, 1907
John S. Drum	March 13, 1908–August 13, 1908
A. F. Hockenbeamer	August 13, 1908–August 16, 1927
D. H. Foote	August 16, 1927–February 2, 1943
E. J. Beckett	February 2, 1943–December 31, 1951
K. C. Christensen	January 1, 1952–

Comptroller

A. F. Hockenbeamer	February 8, 1908–August 16, 1927
E. W. Hodges	August 16, 1927–

* Date of death.

Name	*Term (Inclusive)*
General Counsel	
William B. Bosley	January 24, 1922–December 31, 1943
Thomas J. Straub	January 1, 1944–January 31, 1946
Robert H. Gerdes	February 1, 1946–

Directors

The years stated after each name indicate the beginning of service as a director of the Company and the year during which that service was concluded. Where no terminal year is given the director named was still a member of the board, December 31, 1951.

Name	*Term*
Wallace M. Alexander	1923–1927
Frank B. Anderson	1906–1935
Chas. L. Barrett	1924–1927
James B. Black	1930–
Henry E. Bothin	1906–1923
John A. Britton	1905–1923
Frank E. Buck	1945–
Allen L. Chickering	1927–
John P. Coghlan	1931–
Charles W. Conlisk	1905–1906
James F. Crafts	1950–
W. E. Creed	1920–1927
William H. Crocker	1906–1937
W. W. Crocker	1937–
F. W. M. Cutcheon	1905–1907
E. J. de Sabla, Jr.	1905–1914
Charles H. Dickey	1927–1931
A. B. C. Dohrmann	1924–1930
F. W. Doolittle	1934–1936
P. M. Downing	1929–1944
Frank G. Drum	1905–1923
John S. Drum	1908–1930
Guy C. Earl	1930–1935
E. P. Eells	1907–1908
Fred T. Elsey	1914–1938

Name	*Term*
W. G. B. Euler	1948–
Merril O. Evans, Jr.	1905–1906
James F. Fogarty	1935–1948
D. H. Foote	1909–1943
Herbert C. Freeman	1936–1942
J. E. Gladstone	1914–1915
Edwin Gruhl	1930–1933
Walter A. Haas	1949–
N. W. Halsey	1906–1908
Wm. G. Henshaw	1912–1916
	1918–1924
A. F. Hockenbeamer	1908–1935
Samuel Insull	1912–1916
Alexander N. Kemp	1905–1906
Frank A. Leach, Jr.	1923–1929
George W. Lewis	1905–1906
Norman B. Livermore	1916–1918
	1920–
James K. Lochead	1948–
John Martin	1905–1914
Elliott McAllister	1951–
John A. McCandless	1915–1930
Garret W. McEnerney	1905–1908
Chas. K. McIntosh	1926–1930
	1935–1950
John D. McKee	1914–1948
C. O. G. Miller	1912–1952
L. F. Monteagle	1906–1912
George G. Moore	1913–1914
Henry D. Nichols	1938–
John J. O'Brien	1927–1936
Charles R. Page	1943–1950
Silas H. Palmer	1936–
Cyrus Peirce	1905–1912
N. D. Rideout	1906–1907
Charles T. Rodolph	1916–1918
Edwin L. Shea	1943–1945
Leon Sloss	1907–1911
Louis Sloss	1911–1914

Name	*Term*
Frank D. Stringham	1905–1906
	1907–1909
Walter H. Sullivan	1945–
N. R. Sutherland	1952–
Carl Taylor	1905–1907
Joseph S. Tobin	1906–1911
Nion R. Tucker	1918–1920
Geo. K. Weeks	1905–1906
	1908–1920
A. Emory Wishon	1936–1948
L. Foster Young	1905–1906

Index

C

D

E

F

G

H

I

J

Y

Z